THE CARNIVOROUS PLANTS

The CARNIVOROUS PLANTS

BY

FRANCIS ERNEST LLOYD

D. Sc. h. c. (*Wales*); F. R. S. C., F. L. S.
Emeritus Professor of Botany, McGill University

Dover Publications, Inc.
New York

Published in Canada by General Publishing Company, Ltd., 30 Lesmill Road, Don Mills, Toronto, Ontario.

Published in the United Kingdom by Constable and Company, Ltd., 10 Orange Street, London WC 2.

This Dover edition, first published in 1976, is an unabridged and unaltered republication of the work originally published by the Chronica Botanica Company, Waltham, Mass., in 1942 as Volume IX of "A New Series of Plant Science Books."

International Standard Book Number: 0-486-23321-9
Library of Congress Catalog Card Number: 75-46417

Manufactured in the United States of America
Dover Publications, Inc.
180 Varick Street
New York, N. Y. 10014

PREFACE

The experience which has led to the writing of this book began in 1929 when, examining a species related to Utricularia gibba, I made an observation of some importance in understanding the mechanism of the trap. This begot a desire to study as many other species of the genus as I could obtain for comparison, primarily to determine the validity of my conclusions. My feeling that research in this field was promising was strengthened by the discovery that the pertinent literature was singularly barren of the information most needed, that is to say, precise accounts of the structure of the entrance mechanisms of the traps. And an examination of much herbarium material, because of the meagreness of the underground parts of the terrestrial types resulting from indifferent methods of collection, forced the conclusion that, even had other difficulties inherent in studying dried material not intervened, it would be necessary to obtain adequately preserved specimens. This meant a wide correspondence and, if possible, extensive travel. The uncertainty of achieving the latter made the former imperative.

The responses to my requests for help were numerous and generous from all parts of the world, with the result that there came to me from many sources well preserved material which fairly represented the genus, for it brought to me some 100 of the total of 250 or more species. The most lavish single contribution was put at my disposal by my teacher and friend, KARL VON GOEBEL, who gave me a collection of Utricularia collected by him in the tropics of the Old and New Worlds, and in temperate Australia. Many others, while they may have contributed less in amount, could have been no less generous, for the work of collecting, preserving, packing and posting specimens is by no means an easy job.

Travels included two journeys, one to Africa and one to Africa and Australia, the latter made possible by a parting gift from my colleagues of McGill University on my retirement from the Macdonald Chair of Botany in 1935. At the university centres visited I was afforded all kinds of help: laboratory space, guidance to promising localities and means of transportation. Several summers were spent also at the Botanical Institute of the University of Munich on the original invitation of Professor GOEBEL, seconded, after his death, by Professor F. VON WETTSTEIN and his successor Dr. F. C. VON FABER.

During my preoccupation with Utricularia I had to prepare two presidential addresses, and I was thus led, as has many another in like circumstances, to give an account of the whole field of plant carnivory. My interests were widened in this way, and soon I became imbued with the idea of bringing together, and perhaps of adding to, our knowledge of this fascinating group of plants. This extended my list of desiderata. On my requests sent to various correspondents I received material of every group, some living, some preserved, e.g., living material of Heliamphora nutans from the Edinburgh Botanical Garden, where also I saw and studied Cephalotus.

On the study of the material received from many sources, therefore, the accounts in this book rest, and not, in the first instance, on the published papers *of the many excellent workers who have busied themselves in this field, excepting, however, the studies of fungi, of digestion and, in some forms, of motility.*

In view of so much help I cannot forbear from making some, if inadequate, acknowledgement: —

First of all I should acknowledge the hospitality of the botanical staffs of the Universities visited and made use of as centers of activity during my travels. At the Edinburgh Botanical Garden, Sir WILLIAM WRIGHT SMITH, Mr. M. Y. ORR and Dr. J. M. COWAN (who helped me by raising seedlings of *Utricularia*); at the Royal College of Surgeons, my friend Dr. J. BEATTIE; at the University of Capetown, Miss E. L. STEPHENS who has been a constant help for some years. My stay there was made profitable by the practical assistance in transportation and guidance afforded by Mrs. FRANK BOLUS, Professor R. H. COMPTON, Mrs. M. R. LEVYNS and Mr. A. J. M. MIDDLEMOST; at Brisbane University, Professor D. A. HERBERT and Mr. C. T. WHITE; at the University of New South Wales, Sydney, Professor JOHN MCLUCKIE, Dr. PAT BROUGH, Professor I. V. NEWMAN (now of the University at Wellington, N. Z.) and other members of the staff; at the University in Melbourne, the late Professor A. J. EWART and Miss ETHEL I. McLENNAN; at the Melbourne Herbarium, the late Director Mr. F. J. RAE and Mr. P. F. MORRIS; at the University of Adelaide, Dr. A. E. V. RICHARDSON (of the Australian National Research Council) and Professor J. G. WOOD; and at Perth, Professor J. C. ARMSTRONG and Miss ALISON BAIRD; at the Western Australian State Herbarium, Dr. C. A. GARDNER. Without their knowledge of local conditions and immediate assistance, always put promptly at my disposal, my work would have been much delayed and always less fruitful.

To those who as individuals have given me various forms of help, often involving much effort, I offer these mere thanks into which I ask them to read my highest appreciation. Dr. J. W. ADAMS, Morris Arboretum; Dr. Å. ÅKERMAN, Svalöv; Miss E. BEATRICE ASHCROFT, Auckland University College; Dr. JOJI ASHIDA, Kyôtô; Professor L. G. M. BAAS BECKING, Leiden and Buitenzorg; the late Professor EDWARD BARNES, Madras Christian College, India; Mr. CHARLES BARRETT, Editor, *The Victorian Naturalist*, Melbourne; the late Mr. H. BLATTER, Panchgani, India; Professor Y. BHÂRADWÂJA, Benares Hindu University; Dr. K. BISWAS, Botanic Gardens, Sibpur near Calcutta; the late Dr. H. R. BRITON-JONES, Trinidad; Mr. J. H. BUZACOTT, Maringa, N. Queensland; Mr. E. J. H. CORNER, Botanic Gardens, Singapore; Miss LUCY M. CRANWELL, The Museum, Auckland, N. Z.; Dr. J. M. CURRY, Health Department, Panama (Canal Zone); Mr. F. C. DEIGHTON, Department of Agriculture, Sierra Leone; Professor H. H. DIXON, Trinity College, Dublin; Mr. WM. DUNSTAN, Manager, *The Herald*, Melbourne; Dr. J. H. EHLERS, University of Michigan, Ann Arbor, Mich.; Miss KATHERINE ESAU, University of California, Davis, Calif.; Professor M. L. FERNALD, The Gray Herbarium, Harvard University; Mr. M. FREE, Brooklyn Botanic Garden; Mr. A. V. GIBLIN, Hobart, Tasmania; the late Prof. H. GLÜCK, Heidelberg; Professor T. H. GOODSPEED, University of California; Professor JOHN E. HOLLOWAY, The University, Dunedin, N. Z.; Mr. R. E. HOLTTUM, Botanic Gardens, Singapore; Dr. F. C. HOEHNE, São Paulo, Brazil; Dr. M. HOMÈS, The University, Brussels; Mr. F. W. JANE, University College, London; Dr. W. KARSTENS, Leiden; Dr. S. B. KAUSIK, Central College, Bangalore, India; Professor L. P. KHANNA, Rangoon, Burma; Professor W. KUPPER, Botanical Institute, Munich; Mrs. M. H. LEA, Fairhope, Ala.; Frère LÉON, Cuba; Dr. GUNNAR LOHAMMAR, Uppsala; Mr. ALLAN McINTYRE, Hobart, Tasmania; Mr. C. MACNAMARA, Arn Prior, Ont.; Dr. E. B. MARTYN, now of Jamaica; Mr. O. MELLINGEN, Hanau, Germany; Dr. E. M. MERL, Munich; the late Professor G. E. NICHOLS, Yale University, New Haven, Conn.; Mr. C. E. PARKINSON, Forest Research Institute, Dehra Dun, India; Dr. D. Y. PADMAPERUMA, Royal College, Colombo, Ceylon; the late Mrs. EMILY H. PELLOE, Perth, W. A.; Dr. A. QUINTANILHA, The University, Coimbra, Portugal, later of Paris; Mrs. LESTER ROWNTREE, Carmel, Calif.; Mr. E. O. G. SCOTT, Launceston, Tasmania; Professor em. GEO. H. SHULL, Princeton Unversity, Princeton, N. J.; Mr. N. D. SIMPSON, Botanical Garden, Peradeniya, Ceylon; Dr. C. M. SMITH, De Land, Fla.; Mr. J. H. SMITH, Atherton, Queensland; Mr. H. STEEDMAN, Perth, W. Australia; Mr. E. J. STEER, Capetown, S. Africa; Mr. D. R. STEWART, Albany, W. Australia; Dr. G. H. H. TATE, American Museum of Natural History, New York, N. Y.; Professor R. B. THOMSON, The University, Toronto, Ont.; Dr. J. C. TH. UPHOF, Orlando, Fla.; Dr. C. A. WEATHERBY, Gray Herbarium, and Professor WM. H. WESTON, both of Harvard University; Dr. FR. V. WETTSTEIN,

K. Wilhelm Institut f. Biologie, Dahlem; Professor EDGAR J. WHERRY, University of Pennsylvania, Philadelphia, Pa.; Mr. J. WYER, N. Queensland Natural History Club, Cairns, N. Queensland.

Finally my thanks are due to the Carnegie Institution of Washington, at Stanford University, for technical help.

*   *   *

From time to time during the last 50 or 60 years there have appeared in various popular magazines and newspapers accounts giving more or less detailed descriptions of fabulous man-eating trees. The earliest of these, apparently, is one which was written by Dr. CARLE LICHE, quoted at length by CHASE S. OSBORN in his book *Madagascar, the land of the man-eating tree*. This lurid title was used avowedly to "enmesh the interest of possible readers", not to propagate the faith. A summary of this and of a number of other yarns has been provided by SOPHIA PRIOR in a bulletin issued by the Field Museum of Natural History in 1939. If the reader cares to inform himself concerning this lore, these two sources will set him on his way. Miss PRIOR'S paper is documented, and includes reproduction of some of the illustrations which constitute part of the original but unconvincing evidence offered in the various accounts reviewed by her. Extensive use has been made of the Field Museum bulletin by Dr. ABÍLIO FERNANDES in an article entitled *Morphologia e biologia das plantas carnivoras (see under Drosophyllum)*.

An amusing, perhaps also tragic, circumstance is to be found described in LICHE'S account, in which a highly imaginative illustration shows that, instead of a native maiden being sacrificed by her tribe by yielding her up to the man-eating tree (possibly a fictitious kind of cycad), a beautiful magazine cover blonde was the lamb brought to the slaughter . . .

A certain carnivorous-plant-mindedness shown by the general public has been due also to occasional cartoons in papers and magazines. In these it is usually the flowers which are incorrectly if amusingly represented as the traps. Such contributions to the more evanescent literature are happily intended less for instruction than for titillation. The misconceptions which arise in this way, while doing little harm, awaken curiosity, the mother of knowledge.

All the illustrations in this book are originals, prepared by the author, unless specifically noted otherwise. The names of authorities in many cases are not accompanied by dates. In such cases only a single publication, to be found in the literature lists, can be referred to. Passages in languages other than English have been translated.

The arrangement of chapters may appear illogical. The principle underlying it is the increasing complexity of the traps. But for this, the fungi may be thought to appear in a strange setting.

*   *   *

Finally I wish to acknowledge assistance, in the reading of proofs, of Professor C. B, VAN NIEL, of Stanford University; of Dr. MARY MITCHELL MOORE (Mrs. A. R. MOORE). and Mrs. F. VERDOORN, who also prepared the indices. Dr. MICHAEL DOUDOROFF, University of California, and the editors of CHRONICA BOTANICA have kindly helped me in checking a number of references to the literature.

Caroli Goebelii

Praeceptoris Illustrissimi

Amici Fidelis

MEMORIAE

CONTENTS

INTRODUCTION

Chapter I: HELIAMPHORA

Chapter II: SARRACENIA

Chapter III: DARLINGTONIA CALIFORNICA

Chapter IV: NEPENTHES

Chapter V: CEPHALOTUS FOLLICULARIS

Chapter VI: GENLISEA

Chapter VII: BYBLIS

Chapter VIII: DROSOPHYLLUM LUSITANICUM

Chapter IX: PINGUICULA

Chapter X: DROSERA

Chapter XI: CARNIVOROUS FUNGI

Chapter XIIa: DIONAEA

Chapter XIIb: ALDROVANDA

Chapter XIII: UTRICULARIA, BIOVULARIA and POLYPOMPHOLYX

Chapter XIV: The UTRICULARIA TRAP

THE EARLIEST KNOWN ILLUSTRATION OF *Nepenthes* (*Nepenthes mirabilis* (Lour.) Merr.) FROM RUMPHIUS, HERBARIUM AMBOINENSE 5: 59 (PUBLISHED IN 1747, BUT DRAWN IN THE SECOND PART OF THE 17TH CENTURY). THE PLANT AT THE RIGHT IS *Flagellaria indica*. — THE VIGNETTE ON P. XV HAS BEEN RE-PRODUCED FROM CLUSIUS' RARIORUM PLANTARUM HISTORIA (*cf.* P. 18), ONE OF THE FIRST DRAWINGS OF A *Sarracenia*. THE *Drosera* VIGNETTE ON P. 271 HAS, BY COURTESY OF PROF. BAAS BECKING, BEEN RE-PRODUCED FROM A PRINT, MADE DIRECTLY FROM A 16TH CENTURY BLOCK USED FOR DODONAEUS' HERBALS.

INTRODUCTION

The purpose of this book is to give an historical review and summary of our present knowledge about the carnivorous or insectivorous plants, the former being the better term. Of these there are about 450 or more species, representing 15 genera, belonging, aside from the fungi, to six families, indicated in the present table (TABLE 1), together with their geographic distribution.

TABLE 1

FAMILY AND GENUS	NO. OF SPECIES	GEOGRAPHIC DISTRIBUTION
Sarraceniaceae		
Heliamphora	5	British Guiana; Venezuela.
Sarracenia	9	Eastern N. America: Labrador to S. E. United States of America.
Darlingtonia (*Chrysamphora*)	1	N. California and S. Oregon.
Nepenthaceae		
Nepenthes	65	Eastern Tropics to Ceylon and Madagascar.
Droseraceae		
Dionaea	1	North Carolina and northern South Carolina, U. S. A.
Aldrovanda	1	Europe, India, Japan, Africa and Queensland, Australia.
Drosophyllum	1	S. Portugal, S. W. Spain, Morocco.
Drosera	90	Ubiquitous.
Byblidaceae		
Byblis	2	Australia, from N. W. to S. W.
Cephalotaceae		
Cephalotus	1	Australia, extreme S. W.
Lentibulariaceae		
Pinguicula	30	N. hemisphere in Old and New Worlds.
Utricularia	275	Ubiquitous.
Biovularia	2	Cuba; eastern S. America.
Polypompholyx	2 (4)	S. and S. W. Australia.
Genlisea	10	W. African and E. South American tropics.
Fungi (various genera with trapping mechanisms)	20 or more.	Ubiquitous.

Roridula, formerly regarded as carnivorous, has now been shown by me not to be so, and is excluded from the above list. The "man-eating tree of Madagascar" must at present also be excluded, since the evidence of its existence is elusive.

The table shows that the carnivorous plants are divisible into two groups, one lot (*Sarraceniaceae* to *Cephalotaceae*) belonging to the *Choripetalae*, the rest to the *Sympetalae*, with personate flowers. This wide separation is a remarkable indication that the carnivorous habit has arisen among the higher plants at two points at the fewest, (as well as among the fungi), in the course of evolution. The methods of capturing prey are in some measure common to the two lots, the greatest height of specialization having been reached by *Dionaea* and *Aldro-*

vanda among the *Choripetalae* and by *Utricularia* among the *Sympetalae.* For this reason the arrangement (Table 2) which has been followed is that which groups the plants according to the character of their trapping mechanisms, named for their obvious analogs among human devices. By 'active traps' is meant those which display special movements necessary or contributory to the capture of prey.

TABLE 2

KIND OF TRAP	GENUS
Pitfalls (passive traps), the pitcher plants	*Heliamphora*
	Sarracenia
	Darlingtonia
	Cephalotus
	Nepenthes
Lobster pot (passive trap)	*Genlisea*
Snares (noose, some active; sticky discs, etc., passive)	Certain *Fungi*
Bird lime or fly-paper traps	
Passive	*Byblis*
	Drosophyllum
Active	*Pinguicula*
	Drosera
Steel-trap (active)	*Dionaea*
	Aldrovanda
Mousetrap	*Utricularia*
	Biovularia
	Polypompholyx

The above table mentions merely the form of the trap. There are, however, other characters which contribute in some way to the efficiency of action. These include methods of attracting the prey by means of lures: the odor of violets in *Sarracenia*, of honey in *Drosophyllum*, of fungus in *Pinguicula;* the secretion of nectar by glands either on the traps or on parts leading to them as in *Nepenthes*, etc.; the exhibition of attractive colors and of bright fenestrations in *Sarracenia*, *Darlingtonia*, *Cephalotus;* of brilliant points of light reflected from drops of mucilage in *Pinguicula*, *Drosera*, etc.; the secretion of mucilage in *Drosera*, etc., movements of various degrees of rapidity, as in *Pinguicula*, *Dactylella*, *Drosera*, *Dionaea* and *Utricularia*. There are also, with few exceptions, means for digesting the prey when caught: enzymes and acids are excreted. When these, together with the captured prey, are accumulated in some sort of a receptacle, something much like the animal stomach results. Involved in all this there are special structures: hairs, glands, specialized stomata (*Cephalotus*, *Nepenthes*), waxy excretions (*Nepenthes*), emergencies (tentacles of *Drosera*).

From the purely physiological point of view the carnivorous plants are concerned in a somewhat special way in the acquisition of nutrient substances containing protein, possibly vitamins and perhaps the salts of potassium and phosphorus, and even others. In this way they receive some profit, though what they receive is no *sine qua non*, as it is with many other plants. As PFEFFER pointed out, many fungi are wholly carnivorous, as in the cases of *Cordyceps*, *Empusa*, etc. Among the higher plants are some which get all their food materials indirectly through agencies such as mycorrhizal fungi. Our so-called carnivorous plants are therefore not peculiar in this habit.

What then distinguishes the carnivorous plants from the rest of the plant world? Why should we still share the feelings of the naturalists of the 18th century who regarded them as *miracula naturae?* We do so, I think, because a carnivorous plant in the sense here meant is one possessing a trap which, though merely a constellation of structures and functions, many of them common enough elsewhere among plants, is a special organ for the capture and digestion of animal prey, thus turning the tables on animals, which directly or indirectly are herbivorous.

But may these traps as such be regarded as something unique? The answer to this question must be sought in such analogs as we may find among plants in general.

Pitfalls in the form of pitchers are of rather widespread occurrence. In some flowers the corolla is tubular and the inner surface is supplied with downward pointing hairs, and there is emitted a luring, if not alluring, smell. Flies are attracted and caught, but after effecting pollination, and the hairs having withered, are released (*Aristolochia*). In other flowers one or more members of the perianth are tubular and secrete and hold nectar (*Aquilegia, Marcgravia, Delphinium*). Perhaps the closest parallel is found in the pitcher leaves of some species of *Dischidia*, a tropical genus of the old world. They are invaded by adventitious roots from nearby stems of their own plant, and are often occupied by ants who use them as shelters. Probably in their native habitats they often contain moisture available for their invading roots. An inturned marginal rim surrounding the narrow mouth reminds one of the rim of the carnivorous pitcher, but it seems to have no well marked special function. In some species of *Dischidia* the pitchers are represented merely by dished leaves facing each other. At the other extreme *Dischidia pectinoides* has a double pitcher, one inside the other, according to GOEBEL. *Lathraea squamaria*, a root parasite of Europe, has hollow leaves, the hollow lined with glands. GOEBEL regards them as reservoirs for reserve stuffs. The upper leaf lobes of *Azolla* are also hollow, but these are inhabited by *Anabaena azollae* in symbiotic relationship. Among the liverworts are species in which the leaves are partly converted into "water sacs" (GOEBEL), notably *Frullania cornigera* of New Zealand, though our own species offer sufficiently good examples. *Lejeunea* behaves similarly, but the sacs are simpler. Most impressive are *Colura* and *Physiotum*. In *P. majus* occur nearly closed sacs the mouths of which are guarded by two lips closed together like the lips of a mussel shell (GOEBEL). Moreover one of the lips is moveable, being provided with a hinge region, thus serving as a valve. Precisely how this valve works is not clear. GOEBEL, to whose account I am indebted, points out that such an arrangement is known only in *Utricularia*, but it must be remembered that this comparison loses some of its cogency for the reason that GOEBEL thought the valve of the *Utricularia* trap to be a simple check valve. There is no evidence that these arrangements in the liverworts indicate a carnivorous habit, though they are inhabited, like any liverwort or moss, by protozoa, nematodes, etc. That they are water holders is evident.

The common teasel (*Dipsacus sylvestris*) has been regarded in all probability to be a carnivorous plant by MILLER CHRISTY (1923). This biennial herb is well known for its water catching reservoirs formed by the connation of the opposed leaves at their bases. A large plant attains a height of 6 feet. Eight plants, with an average height of 5 feet 8 inches, were found by CHRISTY to retain an average of a half pint of water. It is of interest to know that the teasel for this reason claimed the attention of TURNER (1551), who remarked the catching of "rayne" and "dew" (Herball, o.iiij, 1551) and GERARD (Herball, p. 1005, 1597) wrote quaintly, as it now appears to us, "The leaves growe foorth of the iointes by couples, not onely opposite or set one against an other, but also compassing the stalke about, and fastened togither, and so fastened that they hold deaw and raine water in manner of a little bason."

CHRISTY rejects the ideas that the primary object of the collection of water is the succour of the plant in times of drought, and the protection of its nectar from predatory insects. The presence of dead insects, rendering the water filthy, seems to point to these as a source of nutriment. "The cups undoubtedly form most efficient traps," FRANCIS DARWIN had said. CHRISTY suspected the water to have some narcotizing or intoxicating substance (F. DARWIN had noticed that beetles drown in it more rapidly than in pure water), and he further expressed the conviction that "the plant does profit by the insects caught in the cups". In view of the general evidence CHRISTY draws the conclusion that the teasel is a carnivorous plant, but without advancing any definite experimental proof.

The lobster-pot of *Genlisea*, though an exceedingly specialized structure, is fundamentally nothing more than a narrow pitcher with its interior armed with downward pointing hairs. Even the curious method of holding the lips of the narrow slit-like mouth in rigid relation to each other by an adhesion of cells finds its parallel in other situations such as the adhesions of algal cells and those of mycelia. In form, the 'prop-cells' responsible find a loose analog in the cystidia of *Coprinus*. But, after all, their structure and method of function is unique.

The snares found among the carnivorous fungi — those having definite traps — are more obscure in their analogies, and, it would appear, have originated within the group. Apparently unique is the noose of *Arthrobotrys*, etc. The adhesive disc is found among the orchids, in which it is the mechanism for attaching the pollinia to visiting insects. Obviously the orchids did not invent this originally — the fungi probably did so. The loop of the pollinia of *Asclepias* is a sort of noose snare (CARRY).

The snare of *Zoophagus* is a variant of the adhesive disc, but is remarkable as a device resembling in its manner of working a common fish-line and hook, or perhaps better an 'eel-bob.'

The plants which catch their prey by means of a viscid secretion are only a few of a multitude of others that excrete sticky substances by which small insects are caught. These substances are in general of three kinds: oily (often aromatic), resinous and mucilaginous. Among the carnivorous plants, only the last is found, as a watery medium is the only one that can carry an enzyme, as in *Drosera*. Adhesive (mucilaginous or resinous) glands are very common, and often small insects are captured, as, *e.g.* in the case of the catch-fly (*Silene*). Suspecting that many such plants might turn out to be carnivorous DARWIN investigated the behavior of some of them: *Saxifraga umbrosa, S. rotundifolia* (?), *Primula sinensis, Pelargonium zonale, Erica tetralix, Mirabilis longifolia* and *Nicotiana tabacum*. But while he thought to have proved that the hairs of these plants can in some instances absorb organic nutrients, he regretted that he did not try if they could "digest or render soluble animal substances." FERMI and BUSCAGLIONE in 1899 tried some of these and still others (*Martynia, Hydrolea, Sparmannia*) for digestion with negative results, whereas those of the recognized carnivorous plants which they tried were positive. This brings into relief the fact that there are many plants which resemble our carnivorous plants so closely that we can decide about them only through experiment.

Though the glands involved are in structure similar in some cases (*Byblis, Pinguicula*) to those found among other plants, those of *Drosophyllum* and *Drosera*, fundamentally the same in structure in both, are unique as entireties. Those of *Drosera* are raised on emergencies which display motility in no respect different, except perhaps in speed, from that of ordinary growth. The histological elements of the glands are common enough; again it is the constellation of characters which stands out.

The most complete analog to a carnivorous plant of this type is one which was until recently regarded as one itself. This is the *Roridula*, of which there are two species, in South Africa. I myself included it among the carnivores in an account published in 1933. Since that time, on receiving material preserved in formalin from Munich, it was at once apparent that the secretion which appears as glistening droplets in the living plant, was intact and still adherent to the glands, and could therefore not be a mucilage. Had the preservative been alcohol this might have escaped attention. The leaves bear many tentacles superficially similar to those of *Drosera*. Examination showed them to be anatomically quite different, and that they exude a resinous secretion. There are no other glands, so that on this evidence the carnivorous habit seems to be quite excluded (LLOYD, 1934). These two species, relatives of *Drosera*, are, like them and *Byblis*, used by certain insects (certain bugs and crab spiders) as habitual feeding grounds. When insects are freshly caught, they are attacked for their body juices. How these commensal forms avoid capture is another matter, but an interesting one.

The trap of *Dionaea* and *Aldrovanda*, with its close resemblance to a steel-trap, has been, and still is regarded by some as "perhaps the most marvellous in the world," to quote MORREN (1875) who, in saying this, was only repeating what DARWIN had already said. It appears to be quite unique when regarded as a total mechanism. But an analog, in some measure at any rate, was suggested by DELPINO, quoted by HOOKER in his Presidential Address at the meeting of the British Association for the Advancement of Science in 1874. HOOKER had already described a plant from Tierra del Fuego under the name *Caltha dioneaefolia* "which," DELPINO in effect remarked, "is so analogous in the structure of its leaves to *Dionaea*, that it is difficult to resist the conviction that its structure also is adapted for the capture of small insects".

Contributory structural features of these traps are the glands, physiologically of two kinds, but of identical (*Dionaea*) or different (*Aldrovanda*) structure, and the sensitive hairs, which are local points of greater sensitivity. The latter only are unique in structure. There is also motile tissue which, startling in rapidity though its movements are, appears to work in much the same way as that of tissues exhibiting geotropic responses, according to BROWN. But should *Caltha dioneaefolia*, as DELPINO suggested, turn out to be quite parallel to *Dionaea*, it would only add another member to a very small unique group.

A curious case of an insect-catching grass, *Molinia coerulea*, briefly described by F. LUDWIG in 1881, may here be indicated as an analog, albeit a very loose one, to the trap of *Dionaea*. It appears that this grass can catch small insects between its paleae, which act as the jaws of a spring trap, after the fashion of a 5-cent spring mousetrap. It is well known that, during flowering, the paleae are forcibly separated by the swelling lodicules, and are held there for the space of anthesis. The lodicules then shrink and allow the paleae to close. If now, during the period, an insect, attracted by the shining, sappy and turgid masses, attacks them by biting or puncturing, the resulting reduction of turgor is sufficient to allow the outer palea to close, which it does "with surprising swiftness" (HILDEBRAND, *fide* LUDWIG) thereby trapping the offending insect. This action, LUDWIG points out, disadvantages the plant in curtailing the time during which the flower would normally remain open. No compensating benefit seems to accrue.

The trap of *Utricularia*, minute though it is, is compared in the present account to a mousetrap. There are mousetraps and mousetraps however, from simple to complex in structure, from a 5 cent dead-fall to an elaborate, automatic self-setting one, which catches them as fast as they come. If to this should be added a disposal plant (Prof. TRACY I. STORER informs me that such a mousetrap has been invented) so that nothing is left at last but hair and bones, the comparison would be fairly complete, especially if the trap should work in any position and at the same time under water. These are constructed of rigid parts, while that of *Utricularia* is composed of soft, yielding parts. Previous to 1911, the *Utricularia* trap was thought to be relatively simple: a soft "pitcher" or vesicle guarded by a simple check-valve; now it is known to have two valves, a tripping mechanism, a spring which opens the door (one of the valves) which then automatically closes, barely to indicate the complexity of the mechanism, complexity and perfection of which are extraordinary. In 1891 GOEBEL said that the *Utricularias* are "among the most interesting of plant forms, whether we view them from the point of view of their morphology, anatomy or biology." If this was true at that date, it is, because of the added knowledge about the complexity of the trap, much more true now, as indeed GOEBEL personally admitted to me in conversation.

For my own edification I have attempted to indicate the structure of a mousetrap which, as closely as may be, duplicates the trap of *Utricularia* without, however, hoping for the reward for him who invents a mousetrap, promised, I believe, by EMERSON. In this I am yielding to the importunities of many of my friends, whose urgings I must assume to be disinterested. I have, somewhat apologetically, relegated the drawings and description (very necessary I fear) to an appendix to the chapter on *Utricularia*.

For such a mechanism we cannot find an analog among other plants. Though it has moving parts, the property of irritability is not used. Particularly, after the door opens, which it does only passively, it instantly recovers its original position all in 1/33 second. Though its movements are made possible by its turgidity, there is no change of turgor — hence the instant reversibility of movement. But this again depends on a structure which finds some analogy in the walls of anthers, but only a partial one. Without further amplification we may regard *Utricularia* as unique.

It is not without interest to note that among the *Lentibulariaceae* we find examples of the simplest traps (*Pinguicula*), the most complex of the pitfall type, (in the lobster pot of *Genlisea*), and the incomparable trap of *Utricularia*, whose only rival is that of *Dionaea*. Which of the two is the more "wonderful" (I refer now to DARWIN's statement that he thought *Dionaea* the "most wonderful plant in the world") will perhaps be a matter of opinion, but the evidence seems to favor *Utricularia*.

How all these traps work and how we came to know about them, it is the purpose of this book to tell. But I have not confined myself to the traps, for it seemed necessary to present an adequate picture of the plants as a whole. This was especially true of *Utricularia*, as, in spite of many studies, a survey of the entire genus (and those of *Polypompholyx* and *Biovularia*) has not been made since the 1891 publication of GOEBEL. No genus more fully substantiates the saying of CARUEL "La pianta cresce ciascuna alla sua idiosincrasia", for which allusion I am indebted to Professor GOEBEL. The survey presented seems to indicate with some fairness the extraordinary variety of form and behavior of these plants, but necessarily as briefly as possible in the interest of space saving.

About the origin and evolution of the carnivorous plants, however much these questions may intrigue the mind, little can be said, nor have I attempted to discuss them. The evidence from fossils is meagre, for these plants, even the most prolific of them, have seldom been preserved. A *Utricularia* (*U. Berendii* Keilhack) is recorded from the old-diluvial of Oberohe (ENGLER and PRANTL). No others, so far as I know, have been recorded. The water lilies are recorded for the Tertiary, and it is probable that *Utricularia* was contemporary. The fact that they have originated at two or more distinct points in the phylogenetic tree is of major importance. How the highly specialized organs of capture could have evolved seems to defy our present knowledge.

J. G. PEIRCE (1926) remarks that the wide distribution of the carnivorous plants and the permanence of their peculiar morphological and physiological characters mark them as descendants of ancient forms, but we have to add that only some of them are widely distributed (*Drosera, Pinguicula, Aldrovanda* (Old World only) and *Utricularia*) while others, though related in one taxonomic group or the other, are of restricted, sometimes very restricted, distribution. The two categories exist side by side in that ancient continent, Australia. Are the latter young scions derived from the more ancient stocks? And may we regard the Australian types of *Utricularia* as ancient types and in some measure as analogs of ancient animal forms of that continent? Since we cannot answer these questions, it is perhaps as well to say no more.

Literature Cited:

CARRY, T. H., On the structure and development of the gynostegium and the mode of fertilization in *Asclepias Cornuti* Decaisne. Trans. Linn. Soc. London, II, 2:173–208, 1881–1887.

CHRISTY, M., The common teasel as a carnivorous plant. Journ. Bot. 61:33–45, 1923.

CRAMER, C., Über die insectenfressenden Pflanzen. A lecture. Zürich, 14 Dec. 1876. Seen. No more explicit data given.

DARWIN, F., On the protoplasmic filaments from the glandular hairs on the leaves of the common teasel (*Dipsacus sylvestris*). Quart. Journ. Micros. Sci. n. s. 25:245–272, 1877.

DRUDE, O., Die insectenfressenden Pflanzen. SCHENK'S Handbuch der Botanik, Breslau, 1881, I:113–146.

FERMI and BUSCAGLIONE (*see* under *Utricularia*).

FRANÇA, C., La question des plantes carnivores dans le passé et dans le présent. Bol. Soc. Brot. 1:38–57, 1922.

GOEBEL, K., Organographie der Pflanzen, 3. Auflage, Jena, 1928–33.

HOOKER, J. D., Address to the Department of Zoology and Botany, 1874. B. A. A. S., Report of the Forty-fourth Meeting, 1874:102–116, 1875.

JONES, F. M., The most wonderful plant in the world, with some unpublished correspondence of CHARLES DARWIN. Nat. Hist. 23:589–596, 1923.

LLOYD F. E., Is *Roridula* a carnivorous plant? Can. Journ. Res. 10:780–786, 1934.

LUDWIG, F., *Molinia coerulea* als Fliegenfängerin. Bot. Centralbl. 8:87, 1881.

MORREN, ED., La théorie des plantes carnivores et irritables. Bull. de l'Acad. Roy. Belg. II, 40:1040 *seq.* (seconde édition revue et améliorée dans Bull. Féd. Soc. Hort. 1875).

OSBORN, C. S., The land of the man-eating tree. Pp. 442, New York, 1924.

PEIRCE, J. G., The physiology of plants. New York, 1926.

PFEFFER, W., Über die fleischfressenden Pflanzen und über die Ernährung durch Aufnahme der organischen Stoffe überhaupt. Landw. Jahrb. 6:969–998, 1877.

PLANCHON, J.–E., Les plantes carnivores. Rev. des deux mondes, 13:231–259, 1876.

Chapter I

HELIAMPHORA

Discovery. — Appearance of *H. nutans*. — Discovery of other species. — Habitat. — Leaf structure. — Leaf forms. — Comparison of species.

The genus *Heliamphora* is based on a plant, *H. nutans*, collected by SCHOMBURGK who found it growing "in a marshy savannah, at an elevation of about 6000 ft. above the level of the sea on the mountain of Roraima," "the fruitful mother of streams," on the borders of British Guiana. (BENTHAM 1840; SCHOMBURGK 1841). IM THURN (1887) described its habitat and appearance. " . . . . . the most remarkable plant of the swamp . . . . . is the South American pitcher plant, *Heliamphora nutans* Benth., which grows in wide-spreading, very dense tufts in the wettest places, but where the grass happens not to be long. Its red-veined pitcher-leaves, its delicate white flowers raised high on red tinted stems, its sturdy habit of growth, make it a pretty little picture wherever it grows. . . . . . it attains its full size and best development . . . . . up on the ledges of the cliff of Roraima and even on the top." (IM THURN 1887).

For many years only the one species, *H. nutans* Bentham ($1 — 1$), was known. The meagre literature deals almost solely with this plant. Four other species are now known. Three of these were discovered on Mt. Duida, Venezuela, by Dr. G. H. H. TATE just previous to 1931, and were described by Dr. H. A. GLEASON in 1931. An examination of the herbarium material (all type specimens in the herbarium of the New York Botanical Garden) was made possible for me through the kindness of Dr. GLEASON, and my notes on these species have been published (1933). A fourth species, also discovered by Dr. TATE in 1937–8 in the same general region, is *H. minor* (TEXT FIG. 1). The three Mt. Duida species, *H. Macdonaldae* ($1 — 2$), *H. Tyleri* and *H. Tatei*, are closely related and furnish a striking example of closely related species arising within a restricted region (LLOYD 1905). Further exploration may show the genus *Heliamphora* to be as prolific of species as the North American *Sarracenia*, or even more so.

Heliamphora grows in a region of vast rainfall, under extremely wet conditions of soil and air. It is cultivated only with difficulty, but successfully at the Edinburgh Botanical Garden, and I am indebted to Sir WILLIAM WRIGHT SMITH for both preserved and living material of the species *H. nutans*, on which the present account is based. The name *Heliamphora* means swamp-pitcher.

The accounts of *H. nutans* given us by ZIPPERER (1885), MACFARLANE (1889, 1893), GOEBEL (1891), and by one of his students, KRAFFT (1896), leave little to be added. The plant consists of a rosette of basal leaves arising from a strong rootstock. It produces a simple racemose inflorescence of white or pale rose colored apetalous flowers. The 4–6 sepals are ovate-acuminate in form, with numerous stamens and a trilocular ovary with a single style. The normal mature leaves may attain a length of 30 cm.; in cultivation, they are rarely longer than 15 cm. On side shoots of the rhizome arise depauperate branches bearing leaves in various stages of arrested development (2 — 2-4), which have been duly described by the above authors.

Structure of the leaf. — The normal pitcher leaf is an insect trap of the pitfall type. Its form is that of a gracefully curved funnel, widening above the base to contract somewhat just below a leafy expansion, the bell (2 — 1; TEXT FIG. 1). The apex of the bell normally ends in a spoon-shaped, thick-walled structure resembling superficially the lid of *Nepenthes*, which stands upright as represented by BENTHAM, and not bent forward as GOEBEL suggested as a protection of the nectar secreted against rain. The spoon is lacking in some of the leaves on plants which I have seen growing in greenhouses, where many of the leaves are small and lacking in vigor, but seems to be normally present and upright in position in wild plants, judging from a photograph made by TATE (LLOYD 1933).

Mrs. ARBER (1941) regards the spoon ("hood" she calls it) as the continuation of the rudimentary curve-over of the pitcher-lip. The indications of this curve-over are stated to be "very slight". My material, derived from the same source as hers, shows no such indication. To be sure, the sides of the spoon are the incurled margins of the leaf apex, but these have no relation, it seems to me, to anything corresponding to a putative "outward roll-over".

The flaring bell is oval in form, the margins sweeping forward to meet at once or to run parallel for a short distance before joining. At this point they continue into two narrow wings running down the mid-ventral surface of the pitcher, toward the base of which they enlarge and spread to form a wide membranous spreading and clasping base. Above the wings are closely approximated, and in this respect *Heliamphora*, according to MACFARLANE, occupies an intermediate position between *Nepenthes*, with widely removed wings and *Sarracenia* and *Darlingtonia* with a single keel (representing fused wings). The outer surface of the pitcher bears numerous twin unicellular trichomes which have inverted V-shaped spreading arms quite unique and peculiar to this plant (2 — 6 and TEXT FIG. 1), stomata, and many minute glands which probably secrete nectar (2 — 10). These are numerous on the wings, and are probably part of a general lure for insects. The inner surface can be divided for the purpose of description into four zones. Zone 1 (2 — 1) is the spoon, which is quite smooth on its concave surface, but here bears a number of glands which are larger than elsewhere, and some of them very large, usually three or four on each flank. These are nectar glands. Zone 2 begins just below the spoon and is indicated by a dense clothing of downward pointing, delicate hairs in great numbers covering the whole of the surface of the bell (which occasionally is smooth), and the upper constricted portion of the tubular part of the pitcher. They are found in reduced numbers for a short space just below the constriction, and here they are very long and straight. Below a certain point, however, the hairiness suddenly ceases, and gives way to the next zone (3) in which the epidermis is glistening smooth. While in zone 2 there are very numerous nectar glands, interspersed between the bases of the hairs, here in zone 3 there are none at all. Below the lower limit of the smooth area there begins zone 4, which again is clothed, but more sparsely than the bell, with downwardly directed hairs. These are very stout and claw-like (2 — 5), while those of the bell are longer and flexible. Both kinds are longitudinally ridged with delicate folds of cuticle, the hairs of the bell especially so. The difference of stature and rigidity is related to their functions. The hairs of the bell afford an unstable footing for insects which are trying to get at the nectar on the surface between them, and their flexibility adds to the instability, while those in the depths of the pitcher have the rôle of retention, and for this purpose the stronger they are the better. There are no glands in zone 4. There are no digestive glands present in this trap.

The abnormal leaves on the reduced side shoots are of various forms (2 — 2-4). The base of the shoot is enveloped in scale leaves. Following these there may be underdeveloped leaves, described by KRAFFT, in which the tube is very slender and would have a very limited function as a trap, and acts simply as a petiole. The bell is relatively large so that the whole behaves as nothing more than a photosynthetic organ. A spoon is not developed. The inner surface of the blade (bell) is free of hairs, but carries nectar glands. At the lower limits of the bell there is a trapping zone of hairs, but the rest of the tube is quite smooth. It is to be noticed that the "tube" is not truly such, since its edges are not fused. This I judge from KRAFFT's drawing, though he does not state so specifically. GOEBEL described a sort of juvenile leaf at the base of normal shoots consisting of a closed tube, winged with two wings as in the normal, but with a much reduced bell with out-turned edges and no spoon. KRAFFT added some details, pointing out that the whole of the inner surface, save a small zone at the base, is lined with downward pointing hairs. The bell, with the exception of the outturned edges, is also hairy, but the spoon — this is not evidently such, nor did GOEBEL recognize it — is without hairs or glands. GOEBEL described a still simpler and more elementary condition in leaves seen on much reduced side shoots. These were small, with an undeveloped bell, and the tube was open, though appearing closed by the juxtaposition of the edges of the leaf margins, or perhaps sometimes closed by the concrescence or adhesion of these edges, a mode of development which he argues is different from that of the normal leaf which arises as a peltate structure. This idea has been elaborated by TROLL who generally supports GOEBEL's thesis that the tube of the pitcher of *Sarracenia* and *Heliamphora* is fundamentally a peltate leaf. The condition of concrescence or adhesion of the leaf margins is actually realized in the case of *H. Tyleri* in its fully developed normal leaves, as we shall see.

The latest described species, *H. minor* Gleason was found by Dr. G. H. H. TATE on Mt. Auyan-Tepui, Venezuela in December, 1937 at an altitude of 2,200 meters. Generally similar to *H. nutans*, it differs in the more sturdy and less graceful leaves, 10 to 12 cm. long. The spoon is larger and deeper, and orbicular in form. The bell is densely hairy only along the marginal zone, with a few scattered small downward directed hairs on the general surface, with many nectar glands. The slight constriction at the base of the bell is hairy, with slender hairs, and very glandular. The twin hairs on the outer surface are finely tuberculate (TEXT FIG. 1).

The other recently described species *H. Tatei, H. Tyleri* and *H. Macdonaldae* (GLEASON 1931) are tall shrubby plants (4 feet), but otherwise present only a few differences which concern us here. The leaf is in all three much elongated, the major elongation being in the bell which becomes tubular, expanding only at the top where it is surmounted by a rather large and massive overhanging lip-like appendage, which, like the spoon in *H. nutans*, carries large nectar glands. The most divergent of the three is *H. Macdonaldae*, in which the inner surface of the bell is quite smooth except along the free margin and for a narrow zone at the lower limit of the neck about 2 cm. wide. The distribution of small glands on the outer surface is much the same as in *H. nutans* except that they do not occur on the outer faces of the extensive stipular wings.

Glands are absent from the interior surface of the bell where the surface is smooth, while even when in *H. nutans* the surface of the bell is smooth, as it sometimes is, glands occur nevertheless.

An adaptive feature of very great interest is one reported by TATE:— "The question arose . . . . . as to how the pitchers, closely packed and unable to bend over as they were, maintained a constant water level and succeeded in getting rid of the excess water poured into them during the frequent heavy rains. Upon examination it was found that each leaf had a small pore in the seam (opposite the midrib) placed just at the juncture of the basal water containing part of the pitcher and the terminal portion, through which the excess fluid might run out. This observation was made on *H. Macdonaldae*, but in all probability holds for other species as well." (TATE, quoted by GLEASON, 1931).

I have examined the material collected by Dr. TATE with much care and interest, so far as it was permitted, and I have found that the condition described above is to be found in its most pronounced form in *H. Tatei*. To understand the morphology involved let us compare the structure of the leaf with that of *H. nutans*, in which the closed tubular portion ends abruptly in a bell, slit for a short distance along the ventral border, the margins running downward as the ventral wings as above described, to be continued as the stipular wings. In *H. Tatei* the leaves are from 40 to 50 cm. long, and the stipules, in accordance with the shrubby habit of the plant, are very long, clasping the bearing stem and adjacent leaf bases. The ventral wings are short and foliose, while the bell is very long, being slit down the ventral side for some distance. The edges of the trumpet are here also confluent with the ventral wings, but above the morphological limit of the slit they are concrescent except for a space of about one centimeter at its lowest limit. Here the edges of the bell remain free, forming a short elongated-oval slit, which we may call the drain-slit or pore (TEXT FIG. 1). The head of water released by flowing through the slit amounts to 5 cm. in some leaves, or possibly more, often less. This would have the effect of lowering the center of gravity of the water loaded leaf very considerably. In *H. Macdonaldae*, in a leaf of nearly the same length (37 cm.), the region of fused edges was much shorter in the only leaf I could examine, while in *H. Tyleri* (of which I examined two leaves) there is but a slight commissure above the drain slit, or it may be quite open, as it is in *H. nutans.* The length of the slit is about 1 cm. more or less, and has ciliated margins, since it lies within the hairy zone of the bell near its lower limit. Owing to the fact that the specimens were dried and pressed "types", I was limited in my examination. Where the slit of the bell in *H. Macdonaldae* seemed to be open, this may have been due to the separation of the fused margins in drying (LLOYD 1933).

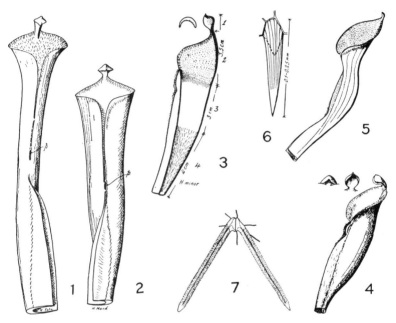

FIG. 1. — 1, *Heliamphora Tatei;* 2, *H. Macdonaldae;* 3, *H. minor,* the zonation of the interior surface is indicated by the numbers 1–4; 4, *H. minor;* 5, *H. nutans;* 6, retrorse hair of *H. minor;* 7, twin hairs of *H. minor.*

It is quite evident that the presence of the drain slit discovered by TATE would render tall plants, which grow to the height of four feet and inhabit a very rainy habitat, far less top-heavy. The upright position of the leaves is further assured by the ample, tightly clasping, stipular wings. At the same time it is to be observed that the adaptation is not equally expressed in all three species, being least so in *H. Tyleri,* in which the slit may not be present at all, the bell being slit all the way down to the limit of the hairy zone. So far as the effect is concerned, this amounts to the same thing, since the water is drained off to the lowest open point of the bell in any case.

Trichomes. — There are two kinds of hairs to be found on the inner surface of the pitcher, those of the bell and adjacent tube, that is of the conducting surface of HOOKER, and those of the basal portion of the tube. They are of identical morphology, but differ in important details of structure. They are unicellular hairs with the bases embedded in a raised mass of epidermis and underlying parenchyma. They taper from the base gradually to the sharp tip, and the cuticle is raised to form folds or ridges, beginning at or near the base and converging on the apex, where they gradually fade away. These ridges are more pronounced on the hairs of the conductive surface, and are much weaker to scarcely distinct on the hairs of the detentive surface. The former are relatively longer, more slender and distinctly flexible, the more so in the lower parts of the conductive surface. KRAFFT suggested that these ridges have use as strengthening elements, but the effect is not to make the hairs rigid. They may make it more difficult for flies to use their foot organs. Their chief efficiency lies, I imagine, in their number and flexibility, so that an insect cannot place its feet on the bell surface, but can only hook onto the hairs which by their flexibility give way and permit the insect to slip into the pitcher. The hairs of the detentive surface on the other hand are short, very thick walled and rigid, thereby making escape difficult. BENTHAM (1840) said of these that "they have all the appearance of ordinary secreting hairs," but this was a mistake. They are certainly not secretory.

The structure of the nectar gland of the pitcher in *Heliamphora* has been described, though not quite correctly, by KRAFFT (1896). There are, for purposes of description, two kinds: (*a*) those which are relatively small and have few cells, about 12 in number (2 — 10). These are found scattered over the whole of the bell, and on the outer surfaces, including the wings, and are regarded as nectar glands by GOEBEL, who detected a sweetness in the excreted fluid; and (*b*) large glands found only on the inner surface of the spoon (2 — 7). KRAFFT spoke of three kinds of glands, distinguishing those on the inner from those on the outer surfaces. But they are all quite the same in structure, differing somewhat in size, those on the outer surfaces being shallower, the glandular cells of a gland having little more depth than that of the surrounding epidermis.

The structure of the smaller glands is as follows: They appear in surface view to consist of six cells, four in a single course in the level of the epidermis, covered partially by two cells, the "cover cells" of GOEBEL. The area of the exposed surface of the gland is about equal to that of a stoma. It is difficult to resist the theory that the glands are derived phylogenetically from stomata, but there is no support for this beyond the suggestive appearance of the two cover cells. Beneath the course of four cells, there is a second inner course of cells which appeared to KRAFFT to be four in number. One usually can count at least six cells, two cells lying beneath the two cover cells. But the glands are of irregular structure, and one cannot say definitely that there are only so many cells. These constitute the gland proper, and are all derived from the epidermis. They are surrounded by a cuticularized membrane, except at the base, which, though being partially covered with this membrane, is not entirely so, there being left a "window" (KRAFFT used this word), so that the active gland cells lie in direct contact with usually two, sometimes one, or three to four, parenchyma cells below.

The walls of these cells which lie in contact with those of the gland immediately above (if we assume an orientation of up and down, the cover cells being up) are always strengthened by curved thickenings like those of xylem vessels. KRAFFT seems to have regarded these cells also to be cuticularized, and the wall thickenings to be on the lateral walls in contact with surrounding parenchyma cells. On both these points he was mistaken. The wall thickenings are found on the walls only where the cells impinge on the gland cells, and are not cuticularized in any part. This arrangement is found also in the glands of *Sarracenia*, as GOEBEL showed, to be described beyond. The function of these parenchyma cells is not known, but it serves to call them transmitting cells. But whether they do more than permit movement of substances from the leaf tissues to the gland, is not known. There is no reason to particularize as to the distinction between the glands of the inner and outer surfaces, beyond the fact that where the outer surface glands impinge on the underlying parenchyma, the parenchyma cells in immediate contact are sometimes so large that it is very easy to recognize the fact that the wall thickenings occur only where the gland cells are in contact with the parenchyma cells. In cases where the section has run through the gland at right angles to the common axis of the contingent parenchyma walls beneath the gland, it becomes apparent why cell walls carrying the thickenings appear to be other than those exactly in contact with the glands, namely, because of the oblique position. In making a drawing one is usually forced to show them as if they were anticlinal, instead of periclinal walls. For this reason one can understand how KRAFFT may have been misled. Viewing the gland from beneath, possible in tangential sections, leaves no doubt about the facts.

The glandular cells and the contingent parenchyma cells were regarded together as constituting the gland by KRAFFT, and the whole was attributed by him to an epidermal origin. But the parenchyma cells are certainly not of glandular nature, judging by their meagre protoplasmic contents, and are of equal certainty not of epidermal origin. One hardly needs to see developmental stages to draw this conclusion. FENNER's account of the origin of the *Sarracenia* nectar gland, which is of the same structure as that of *Heliamphora*, also includes the parenchyma cells.

The large glands are found only on the inner surface of the spoon. KRAFFT correctly traces this type of gland to an epidermal origin, but does not show that in this gland also there are to be found the xylem-like parenchyma cells. He attributes to the gland an identity with the large glands found in *Cephalotus* which, as we shall see when we discuss the latter, is not justified. These glands occur to the number of about 20, larger and smaller in size, the larger ones being in a more lateral position. And these are very large. In surface view they consist of a number of cover cells and first course cells, underlain by about four courses of thick walled cells beneath which lies the mass of glandular cells proper. The periphery of this mass is irregular, as if there was a tendency of the glandular mass to branch or lobe. The contingent parenchyma by the same token intrudes cells between the lobes. So large are these glands that they must contain about 1000 cells. There are only a half-dozen such large glands, the rest within the spoon being of various sizes, but all smaller and showing a structure more obviously like that of the rest of the glands of the inner and outer surfaces. One of the smallest I show in Plate 2 — 7, in which it is seen that some of the parenchyma cells in contact with the gland have spirally and reticulately thickened walls. One finds them in the large glands, but only occasionally; they are very difficult to find, however. In any event the wall thickenings seem to be less pronounced and distinct. The large gland is often in close contact with the vascular tissue.

The cuticularization, as in the small glands of the general surfaces, extends around the gland, with, however, areas furnishing contact with the surrounding parenchyma.

GOEBEL leaned towards the opinion that the glands above described are different in structure from those of *Sarracenia*, but the evidence to be later deduced will, I think, show otherwise. MAC-FARLANE described the glands as being depressed and surrounded by thick walled neighbor cells, "the upper part of which may overhang" the gland. He did not study the gland structure further, as KRAFFT did later, and suggested that the glands of *Heliamphora* stand in an intermediate position between those of *Sarracenia* and those of *Nepenthes*. This idea seems lacking in justification.

Prey and its fate. — That insects are caught by the pitchers of *Heliamphora* was not known to BENTHAM, who handled the first material to reach London. I found insect remains in the pitchers of *H. Tyleri* and KRAFFT did so in the pitchers of *H. nutans* sent to him from England by Veitch and Sons. The odor accompanying decay of insect bodies was noticed by KRAFFT. As there are no digestive glands to be found, we must conclude that the proteins of animal bodies are made available to the plant only by means of bacterial digestion. That no work has been done on this plant can be explained by the rarity of the material, due to the difficulties of cultivation.

Literature Cited:

ARBER (*see* under *Cephalotus*).
BENTHAM, G., *Heliamphora nutans*, a new pitcher plant from British Guiana. Transact. Linn. Soc. 18, 1840.
FENNER, C. A., Beiträge zur Kenntnis der Anatomie, Entwicklungsgeschichte und Biologie der Laubblätter und Drüsen einiger Insektivoren. Flora 93:335-434, 1904.
GLEASON, H. A. and E. F. KILLIP, Botanical results of the Tyler-Duida Expedition. Bull. Torr. Bot. Club 58:277-586, 1931.
GLEASON, H. A., Brittonia 3:164, 1939 (Description of *Heliamphora minor*).
GOEBEL, K., Pflanzenbiologische Schilderungen. Marburg, 1891.
IM THURN, E. F. and D. OLIVER, The botany of the Roraima Expedition of 1884. Trans. Linn. Soc. London II, 2:249-300, 1887.
KRAFFT, S., Beiträge zur Kenntnis der Sarraceniaceen-Gattung *Heliamphora*. Diss. Munich, 1896.
LLOYD, F. E., Isolation and the origin of species. Science, N. S. 22:710-712, 1905.
LLOYD, F. E., The carnivorous plants. Trans. R. S. C. 27:3-67, 1933.
MACFARLANE, J. M., Observations on some pitchered insectivorous plants, I. Ann. Bot. 3:253-266, 1889; II. Ann. Bot. 7:403-458, 1893.
SCHOMBURGK, R. H., Reisen im Guiana... Leipzig 1841.
TROLL, W., Morphologie der schildförmigen Blätter. Planta 17:153-314, 1932.
ZIPPERER, PAUL, Beitrag zur Kenntnis der Sarraceniaceen. Diss. Erlangen, 1885.

Chapter II

SARRACENIA

Discovery. — Known species. — Descriptions of: *S. purpurea.* — *S. psittacina.* — *S. Courtii.* — *S. minor.* — *S. Drummondii.* — *S. flava.* — *S. Jonesii.* — Morphology of the leaf. — Digestion and absorption. — Animal life of the pitchers.

The genus *Sarracenia* is based on TOURNEFORT's original description (1700) of a plant sent to him by Dr. M. S. SARRAZIN from Quebec, Canada. The name was adopted by LINNAEUS (1737). The earliest known illustration of *Sarracenia* is to be found in DE L'OBEL's *Nova Stirpium Adversaria*, evidently of a leaf of *S. minor*, probably received from some Spanish explorer in Florida (p. 430, 1576 ed.). According to UPHOF (Engler and Prantl, 2 ed.) there are nine species. WHERRY (1933) distinguishes between the northern form of *S. purpurea* and a southern form, namely, the subspecies *S. purpurea gibbosa* and *S. purpurea venosa*, respectively. All species are distinguished by the possession of pitcher leaves either upright or decumbent, of considerable variety of form, to be detailed later. The following is a list of the species and their geographic distribution, according to WHERRY (1935).

Species with upright tubular pitcher leaves: —

S. oreophila (Kearney) Wherry. Green pitcher plant. Of very limited distribution: Taylor Co., Georgia, and in the Appalachian Mountains of Alabama (Cherokee, DeKalb, and Marshall Cos.).

S. Sledgei Macfarlane. Pale pitcher plant. S. Alabama, Mississippi, Louisiana and E. Texas. One or two colonies are reported to survive in the Cumberland Plateau of Tennessee, presumably in its ancestral home before the rise of the peneplain of the Cretaceous.

S. flava L. Yellow pitcher plant (*1 — 7*). N. and S. Carolina, Georgia, extreme N. Florida and S. Alabama, in the coastal plain.

S. Jonesii Wherry. Red pitcher plant. There is a singular and striking survival of this plant in an isolated spot in Buncombe and Henderson Cos., N. Carolina. Otherwise it is found chiefly in S. Alabama and in restricted regions nearby in Florida and Mississippi.

S. Drummondii Croom. (*1 — 6*). White-top pitcher plant. Chiefly S. Alabama, with slight extensions into Mississippi, Georgia, and N. Florida. It forms two isolated colonies in Georgia (Sumter Co.) and in Florida (Madison Co.).

S. rubra Walter. Sweet pitcher plant. North Carolina (from Moore Co. southward) through S. Carolina into Georgia, away from the coast except in N. Carolina.

S. minor Wall. (*1 — 9*). Hooded pitcher plant. "Fly-traps" (MELLICHAMP). Eastern half of the peninsula of Florida, in the north of that state, southern Georgia, western S. Carolina and slightly into N. Carolina.

Species with decumbent leaves: —

S. psittacina Michaux (*1 — 8*). Parrot pitcher plant. From a

short distance E. of New Orleans, Mississippi, through S. Alabama,
S. Georgia to the coast and in N. Florida.

S. purpurea venosa (Rafinesque) Wherry. Southern pitcher plant.
This species has an interrupted distribution from southern New Jersey
to S. Mississippi. Only small isolated colonies are to be found between N. Carolina, where it is widespread, and a similarly widespread area in S. E. Georgia, extreme N. E. Florida, S. Alabama,
from which a narrow tongue extends to near the Mississippi River
N. of New Orleans.

S. purpurea gibbosa (Rafinesque) Wherry. (*1 — 3-5*). Northern
pitcher plant. Found throughout a vast area, beginning with a narrow strip embracing the coastal regions of Maryland, Delaware and
New Jersey, it spread westerly through N. Pennsylvania, N. Ohio,
N. Illinois, Wisconsin, through the whole region north and east to
the Atlantic coast, and N. W. through the region of Winnipeg into
uncharted regions. The northern limits are not known.

Sarracenia purpurea Linn. has had a long history, and we are indebted to HOOKER (1875) for digging out the facts. From an early
sketch by an unknown author, which found its way to Lisbon and
thence to Paris, CLUSIUS (Rariorum pl. historia, 1601, p. lxxxij)
published a figure, which thirty years later was copied by JOHNSON
in his edition of GERARD'S Herbal, in the hope that someone would
find the plant. The hope was realized when JOHN TRADESCANT,
whose name is perpetuated in the genus *Tradescantia*, found it in
Virginia and succeeded in bringing it alive to England in 1640. In
1700 TOURNEFORT described the plant, naming it *Sarracenia* (or *Sar-
racena*) in 'honor of Dr. M. S. SARRAZIN, who had sent it to him from
Quebec. The name was adopted by LINNAEUS in his *Hortus Clif-
fortianus*, 1737. The plant in question is then called *Sarracenia
purpurea* L., and is the best known of all the species chiefly by reason
of its above mentioned wide distribution.

Quite naturally the structural features of these peculiar plants
were the first to attract attention. The terminal lobe or flap not
only looked like a lid, but was believed by MORISON (Plantarum
Historiae, 1699, 3:533) to be hinged and capable of movement, as
many non-botanists believe today. LINNAEUS and others adopted
this idea, thinking this behaviour to conserve the water within. BUR-
NETT (1829) seemed very sure of this. "In many instances the apparatus is fitted with a lip or lid, by which the mouth may be shut or
opened; the machinery of which limb is so contrived that, when the
cavity within is well supplied, it closes to prevent evaporation; and
when the stock is diminished or consumed, the lip is raised, so that the
mouth is again raised to receive the falling rain or rising dew."
CATESBY (Nat. Hist. of Carolina 2:69, 1743) had the idea that the
hollow leaves were a refuge for insects from the animals (frogs, etc.)
which might devour them. WILLIAM, son of CHARLES BARTRAM, in
his *Travels in N. and S. Carolina, Georgia and Florida* (1791) recorded the objection suggested earlier by COLLINSON (see SMITH,
1821) that many insects, on the contrary, are caught and destroyed
in the pitchers.

Later more meticulous observations on *S. adunca* led MACBRIDE

(1817) to find that the tube of the pitcher leaf is lined with down-wardly pointed hairs, which he could "plainly see at the bottom of the tube," and he saw also that there is about the mouth of the tube a viscid substance which attracts flies.

Then MELLICHAMP, a physician like MACBRIDE, resident of the same region and a contemporary of HOOKER, did the first real experimentation on this plant and compared the rate at which fresh venison showed disintegration in the pitcher fluid and in distilled water, concluding that bacterial action was at work. He found also that the pitcher fluid did not allow the escape of flies when they fell into it as water does, indicating that there is an "anaesthetic action." There is also, he saw, a nectar baited pathway up the outside of the pitcher to its mouth. Thus MELLICHAMP'S work opened up the field of physiological research to which reference will be made later.

Since then there have been numerous descriptions of the structure of the various plants of the genus, not always of unimpeachable accuracy. We now consider this aspect of the matter in what follows.

Sarracenia purpurea is the most widely distributed, and longest and best known, species, ranging from Labrador to Florida along the Atlantic seacoast of N. America, and westward to Wisconsin and Minnesota, successfully withstanding the rigors of the northern winters. It has been successfully introduced in Switzerland. With *S. psittacina* Michx. it is associated in the section *Decumbentes* Uphof, both being characterized by having their leaves more or less spreading as a rosette. It is to be found in bogs, usually in company with much *Sphagnum*, anchored therein by its strong ascending rhizomes clothed with the remnants of dead leaf bases and sending out thick fibrous roots. It may often be found in company with other plants, making large floating or semi-floating masses of vegetation about the edges of ponds, as described by MACFARLANE and STECKBECK for Davenport Lake, near Toms River, N. J., U. S. A. (1933). In common with carnivorous plants in general the roots are devoid of mycorrhiza (MACDOUGAL 1899).

It is a beautiful plant ($1 — 3$). Its leaves, which have a very graceful form, are clustered into a rosette and are deep green with rich crimson markings along the venation of the "flap" and more or less uniform similar coloration in the upper portion of the body of the leaf, depending on the exposure to light.

Form and structure of the leaf. — The pitcher leaf of *Sarracenia* has many times been the subject of description from the anatomical point of view by VOGL (1864), MACBRIDE (1817), MELLICHAMP (1875), HOOKER (1875), ZIPPERER (1885), GOEBEL (1891), MACFARLANE (1889, 1893).

Aside from the cotyledons, which present no especially peculiar features, there are two forms of the pitcher leaf, a juvenile and a mature, both mentioned by TROLL (1932). The mature form may be likened to an elegant cornucopia curving however only in one plane. Arising from a winged base, the wings embracing the bearing stem, it becomes cylindrical for a shorter or longer distance according to circumstances. The lower part of this is solid; in its upper part may be found the deepest portion of the hollow interior of the pitcher.

Along the upper (ventral) surface of the cylindrical petiolar portion arises very gradually a single ridge, the *ala ventralis*, which attains considerable depth further up the leaf ($1 — 4$; $2 — 12$). At the same time the leaf becomes expanded into a curved conical hollow vessel, extending to the mouth. As this point is approached the ventral wing begins to show evidence of a double character in that its edge is longitudinally fissured to form two parallel ridges which are continuous with the edges (nectar roll) of the bell, which in this species has a very peculiar form. The abaxial two-thirds are expanded into a cordate "flap," the sides of which where they meet the adaxial part of the bell become helicoidal. The edge of the helix can be seen to continue as the edge of a convolute margin of the pitcher — the adaxial part just mentioned which I have called the nectar roll, and which is nothing more or less than the adaxial part of the bell. TROLL'S (1932) description says that the abaxial part of the pitcher is lengthened as the lid. This is true enough as far as it goes, but this and all other descriptions, as far as I am aware, neglect to point out the nature of the curious rolled margin around the adaxial limb of the opening. At the midpoint of this rolled margin there is on the surface no sign of its nature. Examination by means of sections, however, shows that the two ridges of the ventral wing spread to right and left to continue as its involuted margins. One is reminded of the volutes of the capital of an Ionic column. To sum up in a word, the flap and nectar roll are to be taken together as the edge of the pitcher, wide and leaf-life abaxially and tightly rolled outwardly adaxially.

But this comes out quite clearly in the juvenile form of pitcher, found on seedlings and delicate shoots. These are slender, the tubular portion being narrow and only very gradually widening toward the mouth ($2 — 13$). This is surmounted by an overhanging hood-like expansion, the margins of which do not become rolled along the abaxial reach of the mouth, but run obliquely, meeting to form the ventral wing. According to this description the ventral wing is a single structure below and double above, so far as external evidence goes.

Mrs. ARBER (1941) has recently argued that the lid in *Sarracenia* "is merely a localized development of the collar". This may be questioned on the evidence above stated, that the collar (nectar roll) is not present in juvenile leaves.

The whole of the outer surface of the mature pitcher is supplied with scattered nectar glands ($2 — 15, 16$). It is also somewhat rough and hairy with scattered trichomes ($3 — 2$) with peculiar thickenings in the form of waves of surface expansion rather than continuous ridges, such as occur on the trichomes of the interior. The external glands may be regarded, as MACFARLANE suggested, as alluring in function, leading creeping prey to the mouth.

The internal surface shows, as HOOKER pointed out, distinct zonation. He recognized four zones and described them as follows. Zone 1 ($2 — 12$) embraces the cordate emarginate flap. The epidermis carries stomata, glands and strong downwardly directed hairs. The lower limit of this zonation is clearly marked by an irregular line where the character of the epidermis cells abruptly changes. In zone

2, the epidermis cells have very thick outer walls each ending in an umbo, and more or less imbricated with its neighbors below ($2 — 14$). There are numerous glands here. The appearance to the eye is velvety, the surface being broken up by the imbrication and by the very numerous, fine, downwardly directed ridges concentering on each outer cell wall on the umbo. This zone forms a collar about 1 cm. in width. While zone 1 is highly colored with red along the venations, green between, zone 2 is less colored, though the red still follows the main veins. There are no stomata here.

Zone 3 is smooth and glassy and reflects the light strongly. The epidermal cells have wavy thick walls, and except for a narrow strip just below zone 2, there are throughout numerous glands (I count 15-20 per mm²), but no stomata. This zone occupies about one-half the whole interior. Below it is zone 4, which is devoid of cuticle (BATALIN 1880) except for a small space surrounding the base of each hair. These are numerous, downwardly pointed, long, slender and glassy, and are effective in the detention of prey. The lack of cuticle can be very easily demonstrated by exposing the interior surface of a leaf to a weak solution of methylene blue (or other suitable dye) or potassium permanganate. It shows some discoloration, being brownish as compared with the rest of the surface. At the lower limit of zone 3 the sinuous walled epidermis abruptly changes to an epidermis with plain walls, and the cells appear strictly isodiametric. There are neither glands nor stomata.

For the above zones we may adopt HOOKER's descriptive terms, which, for zone 1, is attractive, zone 2, conducting, zone 3, glandular, and zone 4, detentive, even though these terms are incomplete in significance. Zone 1 is not only attractive but is also a place of very insecure foothold, because of the form and direction of the hairs. Zone 2 is also both attractive because of the nectar secreted, as in zone 1, and affords a precarious foothold. Zone 3 has a hard, glassy surface, extending the glacis of zone 2, all three zones forming a *facilis descensus Averno*. Zone 4 is probably not only detentive, but also absorptive.

And to these should be added a fifth zone. This is a relatively narrow zone below zone 4, in which the cuticle is permanent, and which is hairy only in its upper part, the lower being completely smooth. There are no glands, and the epidermal cells are quite like those of zone 4. FENNER (1904) calls this zone (but he was describing *S. flava*) an absorption zone, but I think without good reason. It is true that these cells do not completely resist the entrance of methylene blue, but this enters them much less easily than into the cells of zone 4, though evidently more easily than into those of zone 3, which are completely resistant.

MacDOUGAL recognized the zones as I have described them. When subjected to total darkness, the petiolar region of the leaf elongates greatly, while the upper zones become shorter, zones 1 and 2 showing the greatest reduction in size. Fully etiolated leaves are twice the length of normal ones, but the petiolar region, including the basal part of the pitcher, is five times the normal length. The ventral wing does not develop, the leaf being wedge-shaped in transverse section. The ascidium is present. Corresponding dimensional changes take place in the component cells, but there is also, according to MacDougal, an actual increase in the number of cells in the elongated portion of the detentive region (which partakes in elongation with the petiole) and an actual decrease in the number of cells of the conductive surfaces (zones 1 and 2). Thus the pitcher of *Sarracenia* behaves, in relation to light, as if it were a leaf blade (zones 1, 2 and the upper part of 3) and the rest as if it were petiolar (1903, pp. 173-6). *Iris*, when grown in the dark, grew only slightly in excess of the normal. We recall that Goebel compares the *Sarracenia* leaf with that of *Iris*.

The juvenile leaves, which are also pitcher leaves, differ in some details from the mature. While they display the same zonation, the characters as they have been described for the mature leaves overlap. They can be described as follows:

Zone 1 is the same as in the mature leaves. The margin of the flap is ciliated with more or less curved blunt hairs. The epidermal cells are sinuous walled, the glands present but few. Stomata are present and the hairs stout and curved.

Zone 2. The epidermis of zone 1 changes abruptly in that all the cells become trichomatous, but very short and produce the effect of imbrication, as described above. Glands are large and numerous, more so towards the lower limit of the zone, where the epidermis again changes.

Zone 3. The epidermal cells are again sinuous walled but, unlike the mature leaf, there are numerous trichomes. Glands are here also present, but no stomata.

Zone 4. The epidermal cells become straight, the cells isodiametric, with numerous very slender hairs, and no glands, and no cuticle.

Zone 5 has the same sort of epidermis as zone 4, but is devoid of hairs.

As we shall see, the juvenile leaf of *S. purpurea* resembles in structure that of *S. psittacina*.

We come to the details of the glands and trichomes. The glands (3 — 1) are all of one type (the "*Sarracenia* type," Goebel, 1891). Viewed as part of the general surface, each gland exposes normally six cells to view, four in a rough circle and two, the cover cells (Goebel) in the middle (2 — 15). The cover cells overlap the four bordering cells to a greater or less extent. Those on the outer surface have relatively large cover cells, which jut out further beyond the general level of the surface. Those of the glands of zone 2 are relatively much smaller.

The outer surface glands (2 — 15, 16) are the smallest and simplest in structure, derived from a single epidermal cell, according to Zipperer and to Fenner. Undoubtedly the gland is of epidermal origin, and the idea is not precluded that it may represent originally a stomatal apparatus, the cover cells arising originally as guard cells. But this is admittedly speculation. The four peripheral cells lie in the general level of the surrounding epidermal cells, while the two cover cells are conical and are wedged in between the peripheral cells. Against the interior faces of the peripheral cells there is usually one, sometimes two cells, the adjunct cells, which appear to be derived from the parenchyma. The walls of the adjunct cell, or cells in contact with the gland cells, are variously thickened, reticulately and circularly, as represented by GOEBEL (1891). FENNER thought that the adjunct cells are also derived from the epidermis (FENNER called them "Durchlasszellen"), but their denser protoplasmic content indicates that they have more than a passive role. The outer walls of the cover and peripheral cells are all cuticularized, staining with fat stains (Congo Red, etc.) except a part of those making the contact with the adjunct cell or cells. These walls resist sulfuric acid along with the outer walls of the surrounding epidermal cells. But methylene blue easily permeates these glands in the living leaf.

The interior glands (3 — 1) are of similar structure, but are of two courses, evidently, as FENNER indicates, derived from originally four peripheral cells. The gland, aside from the adjunct cells, therefore consists of normally 10-12 cells, the outer course having four peripheral and two cover cells, the inner course usually four to six cells. The cover cells are slenderly conical, are wedged in the middle of the outer peripheral cells, extending inwardly till more or less in contact with the inner course. Their walls are considerably thickened and cuticularized throughout. The base of the gland is in contact with two to four or five adjunct cells with reticulate, circularly or spirally thickened walls of contact which give a positive reaction with phloroglucin and HCl. Here, however, there is no suberization of the gland cells so that there is left a "window" (FENNER'S term) allowing communication by ready diffusion between the adjunct and gland cells proper. The glands of the nectar roll, while identical in structure with those elsewhere, show a certain distortion consequent on the growth movement resulting from torsion during the development.

The structure of the glands in whatever zone they occur is the same, though they function differently. On the outer surface of the pitcher and on the inner in zones 1 and 2, they secrete nectar. Though HOOKER was in doubt on this point, I am sure of it from my own observation. I have also, on a warm, sunshiny day watched flies in numbers busily sucking the nectar and some of them getting trapped by slipping down the surface of zones 1 and 2. The glands of zone 3, however, probably secrete digestive ferments, judging from the results of HEPBURN et al. (1927), to be discussed later.

Sarracenia psittacina Michx. — This species (1 — 8) is associated with *S. purpurea* in the *Decumbentes* by UPHOF, because of the position of the leaves which lie more or less parallel with the ground. The leaf considered as a trap, is, however, quite different in this species, and is much more efficient mechanically — or at least it appears so. No account I know of quite brings this point out. The leaf which GOEBEL described as the "first pitcher leaf" is a juvenile form (3 — 5).

Its habitat is low, wet, sandy meadows subject to inundations by the acid waters of nearby swamps (WHERRY).

It is regarded taxonomically as associated with *S. purpurea*, but it is as much or more like *Darlingtonia*. The pitcher consists of a narrow, tapering curved tube (3 — 4), somewhat flattened dorsiventrally, with a wide ventral wing, and with the top of the pitcher curved over to form a hood, with an entrance of narrow caliber facing horizontally, instead of downwards as in *Darlingtonia*. It is deep red in color, mottled by angular white fenestrations which allow diffused light to enter the tube on all sides, more especially on the ventral aspect of the tube which, because of the decumbent position of the leaf, lies uppermost. In some other species, the fenestrations occur on the dorsal aspect of the tube. The pitchers are rigid, and are of striking shape, suggesting the specific and common name. The above mentioned fenestrations have a more opaque look than those of *Darlingtonia*, and on examination they were found to have extensive intercellular spaces, the effect of which is to diffuse the light, thus producing a snowy whiteness.

The form and structure of a pitcher can be best seen in one cut sagittally ($3 - 4$). The upper part of the tube is strongly curved, so as to direct the opening toward the leaf base. The end of the mid-vein is indicated by a low umbo, the organic apex of the pitcher. Beyond this point the hood is closed by the forwardly curved lobes of the "flap," the margins of which are closely apposed, sometimes even to mutual adherence, though sections show their histological independence ($3 - 6$). The more ventral reaches of these lobes are enlarged and bend inwards to form the entrance tube. Inspection of this shows that it is formed partly by the upper short stretch of the ventral pitcher wall and the proximate parts of the lobes, a condition duplicated in the aberrant juvenile leaf of *Darlingtonia* ($5 - 3$). Thus is formed a short cylindrical entrance tube ($3 - 6$), making the trap of the lobster-pot type. The inner free edge of the entrance tube is stiffened not only by the strong epidermis, but by a weal running parallel to the free edge ($3 - 4$). This weal is continuous with the exact edge of the lobes above the entrance tube, and must be regarded as the morphological margin. The edging beyond this forms a shelf bearing numerous nectar glands, and is clothed on both sides with tessellated epidermis of umbonate, striated cells, characteristic of the inner general surface of the entrance tube, where also glands are found.

This shelf corresponds exactly with the inwardly curved nectar roll of *Darlingtonia* ($5 - 10$), from the pitcher of which that of *S. psittacina* differs in the fact that the organic apex of the tube lies within the periphery of the hood, while in *Darlingtonia* it lies beyond. The two lobes of the fishtail appendage of *Darlingtonia* correspond to the two lobes of *S. psittacina*. MACFARLANE regarded this species as the most aberrant of all the species of *Sarracenia*, and its similarity to *Darlingtonia* supports this view. It is on the whole more similar to *Darlingtonia* than to *S. purpurea*.

The earlier stages in the development of the leaf are practically indistinguishable from that of other species examined. The feature peculiar to this species, however, the infolded edge of the flap, is a character which appears quite late in the course of development. In a leaf which, though embryonic in form, was large enough to be exposed to the light, the hood measured about 0.75 mm. and in this the fold has just commenced to develop ($5 - 11$). In one with the hood 2 mm. long the ingrowth was marked, but far from fully developed.

In this early stage the structure resembles that of *Darlingtonia*, save for the forward developing fishtail appendage, which here does not appear at all.

The interior surface of the pitcher presents a zonation which corresponds roughly with that in *S. purpurea*, but is by no means as distinct as in that species. This lack of distinction arises from the overlapping of the zones 3 and 4, and the restriction of zone 2 to the inner surface of the entrance tube, the ventral portion of which is part of the pitcher tube proper. This point must be appreciated as otherwise it would be difficult to recognize zone 2 at all.

Zone 1 (3 — 4) is the whole of the inner surface of the hood excepting the inturned edge of the re-entrant tube. The epidermis is of wavy-walled cells with stomata and many nectar glands, and scattered, relatively few downwardly directed, curved weak hairs, as compared with the flap of *S. purpurea*, or *Heliamphora*. Since the chief mechanism for the capture of insects is the re-entrant tube, these hairs are of little importance. This is compensated for by the presence of very many stiff hairs in the dorsal aspect of the dome, to which zone 3 reaches.

Zone 2 corresponds to this zone in *S. purpurea* in function, though it is not a complete zone geometrically speaking. It embraces a short reach of the ventral wall of the pitcher with the contiguous sides of the re-entrant tube, including the shelf, which is within the morphological edge of the lobe. The shelf and the inner surface of the tube sides are clothed with an epidermis of tessellated straight walled cells each with a low striated umbo, pointing inward and downward, as in zone 2 of *S. purpurea*. Glands are present, in greater number proximally than distally. They are absent under the shelf, but the shelf itself bears a great many. This is the principal lure evidently, but the insect which advances into the re-entrant tube to sip the nectar is invited to enter further by the shining white fenestrations, mullioned in red, of the pitcher wall. The outer surface bears many small glands also, which, with those of the general outer pitcher surface, constitute a general lure.

Zone 3. Like zone 3 of *S. purpurea* this carries some stomata and many glands, but, unlike that species, the whole surface is clothed with a dense felt of downwardly pointed, slender stiff hairs, continuous with those of zone 4. It may be described as an advance of zone 4 to overlap zone 3. The parallelism between this species and *S. purpurea* is seen in the many glands of this zone. These are possibly peptic glands, though the evidence is at present not conclusive (*see* p. 34). The epidermis is of a mixture of wavy-walled cells, and smaller straight walled cells, these becoming more numerous as the next zone 4 is approached. It is underlain by a course of wavy-walled cells, the walls of which are thick and afford stiffening to the pitcher wall.

Zone 4 is devoid of glands, but has a dense clothing of trapping hairs down to the very end of the pitcher tube, where they are shorter, fitting better the reduced bore of the tube, and leaving a lumen. MACFARLANE described the whole of zones 3 and 4, as above delimited, as the detentive zone, but having glands in the upper one-third. In *S. purpurea* zone 3 is secretive, and has a glissade surface, while in *S. psittacina* the surface is hairy.

The structure of the glands is like that in *S. purpurea* (*3 — 3*).
GOEBEL described the seedling leaves which appear directly following the cotyledons. In form they resemble closely the juvenile leaves of *S. purpurea*. The leaves of the two species in the juvenile state are regarded by W. P. WILSON (1888) as indistinguishable, and he regarded them as closely related. The presence of the umbo, however (*3 — 5*), clearly separates *S. psittacina* from *S. purpurea*. The forward margin of the mouth is simple, and the inturning valvular nectar roll with its marginal thickening is absent. Absent also are the two lateral lobes. The interior surface is divided into four zones: (*1*) the under surface of the hood, with scattered retrorse hairs with interspersed glands; (*2*) the gliding zone with a lining of imbricated cells with downward directed points; (*3*) a wide zone with many long downward pointed hairs with glands between; and (*4*) the bottom zone with smooth epidermis. GOEBEL'S zone (*2*) corresponds to zones 2 and 3 in my description of the adult form of leaf above.

Sarracenia Courtii. — This is a hybrid between *S. purpurea* and *S. psittacina*, and in its structure reflects the characters of both in the zonation of the pitcher leaf. As in *S. purpurea*, the conductive zone, zone 2, is broader than in *S. psittacina*, and occupies a transverse band around the interior of the leaf, narrowing dorsally, thus separating zones 1 and 3 almost completely. Zone 3 is much less hairy than this zone in *S. psittacina*, but is glandular, as in that species. The general aspect of *S. Courtii* resembles that of *S. psittacina*, but the plant is larger.

Sarracenia minor. — In this species the leaf stands in a vertical position, and the opening is overhung by a wide, domed lid (*1 — 9*; *3 — 7-9*). The wall of the pitcher opposite the opening, and for some distance up and down, is fenestrated with white patches as in *Darlingtonia*. These are slightly thinner areas of the wall, devoid of chlorophyll, and there is no palisade tissue anywhere. These white spots may be regarded as a visual lure for insects. The lower edge of the mouth is thickened by an outwardly reflexed edge of the wall, as in *S. purpurea*, to form the nectar roll. The body of the pitcher is a tapering tube slightly curved, and carrying a wing in front — the *ala ventralis* — which has a double edge above, the edges flowing right and left into the edge of the lid, but a single one below, and is not confluent with the stipular wings of the leaf base. The ventral wing starts at the top of the tube and attains its greatest width about half way down.

The outer surface is sparsely hairy with short, curved hairs with finely tuberculated walls. There are numerous glands scattered all over the outer surface, and these are especially active in secretion along the upper part of the edge of the wing, where drops of nectar which have been excreted by them may be seen (*3 — 9*). I have not seen nectar collecting visibly elsewhere on the outer surface. The interior surface presents a zonation visible to the eye but somewhat different from that of *S. purpurea* and more like that of *S. psittacina*. MELLICHAMP (1875) recognized three "belts" or zones: (*1*) embracing the internal honey secreting portion; (*2*) a belt lined with soft and velvety pubescence affording no foothold for most insects; and (*3*) that of coarse straw-colored hairs extending to the bottom of the tube where a watery fluid is secreted. Essentially correct, this description does not specify closely enough the distinction which actually exists. Though the zonation does not stand out so clearly as in *S. purpurea*, we can nevertheless recognize four zones.

Zone 1, that of the under surface of the lid which ends in an oblique line extending obliquely upwards from the lower margin of the mouth. This is covered rather densely with curved hairs downwardly directed. Interspersed are numerous nectar glands which are evidently active, for one can see minute drops of nectar studding the surface. At the line of demarkation the epidermis abruptly changes to a smooth, continuous surface of tessellated cells, each of which is downwardly sharply umbonate (*3 — 10*). Interspersed are very numerous glands which are very active. In the upper part stand large drops which run together to form a flood of nectar. This is continuous along the lower lip of the mouth and for a centimeter down from there and elsewhere around the tube. This I call zone 2. At its lower limit the umbonate cells give way gradually to cells of identical structure, but having the umbo lengthened into a longer slender spike, still with many glands scattered between. This zone measures about 3 to 4 cm. in depth. It is evidently glaucous, with a white sheen. This is zone 3. Below begins zone 4, recognizable to the eye by the pale green, non-glaucous appearance. It soon becomes brownish in color and bears numerous scattered long slender hairs with a detentive function (*3 — 11*), with more or less straight walled cells between. In the upper part of this zone there are a few glands, but none much below a depth of 1 cm. Below the epidermis in zones 2, 3 and 4, the pitcher wall is conspicuously strengthened by a hypodermis of wavy walled cells with walls rather thin above, but in the general region of zone 4 very thick and underlain by a second course of wavy walled cells with thinner walls. It is obvious that these cells add materially to the rigidity of the tubular wall. The epidermal walls themselves are straight or only very slightly wavy. The edges of the lid are continuous with the true edge of the lower reach of the mouth border. The nectar roll, as in *S. purpurea*, is covered with tightly imbricated umbonate cells with numerous nectar glands (*3 — 10, 12*). On the whole, the pitcher lining is similar to that of the juvenile pitchers of that species, in which, however, zone 3 is much shallower than in *S. minor*. In general form this species resembles *S. purpurea* with its bell turned forward so as to shade the opening, but as far as the epidermal lining is concerned is more like either the juvenile leaves of *S. purpurea*, or the mature leaves of *S. psittacina*. In the course of evolution it is possible that *S. purpurea* has been derived from a plant resembling *S. minor* simply by a change in the posture of the leaves from vertical to spreading, and by an extension of one zone at the expense of another. A change from *S. minor* to *S. psittacina* could have been accomplished by an additional elaboration of the region surrounding the mouth by extending the dimensions of the nectar roll, and reversing it, curling it to the inside instead of to the outside. This is speculating, of course.

Sarracenia Drummondii. — This is a tall species, the trumpet-shaped leaves attaining a length of 2–3 ft. and standing in a strictly erect posture (*1 — 6*). The tapering tube gradually widens to the top, but contracts somewhat just below the opening, the bulge being scarcely wider than the opening, which is oblique. About two-thirds of the margin is occupied by a nectar roll, the free edges of which are continuous with the two edges of the ventral wing, as in other species already described. The abaxial third of the edge of the opening is extended into a spreading, over-hanging lid supported by its broad stalk. The posture changes somewhat with age, passing from a more horizontal to a more oblique position, and, according to GOEBEL and others, serves to divert rain water from the interior of the tube. The lid and upper portion of the tube are highly colored in a motley of white and red, with green except in the white fenestrations, which occur here as in *S. minor* and *Darlingtonia*.

The external surface is supplied with small nectar glands and is roughly hairy on the upper part of the tube. The hairs, which are like those in *S. purpurea*, point in various directions, and not uniformly in one direction.

The internal surface is clearly divisible into zones. Zone 1 is the inner surface of the lid as far as a distinct line crossing the isthmus supporting it. There are many glands and stomata, and the surface is studded with curved, downwardly pointed hairs of slender form and bending under the pull of a fly's foot. Zone 2 starts at the line across the stalk of the lid, and, including the nectar roll, extends downward inside the tube a distance of 18 cm. in a leaf 60 cm. tall. The surface is clothed with oval cells which form short sharp hairs, retrorse as elsewhere. There are large nectar glands on the nectar roll and in the upper one-half of the zone, but none below. There are no stomata (ZIPPERER). This is the conducting zone (MACFARLANE). Zones 3 and 4 are not separable to the eye except for the fact that, in the upper region of the combined zones, which are detentive, there are a few glands in a narrow belt just below the lower limit of zone 2. Though to the eye the line of demarcation between zones 2 and 3 is distinct, the transition under the microscope is not a very sudden one, since the change from very short hairs (zone 2) to the very long ones of zone 3 is gradual. In zone 2, every epidermal cell is a trichome (except of course where glands occur); in the zone below this is true only of relatively few epidermal cells. In the upper part of zone 3, the epidermal cells have more or less sinuous walls, giving way soon to cells with oval outline, and this region we may recognize as zone 4. The bottom of the tube is quite smooth for nearly five cm. From the whole of zones 3 and 4 the cuticle is absent. The tube throughout its length is greatly strengthened mechanically by the presence of a wavy thick walled second layer.

MACFARLANE denied the presence of glands in the upper part of the detentive zone, saying that there are stomata surrounded by groups of cells. I think he was mistaken in this. The glands, which are few in number, are somewhat distorted, owing to the character of the epidermis of many imbricated hairs, but are nevertheless clearly glands. There are no stomata (ZIPPERER).

In addition to the normal pitcher leaves there are others in which the tube is not developed. The leaf then consists of a cylindrical stalk with a wide ventral wing. At the apex there is more or less of a depression. Such leaves are photosynthetic only, and have been compared by GOEBEL to the unifacial leaf of *Iris*. These leaves develop later in the growing season (GOEBEL).

Having favorable material at Munich, I arranged the upper part of a leaf under a bell jar and put a blue bottle fly inside. The leaf stood vertically in shallow water in a vial. The fly was soon attracted by the nectar secreted by the glands of the external surface and gradually worked his way by an erratic path to the rim. Mounting this he began to sip the nectar, either on the under surface of the lid as far as he could reach without letting go his hold with his hind legs on the edge of the lid, or of the rim. Swinging about he explored the surface inside the rim, always hanging on by his hind legs; and it was evident that he was aware of the precarious foothold, for he was loth to free his hind foot or feet. But on getting what seemed to be a foothold and reaching as far as possible for the nectar, he would let go and then invariably fall plump into the abyss. A bit of the tube was cut away above the water level so that he could escape, and in consequence he performed for me again and again. His actions were repeated a dozen times without failure of being trapped. If he ventured on the under side of the lid, as he sometimes did, he could remain there as long as he grasped the edge with one foot, seizing the hairs with the other; but the moment he let go of the edge, down he fell into the tube. There is therefore no question but that the surface of zones 1 and 2 is one which gives no foothold to such flies and, to infer from the variety of prey found in the pitchers, to most other insects as well.

Sarracenia flava. — This species resembles *S. Drummondii* in many respects, but is stouter and coarser, and its prevailing color is greenish-yellow, with the latter color quite dominant. The tube tapers gradually from the mouth down, being widest at this point. The lid is more erect and has a narrower and stouter neck, and is backwardly recurved at the edges. The apex, instead of being emarginate as in some species, is acute (*1—7*). A leaf 24 cm. long, examined at Munich, shows zonation as follows.

Zone 1 is the under surface of the lid and carries many short, stout, downwardly pointed hairs and many nectar glands. The lower limit of this zone is very irregular, the hairiness following the prominent veins, the spaces between being smooth and glaucous and continuous with zone 2, which is lined with an epidermis of imbricated pointed cells with many glands scattered over the surface. This zone extends about 2 cm. downwards, and includes most of the neck, the nectar roll and a narrow zone below it, as in *S. minor*. This is deep yellow, glaucous and the imbricated cells of the epidermis are short pointed. There are glands present in great numbers, and, quite as in other species described, this is a dominant place of lure. The lower limit of this zone is not defined but fades into zone 3 (8 cm. deep), in which the imbricated cells have longer retrorse points. The number of glands is reduced so that in the lower regions there are none to be found. The whole area is glaucous. The lower limit of zone 3 is very irregular, but readily distinguished by the eye by the change in color, due to absence of cuticle in zone 4. Under the microscope there is a sudden transition from imbricated apiculate hairs to scattered, very long, curved ones, characteristic of zone 4. Underlying both zones there is a hypodermis of wavy, thick walled cells. The lowest portion of zone 4 is quite smooth, is lined with a small, straight walled epidermis, and is 6 cm. in depth.

Sarracenia Jonesii. — Living material from Flat Rock, North Carolina, collected by Dr. L. E. ANDERSON through the courtesy of Professor F. A. WOLF, was examined and showed quite the same characters of the epidermis and of zonation as have been described for *S. Drummondii* and *S. flava.* Such differences as occur are those of the shape of the lid, which is smaller and ovate, similar to that of *S. minor* save that it is more erect and apiculate. The color is green, veined with red, with no fenestrations. There are no glands in the lower part of zone 3, or in zone 4.

Morphology of the leaf. — TROLL (1932) has summarized our knowledge on this subject, adding his own views.

BAILLON (1870) compared the leaf of *Sarracenia* with that of *Nelumbo*, expressing the opinion that "the wide but shallow cone of the (peltate) leaf of *Nelumbo* becomes in *Sarracenia* deeper and narrower in such a manner as to produce definitively the form of a long, obconical trumpet," thus recognizing the relation between the epiascidiate pitcher of *Sarracenia* with peltate leaves.

As we have already seen, the pitcher consists of a spreading bifacial leaf base surmounted by a tubular, gradually widening pitcher bearing a strong ventral wing and the foliaceous flap continued in front as the nectar roll. When the ascidium fails of development, as it sometimes does (as in *S. flava*, etc.), the leaf presents a certain likeness to that of *Iris* and the phyllodia of *Acacia* sp. ASA GRAY (1895-7) designated the ventral wing or keel as a "phyllodial wing." Various earlier authors (LINDLEY 1832, SAINT-HILAIRE 1840, MORREN 1838, DUCHARTRE 1867) regarded the pitcher as a leaf blade with the margins fused, some of them thinking the tube to be the winged petiolar region and the flap the leaf blade. GRAY accepted this view, saying, "they are evidently phyllodia." Of them, however, MORREN believed the flap to be only the apical portion of the leaf blade, the most of which is involved in the tube. MACFARLANE (1889-90) was firmly of this opinion. He regarded the keel as compound of the fused leaf edges, comparing the condition with that in the leaf of *Iris* as he interpreted the anatomy of this. The single keel of *Sarracenia* is equivalent to the pair of apposed wings of *Heliamphora* and the more widely separated ones in *Nepenthes*, according to the nature of the fusion. The flap of *Sarracenia* is to be regarded as compound of two pinnae, as is the lid of *Nepenthes* (1893). TROLL regards this view as false, based on a misconception of the morphology of the *Iris* leaf, which he insists is congenitally a strictly unifacial leaf. He accepts GOEBEL'S intrepretation that the *Sarracenia* pitcher is a unifacial leaf in the form of a tube and turns to the development of it for support. He recalls that in plants with swordshaped leaves the leaf blade (Oberblatt) arises as an outgrowth of the back mass (abaxial side) of the leaf base (GOEBEL 1881), which then enlarges its own apex behind and above the "primary leaf apex," that of the leaf base proper.

The development of the embryo leaf follows the same course except that the upper side of the primordium of the lamina is not completely suppressed but is limited to a minute depression between the leaf base and the apex of the leaf blade (Oberblatt). This is limited below by an as yet extremely narrow transverse zone, which corresponds to the transverse zone of a peltate leaf, and at the same time may be taken as an indication of a unifacial petiole primordium, one, however, which experiences no further development. It is important to note that the leaf blade apex does not rise much above that of the leaf base and that therefore the leaf blade stands nearly normal to the base. This, however, soon changes. The apex now grows rapidly and the primordium widens, flattening dorsiventrally, and changes in curvatures ensue to produce the helmet-shaped form of the lid. Meanwhile the adaxial side elongates and the keel appears, below which the transverse weal of the leaf-base runs; otherwise said, the edges of the leaf base are not concurrent with the keel. The similarity to the *Iris* leaf is unmistakable, only allowing that the leaf blade is hollow. Thus the unifacial character of the leaf blade comes into expression, not as a shallow saucer but as a narrow furrow. The upper side of the lamina primordium is at first confined to the adaxial side of the leaf blade. Growth progresses less by spreading than by upward growth of the margins to form the tubular leaf. The petiole is not developed, but instead the blade greatly lengthens, in *S. flava* to the extent of 1 meter. The terminal portion, whose edges are free, becomes the lid.

I have examined the development of the leaf of *S. minor* and can generally agree with TROLL. In this species, however, the primordia stand out perhaps more clearly because of the greater tendency to grow in length, as compared with *S. purpurea*. In this, however, all leaves do not act alike, for there is sometimes a greater lengthening of the petiolar region, so that even in this species the petiole is not absent, though normally much reduced (2 — 12).

In *S. minor* the earliest stage of development available was a leaf only 0.1 mm. in height in the form of a low cone, its base reniform, about 0.4 mm. in greatest diameter, its convex edge adaxial (3 — 13). The extremities of this edge had a talus-like slope, the cone melting into the overhanging front of the body of the leaf. This rose to a very low apex, evidently a growing point, scarcely evident as a distinct boss. There could be seen a very shallow groove from the top down the adaxial face of the overhanging mass. In this very early and undifferentiated condition there is recognizable a leaf base with very thick edges, a groove, a sign of the coming invagination, and a very low boss. It is not, however, possible to localize a definite growing point for the leaf base, while even at this young stage, the apex of growth of the leaf blade is just visible.

In a leaf 0.3 mm. (3 — 14, 15) in height the apex stands out well, and below it adaxially one now sees a short groove, the leaf base margins distinctly passing transversely across, some distance below the groove. But there is no conclusive evidence that the only apex ever seen, the leaf-apex, is secondary, as in the case of *Iris*, though I hesitate to deny the parallel accepted by TROLL.

In a leaf 0.8 mm. long (*3* — 16) the initial groove is surrounded by a lip which is evidently the rim of the pitcher, surrounding the mouth. With further growth this is raised upward on a laterally compressed stalk on the adaxial side of which the wing now appears as a solid longitudinal outgrowth. In these later stages it is quite evident that the margins of the leaf base meet transversely, and that the wing arises quite independently of it. The zone between the lower end of the wing and the upper end of the leaf base must, I think, be regarded as petiolar. It is solid, and has unifacial structure. In the mature leaf one can see that the wing is, near the mouth, slightly doubled (*3* — 17, 18).

Digestion and absorption. — It was once thought that the tubular leaves were a device for holding water. COLLINSON wrote to LINNAEUS, "the leaves . . . . . are open tubes, contrived to collect rains and dews, to nourish the plant in dry weather." This prompted LINNAEUS to regard *Sarracenia* leaves as derived morphologically from those of *Nymphaea*, but adapted to holding water for its needs, thus enabling it to occupy drier situations, incidentally providing water for thirsty birds. But as GOEBEL, from whom we have drawn these notes, remarks, *Sarracenia* lives in swamps, a fact with which WILLIAM BARTRAM was familiar, but who yet thought that the water caught by the hollow leaves was for the "refreshment" of the plant.

GOEBEL, however, showed that it is easy enough to demonstrate that the pitchers can and do absorb a not inconsiderable amount of water: 6.8 cc. out of 20 cc., and 2 cc. out of 10 cc. in two cases. Fibrin which he introduced remained unaffected, and meat extract, neutralized with sodium carbonate, was attacked by bacteria. These and other similar experiments led GOEBEL to the conviction that while absorption can take place, there is no digestion beyond that attributable to bacteria, and there is no antiseptic action. Previous to GOEBEL several authors had expressed suggestions, opinions, even convictions about the matter. Sometimes the remarks made did little more than show that a question had arisen in the mind, as in the case of MACBRIDE (1817). HOOKER (1875) merely recognized a possibility that digestion occurs. MELLICHAMP (1875) was the first to do some experiments which, though crude, led him to conclude that the fluid of the pitchers hastens the decomposition of insects, without at all evaluating the role of bacteria. BATALIN (1880) interpreted the exfoliation of the cuticle in the deeper zone of the pitcher as evidence that in the absence of glands, which he incorrectly stated to be absent from *Sarracenia*, digestive stuffs (Lösungsmittel) for the solution of proteins were released. No experiments to prove the occurrence of digestion were done. SCHIMPER (1882) showed that changes, due to the absorption of food materials, occur in the epidermal cells similar to the changes called aggregation by DARWIN, but he could not find, from experiments, that there is evidence of digestion aside from bacterial action. That nitrogenous compounds are absorbed was shown by HIGLEY (1885). ZIPPERER (1885), concerned chiefly with anatomy, did only two superficial experiments, one proving to his mind that diastase, and a second that a pepsin is present.

Following GOEBEL, LAMBERT (1902) showed absorption to take place in certain regions, by following the entrance of methylene blue or fuchsin. That digestion occurs was no more than a conviction without proof. FENNER (1904) like SCHIMPER observed that absorption takes place and is followed by cytological changes in the epidermal cells. He observed quantitatively considerable amounts of fluids absorbed. As to digestion he expressed the opinion that *Sarracenia flava* is an insectivorous plant with a digestive enzyme. ROBINSON (1908) found evidence that sucrose and starch can be digested to, presumably, simple sugars by the pitcher fluid, confirming ZIPPERER as to starch, but none that there is either fat or protein digestion.

Thus stood the evidence when in 1918 HEPBURN, ST. JOHN and JONES started their exhaustive studies on these physiological questions presented by *Sarracenia* (and *Darlingtonia*, mentioned elsewhere). These authors did an immense lot of work and travelled extensively for the purpose of doing field experiments. To their results we now turn.

For the purpose of learning about the presence or absence of digestion, they examined *S. flava, Drummondii, Sledgei, rubra, minor, psittacina* and *purpurea*. Tests were made on the fluid from both unopened and opened pitchers, with and without the addition of weak acid (HCl) and alkali (sodium carbonate), and always in the presence of trikresol as a bactericide. Carmine fibrin was used as a substrate in the field, and this, edestin, casein and coagulated egg albumin in the laboratory. The evidence was strengthened by duplication, triplication, or even quadruplication of the tests. Generally composite samples of fluid drawn from a number of pitchers were used. All experiments were done quantitatively, even to measuring the amount of substrate, a matter of importance often disregarded.

In *S. flava* a protease was shown to act on fibrin in both closed (that is, still unopened) and open pitchers. It is more active in weak acid (0.2 %), than in weak alkali, but there was no action in their absence. Edestin was digested in 1.5 to 2 hours. The fluid from closed pitchers was vigorous, acting completely in 30 min. at 37.5° C. and almost so at room temperature. Casein was partially digested in 2 hours. With coagulated egg-white negative results only were obtained.

S. Drummondii and *S. Sledgei.* — When the fluid of closed pitchers was acidified and then tested the results were purely negative. With that of open pitchers, six experiments of eight were negative, but partial or complete digestion occurred in two on sustained exposure (49–57 days). When neither acid or alkali were added the fluid of closed pitchers failed to act even after 50–55 days in four experiments; in two others digestion occurred in 7 and 21 days respectively for *S. Drummondii*. For *S. Sledgei* one experiment was negative, while others acted slowly but completely in 37 to 49 days. The results stand in marked contrast with those in which the fluid was modified by alkali, showing that digestion occurred in 1.5 to 18 days in 20 experiments, while in two others it required 32–36 days, the slowness being due to a reduced concentration of sodium carbonate, which was probably neutralized by the acid proper to the fluid which had been shown to be present. There was no marked difference between the fluid of open and of closed pitchers. It was concluded that a protease was present which, however, acted best in an alkaline medium.

Edestin was slightly attacked by the fluid of open pitchers. Casein was digested completely in 2–8 hours at 37.5° C., and coagulated egg-white, in the absence of acid or alkali, was not attacked, nor was it in the presence of acid, but, on the addition of alkali, "incipient digestion was noted in 24 hours, marked digestion in 48 and 144 hours and advanced digestion in 168 and 216 hours respectively" for two experiments.

S. rubra. — Only a single sample of fluid was available, but this on division showed that in the presence of alkali digestion proceeded rapidly, 0.01 gram of fibrin being completely digested in 1.3 cc. of fluid in 2 hours. In the part with acid added "partial solution was noted at the end of 9 days, complete solution at the end of 50 days."

S. minor. — Experiments were done in the field. No digestion occurred in 30 days (trikresol present) in the absence of acid or alkali, but it did occur when either acid or alkali was added to the fluid, but less vigorously in the alkaline, than in the acid medium. This species therefore stands in contrast to the others aforementioned.

S. psittacina. — Field observation showed that fluid was being secreted in the pitchers, but in such small amounts that it had to be collected by dilution with water (0.5 cc. in each of 50 pitchers free of insects). The results were inconclusive, but indicated that a protease is present which is active in the presence of acid.

Sarracenia purpurea. — The secretion in this species is very small in amount, being found as beads of moisture on the walls. Experiments were done by flushing the pitchers, emptying, and adding 10 to 15 cc. of water to each pitcher. After some days this was removed and tested. The fluid thus obtained showed an ability when alkaline to digest fibrin to a marked extent in 8, 24, 72, and 87 hours (4 samples), and completely in 42, 48, 120, and 135 hours, respectively. Three other experiments gave positive results in 42 and 87 hours. In acid, the results were equivocal.

The general conclusions reached by HEPBURN and his colleagues are that a protease is present in all the *Sarraceniae*, but that in most cases it acts best in an alkaline medium. In some cases, however, it acts in an acid medium.

It was shown experimentally that pitcher fluid retains its power of digestion after being kept at room temperature for as long as 370 days, either with or without a bactericide; and that this is also retained on dilution, which is of importance in view of the fact that dilution by rain may always be expected in the habitat. In contrast with *Nepenthes*, neither mechanical nor food stimulation was found to have any effect.

In the fluid of closed pitchers there is evidence that there are both invertase and lipase, while maltase, emulsin, diastase, urease, and esterase were present. It will be recalled that ZIPPERER claimed the digestion of starch and ROBINSON that of sucrose and starch.

It is generally understood that the water of swamps and sandy soils is acid, though not always. WHERRY found bog water to be sometimes alkaline, though the sphagnum hummocks would contain acid water. Generally he found that when growing in acid water, the pitcher fluid was acid, but not always in the same degree. But occasionally the fluid would be alkaline or neutral. On the same plant the fluid of a young pitcher might be alkaline, and of old pitchers acid — this for *Sarracenia purpurea*. HEPBURN *et al.* found for some southern species acidity and alkalinity about equally distributed for *S. Drummondii* and *S. Sledgei*. Five pitchers of *S. flava* all held acid fluid.

HEPBURN and ST. JOHN examined the bacterial content of closed and open pitchers. Closed pitchers were always sterile. The fluid of open pitchers which had captured prey always contained bacteria, as is to be expected, and these always digested several different substances. The interesting fact is pointed out, however, that these "bacteria digested the proteins so slowly that their part in the digestion of prey must be a minor one in the genus *Sarracenia*, the protease of the pitcher liquor playing the leading role." "The bacteria apparently live in symbiosis with the *Sarracenias*, drawing their nutriment from the digested insects, and aiding, to a certain extent, in the digestion of the prey." An exception must be made for *Darlingtonia* where there is no digestion by the pitcher fluid proper (see beyond). Reference is made to the odors of putridity and of ammonia and amines noticed when such bacteria are active.

The earlier observations of others that water is absorbed was verified, and it was further found that, when nitrogenous substances in solution were used, the absorption of the solutes proceeded more rapidly than that of the water. In the presence of a phosphate buffer, the nitrogenous compound would be absorbed while the total amount of water increased. When a neutral phosphate solution was used, the absorption of the phosphate was less rapid than that of the water. The percentage of compound absorbed usually increased with the length of the period of absorption. The actual entrance of substances into the tissues was demonstrated by the presence of the lithium ion, after introducing lithium citrate into the pitcher fluid. It is thus indicated that the products of proteolysis and phosphates are absorbed by the walls of the pitcher and utilized by the plant. Data on the chemical composition of the tissues are also furnished, but are of only secondary interest here.

This brief summary of the work of HEPBURN and his colleagues, it is gratifying to record, has furnished a comprehensive view of the physiology of the pitchers of *Sarracenia* in its relation to digestion, which might have remained unwritten but for their evident enthusiasm and diligence.

Animals which live in the pitchers of Sarracenia and Darlingtonia. — It is a matter of common observation that the pitcher plants attract a horde of insects of all kinds: "ants, wasps, bees, butterflies and moths" by their nectar, and other forms (beetles, spiders) for other reasons. Spiders frequent the opening of the pitcher in the not vain hope of visits of small insects which may be caught by them. EDWARDS observed this in *Darlingtonia*. They occur on *Drosera*, *Byblis*, *Nepenthes* and probably others for the same reasons. Minute wasp-like creatures parasitize pitcher inhabitants. The caterpillars of a moth live in burrows formed by feeding on the tissues of the rhizome, and form characteristic, more or less upright, above-ground tubes of the debris. This is *Papaipema appassionata*, the moth being maroon and yellow in color. Of especial interest here are those which habitually use the pitchers as their homes, and live in them and nowhere else. They find their food either in the tissues of the pitcher walls, or in the mass of dead insects caught by the trap, or merely live in the water from which, however, they must derive their food. Animals other than insects include a small tree-toad and a small chameleon lizard, whose bones are sometimes found in the inclosed debris. The toad rests just inside the mouth of the pitcher, doubtless awaiting the chance of capturing prey. But to come to the obligate inhabitants:

A small mosquito (*Wyeomyia Smithii*) lays its eggs in the pitchers of *Sarracenia purpurea*. In the pitcher fluid (always diluted by rains) the larvae grow to maturity, hibernating frozen in ice during the winter. It is harmless to man. It is said not to breed elsewhere, and is found well beyond the Canadian border, though it is tropical in its affinities.

Similarly the larvae of a minute gnat, *Metriocnemus Knabi*, breeds in the same manner. A closely related species, *M. Edwardsii*, described by JONES (1916), was discovered to occur in the pitchers of *Darlingtonia californica* by Mrs. AUSTIN about the year 1875. The larvae are minute thread-like "worms" circulating in the decaying insect debris, which appears as writhing masses, so numerous are the larvae. According to HEPBURN and JONES (1919), such forms preserve themselves against the digestive action of the surrounding fluid by means of antienzymes. In this connection it may be mentioned that, in discussing the anthelmintic action of papain (in the crystalline form), BERGER and ASENJO (1940) tested the effect of this enzyme on *Ascaris lumbricoides* (from pig intestine) and found that these organisms were attacked, that is, ulcerations were formed on them inside of 16 hours in a 0.02% solution in a phosphate buffer of pH 5, and the animals were completely digested in 16 hours in a 0.11% solution. The same authors showed that the bromelin of fresh pineapple juice acts similarly. Evidently *Ascaris* has no sufficient protection against this enzyme in the concentrations used, though presumably it has an antienzyme which protects it within its normal environment.

The most intriguing of all the animal associates are three closely related species of a small moth of the genus *Exyra*, because of the striking adaptations which they display to a special environment (JONES 1921). These moths lay their eggs singly or in groups in the mouth of the pitcher. When laid singly, the hatched larva enters the tube and feeds on the superficial tissues of its wall. This is true of the species *Ridingsii* and *semicrocea*. If more than one larva happens to occupy a pitcher, one of them ruthlessly drives out or kills its neighbors. The third species, *Rolandiana*, lays a group of eggs in a pitcher of a single plant (of *S. purpurea*), and when hatched the larvae spread to various closely placed pitchers, readily possible in this species because of the dense massing of the pitchers (*1 — 3*).

Eventually only a single larva occupies a pitcher. The wide separation of pitchers of *S. flava, rubra, Drummondii, Sledgei* and *minor* are a practical hindrance to such movements of very young larvae from one pitcher to the other, and it is in these that the other species of *Exyra* lay their eggs singly. "Thus," says F. M. JONES, "the habit of growth of the food plant determines the egg-laying habit of the associated insect" (1921).

The newly hatched larva is very small (2.6 mm.), and being translucent and half buried in the tissues on which it feeds and partly covered by debris enclosed within the tube, seems pretty well protected without further ado. *E. Ridingsii* on hatching retires to the grooves in the lid-stalk of *S. flava*, and there forms for itself a small tent of silk and frass, on the floor of which it continues feeding. The older larvae of all three species make use of a method of isolating themselves from the outside world as follows. They spin a diaphragm of silk webbing across the mouth of the tube, either transversely or more or less obliquely according to the position of the lid, and in *S. psittacina*, across the mouth of the entrance tube. Any accidental openings are closed by webbing, and thus they immure themselves in a food chamber from which rain is prevented entrance. Larvae of a spring brood, when they find themselves in young tender pitchers, use another quite extraordinary method of insuring for themselves a safe retreat. The young larva then eats away a ringing groove near the top of the pitcher. Above this the pitcher wall dies, dries, and becomes indurated, sagging over and barring the entrance. In the chamber thus formed the larva feeds and hibernates. In the pitchers of *S. flava*, which die down during the winter, the larva retires to the lower regions of the pitcher, and there ensconces itself in a chamber plugged by webbing and frass, where it awaits the spring. A curious variant of this habit is displayed by the caterpillar of *Exyra Ridingsii*, which before pupation prepares for the future by cutting an emergence hole above its point of pupation, so that the moth may easily escape, and below a small hole for the drainage of water, so that its pupation chamber may not be flooded. It then forms its chamber by webbing spun loosely so as to allow water to pass, and then spins its cocoon of webbing and frass. *Exyra semicrocea*, when it pupates in the pitchers of *S. psittacina*, handles its situation somewhat similarly, but with special attention to the peculiarities of the host plant. Usually when the larva intends to pupate it passes into an uninjured pitcher. Since that of *S. psittacina* has a lobster-trap entrance, out of which escape would be difficult — not because of the size of the opening, but because of its re-entrant character — the larva first cuts an escape hole in the roof region of the hood.

After hibernation the larvae (the third instar), are voracious, and, emerging in the spring, attack not only the pitcher, but the flowers and young fruit which they devour. When ready to pupate the larva cuts a hole in a young growing leaf still unopen, ascends the tube, and feeds on the inner tissues. This causes the tops of the pitchers to wither and the dead portion to topple over. *E. Rolandiana* does the same in *S. purpurea*. The larvae of these moths have lateral tubercles or "lappets" which, according to JONES, prevent them from

entering and so getting pinched in too narrow spaces. The species
(*E. Rolandiana*) peculiar to *S. purpurea*, with its wide, amply spacious
pitcher, does not possess the lappets. These in the very young larvae
are scarcely more than bristles, but with successive instars the tubercle
becomes larger, and armed with a prominent bristle.

A solitary wasp, *Chlorion Harrisi*, habitually makes use of *Sarracenia* pitchers for its nest of several stories which are supplied with
food and each an egg. Dr. JONES informs me, however, that this
insect is not confined to *Sarracenia*. He found it in 1939 nesting in
abandoned beetle-burrows on Martha's Vineyard, Vineyard Island,
where *Sarracenia* does not occur.

A fly, *Sarcophaga*, produces large white maggots which feed upon
the remains of insects in the pitchers. The protective enzyme studied
by HEPBURN and JONES was extracted from *Sarcophaga* larvae. Several species of this genus, peculiar to *Sarracenia*, were described by
RILEY.

There is a minute fly (2–3 mm.), *Dorniphora venusta*, which is found
in the pitchers of *S. flava* late in the season when they are relatively
dry and have lost their trapping abilities, as they apparently do
(JONES, 1918). The larva feeds upon the captured insects.

Another small fly, 3–3.8 mm. in length, described under the name
Neosciara Macfarlanei by F. M. JONES (1920) has similar habits, and
is found in the vertical tubed *Sarracenias*. Its presence is betrayed
by a frothy looking product of the larvae about to pupate, which
fills the pitcher tube just above the mass of dead insects on which
they have fed. Both these flies, as well as the *Sarcophagids* above
mentioned, appear to be confined to *Sarracenia*, but some doubt
remains as to this.

The purpose of the above brief account is merely to point out
the more general facts about the constant insect associates of *Sarracenia* and *Darlingtonia*. To exhaust the present knowledge of all
the insects which attack and feed upon and pollinate these plants
would go beyond our purpose. A general summary of this knowledge
is supplied by JONES in WALCOTT's book of illustrations of the *Sarracenias*, in which a bibliography is to be found. It is upon this
author that I have depended for these notes. It may be added as a
matter of speculation that further investigation would certainly dis-
cover many other associates, including crustacea, protozoa and pro-
tophyta, some of which might turn out to be obligate inhabitants,
as in the case of *Nepenthes*.

Literature Cited:

ARBER (*see* under *Cephalotus*).
BAILLON, H., Sur le développement des feuilles des *Sarracenia*. C. r. Acad. Sci. Paris
    71:630, 1870. Also in Adansonia 9:331, 1868–1870 (*through* TROLL).
BARTRAM, WM., Travels in N. and S. Carolina, Georgia and Florida. Philadelphia 1791.
BATALIN, A., Über die Function der Epidermis in den Schläuchen von *Sarracenia* und
    Darlingtonia. Acta Hort. Petropol. 7:345–359, 1880.
BERGER, J. & C. F. ASENJO, Anthelmintic activity of crystalline papain. Science II, 91:
    387–388, 1940.
BURNETT, G. T., On the functions and structure of plants, with reference to the adumbra-
    tions of a stomach in vegetals. Quart. Journ. Sci. Lit. and Art, Vol. for Jy.–Dec.,
    1829:279–292.

CANBY, W. M., *Darlingtonia californica*, an insectivorous plant. Proc. A. A. A. S. 1875, B:64–72.

CATESBY, Nat. Hist. of Car., Vol. 2, p. 69, 1743 (*through* HOOKER).

COLLINSON, (*see* SMITH 1765).

DARWIN, (*see* under *Drosera*).

DUCHARTRE, P. E., Élémens de botanique. Paris 1867 (*through* TROLL).

FENNER (*see* under *Nepenthes*).

GOEBEL, K., Blattentwickelung von *Iris* (under the heading of "Litteratur"). Bot. Zeitung 39:95–101, 1881.

GOEBEL, K. (*see* also under *Nepenthes*).

GRAY, ASA, Sarraceniaceae. Synoptical Flora of North America 1:79, 1895–7, New York.

HEGNER, R. W., The protozoa of the pitcher plant (*Sarracenia purpurea*). Biol. Bull. 50: 271–276, 1926.

HEPBURN, J. S., F. M. JONES, & ELIZ. Q. ST. JOHN, The absorption of nutrients and allied phenomena in the pitchers of the *Sarraceniaceae*. Journ. Franklin Inst. 189:147–184, 1920.

HEPBURN, JONES & ST. JOHN, The biochemistry of the American pitcher plants (*Secondary title:* Biochemical Studies of the North American *Sarraceniaceae*). Trans. Wagner Free Inst. of Science 11:1–95, 1927. Full bibliography.

HIGLEY, Bull. Chic. Acad. Sci. 1:41–55, 1885 (*through* HEPBURN).

HOOKER, J. D., Address to the Department of Botany and Zoology. Rep. 44th Meeting Brit. As. Adv. Sci. Belfast 1874:102–116, 1875.

JONES, F. M., Pitcher-plant insects. Ent. News 15:14–17, 1893.

JONES, F. M., Pitcher-plant insects, II. *Ibid.* 18:413–420, 1907.

JONES, F. M., Pitcher-plant insects, III. *Ibid.* 19:150–156, 1908.

JONES, F. M., Two insect associates of the California pitcher-plant, *Darlingtonia californica*. *Ibid.* 27:385–392, 1916.

JONES, F. M., *Dorniphora venusta* Coq. in *Sarracenia flava*. *Ibid.* 29:299–302, 1918.

JONES, F. M., Another pitcher-plant insect. *Ibid.* 31:91–94, 1920.

JONES, F. M., Pitcher plants and their moths. Nat. Hist. 21:296–316, 1921.

JONES, F. M., Pitcher plants and their insect associates. *In* WALCOTT, 1935, pp. 25–34.

KRAFFT (*see* under *Heliamphora*).

LAMBERT, Ann. de Hygiène et de Méd. col. Paris 1902, 5:652–662 (*through* HEPBURN).

LINDLEY, J., Introduction to Botany. London, 1832.

MACBRIDE, JAMES, Trans. Linn. Soc. London 12:48–52, 1817.

MACDOUGAL, D. T., Symbiotic saprophytism. Ann. Bot. 13:1–47, 1899.

MACDOUGAL, D. T., The influence of light and darkness upon growth and development. Mem. N. Y. Bot. Gard. 2, 319 pp., New York 1903.

MACFARLANE, J. M., & D. W. STECKBECK, *Sarracenia purpurea* var. *stolonifera*, A noteworthy morphological and ecological type. Bull. Misc. Inform. Kew, No. 4, 1933:161–169.

MACFARLANE (*see* also under *Nepenthes*).

MELLICHAMP, J. H., Notes on *Sarracenia variolaris*. Proc. Am. Ass. Adv. Sci. 23 meeting. 1875, B:113–133.

MORREN, CH., Morphologie des ascidies. Bull. Acad. R. Belg. Bruxelles 5:430, 1838 (*through* TROLL).

RILEY, C. V., On the insects more particularly associated with *Sarracenia variolus* (spotted trumpet-leaf). Proc. A. A. A. S. 1875, B:18–25.

ROBINSON, WINIFRED J., A study of the digestive power of *Sarracenia purpurea*. Torreya 8:181–194, 1908.

SAINT–HILAIRE, A. DE, Leçons de botanique etc. Paris 1840 (n.v.).

SCHIMPER, A. F. W., Notizen über insectenfressenden Pflanzen. Bot. Zeitung 40:225–234; 241–248, 1882.

SMITH, Correspondence of LINNEAUS. Vol. 1, p. 69, 1821. Reference to COLLINSON (*through* HOOKER, 1875).

TROLL, W., Morphologie der schildförmigen Blätter. Planta 17:153–314, 1932.

UPHOF, J. C. TH., Sarraceniaceae. Die natürlichen Pflanzenfamilien, 2. Aufl., Vol. 17b: 1–24, 1936.

VOGL, A., Phytohistologische Beiträge, II. Die Blätter der *Sarracenia purpurea* Linn. Sitzungsber. Wien. Akad. Wiss. Math.-Wiss. Kl. 50:281–301, 1864.

WALCOTT, MARY V., Illustrations of North American pitcher plants. Smith. Inst. Wash. 1935 (containing contributions by WHERRY and by JONES).

WHERRY, E. T., Acidity relations of the Sarracenias. Journ. Wash. Acad. Sci. 19:379–390, 1929.

WHERRY, E. T., The geographic relations of *Sarracenia purpurea*. Bartonia No. 15, 1933:1–8.

WHERRY, E. T., Exploring for plants in the southeastern states. Sci. Mo. 38:80–85, 1934.

WHERRY, E. T., Distribution of the North American pitcher plants. WALCOTT, 1935, Pp. 1–23.

WILSON, W. P., On the relation of *Sarracenia purpurea* to *S. variolaris*. Proc. Acad. Nat. Sci. Phila. 1888:10–11.

ZIPPERER, PAUL, Beitrag zur Kenntnis der Sarraceniaceen. Diss. Univ. Erlangen. Munich 1885, Pp. 34.

Chapter III

DARLINGTONIA CALIFORNICA

Discovery. — Distribution. — Habit. — Leaves: kinds. — Structure. — Place of absorption. — Development of leaf. — Digestion and absorption.

The genus name *Darlingtonia* is used here because of its wide familiarity and use in horticultural literature. Under the International Rules of Botanical Nomenclature this name is invalid because of being a later homonym, and is to be replaced by *Chrysamphora* Greene.

This highly localized pitcher plant of Oregon and California called locally the "cobra plant" was discovered in October 1841 by Mr. J. D. BRACKENRIDGE, Assistant Botanist of the U. S. Exploring Expedition, under Captain WILKES, on a journey from Oregon to San Francisco. It was found in a marsh bordering a small tributary of the Upper Sacramento River a few miles south of Mt. Shasta. In the opinion of JOHN TORREY, who described it in 1853, it was sufficiently different from *Sarracenia* to warrant the new generic name which he gave it, dedicating it to his "esteemed friend" Dr. WILLIAM DARLINGTON, of West Chester, Pa., "whose valuable works have contributed so largely to the scientific reputation of our country." The range of this species is now known to extend into the Siskiyou Mountains of S. Oregon, down to sea-level along the coast (I found it 6 miles north of the town of Florence) and in the contiguous region of California. As an example of a restricted geographical distribution, this is comparable to that of *Cephalotus follicularis* in S. W. Australia.

Darlingtonia has the same general habit of growth as that of the other *Sarraceniaceae*, a strong perennial rootstock, bearing a sort of rosette of leaves and clothed with the dead remains of older leaves. The larger leaves attain a length of 2-3 feet ("3 ft. 6 in.", EDWARDS) and present a unique appearance, owing to the torsion of their tubes and the large motley domes with their fishtail-shaped appendages. "The leaves are most beautiful and singular, having a fanciful resemblance to a number of hooded yellow snakes with heads erect in the act of making a final spring, suggesting the name 'caput serpentis'," wrote EDWARDS in 1876. He states that the leaves all twist in the same direction, which is not the case (KURTZ) $(4 — 1-5)$.

There are two kinds of leaves, juvenile, produced by seedlings and by small shoots, and the leaves of maturity. The juvenile leaves $(5 — 1-4, 6; 6 — 17)$, which have been described by GOEBEL, follow directly on the very simple lanceolate cotyledons, and on small lateral shoots of restricted growth on rhizomes. They are tubular, tapering downwardly, with a clasping base. The opening is oblique, the leaf being drawn out on the abaxial side into a tapering acute or bifid apex. The edges of the opening are simple, that is, are not curved in- or outwardly. On the adaxial aspect the opening is bayed or sometimes slit downwards. The whole outer surface of the leaf is studded with somewhat raised stomata and many nectar glands which

scarcely exceed the stomata in size. These glands are found even
on the outer surface of the overhanging apex. The inner surface can
be roughly divided into three zones. The uppermost embraces the
whole of the apex and some distance into the interior from the opening. The inside surface of this portion is furrowed longitudinally from
the extreme apex to a point well within the tube. The floor of this
furrow is lined with smooth epidermis which for some distance forms
a low swelling on each side of the furrow. Among these cells are a
very few groups which have distinctly the structure of a nectar gland,
but I have not been able to determine positively that nectar is secreted. They seem not to be quite so highly specialized in form at
least as the glands of a mature or adult type of pitcher. The epidermis in general of this zone is of the "fishscale" type, that is the cells
are imbricated and are downwardly sharply pointed, the more sharply
the more deeply placed in the pitcher. As zone 2 is reached, fewer
of the cells are trichomes, which are now much longer, the remaining
cells being quadratic and elongated to some extent. In the depths
of the pitcher, hairiness ceases, and the epidermis, in zone 3, is quite
smooth. Like the senile leaves, the juvenile tube leaf is twisted
through 180 degrees from base to apex, so that the opening comes
to face downwards, more or less. In size they may be as small as 1
cm. and up to 10 cm.

Occasional juvenile leaves display aberrancies from the normal
course of development. Rather frequently one finds a leaf with the
apex forked, and having no median vein, clearly corresponding to
the fishtail appendage of the adult leaf. Accompanying this condition there may or may not be developed an *ala ventralis*. In most
cases the rim of the mouth remains simple, but in one leaf I found
that a distinct nectar roll had been developed along both sides, but
not meeting anteriorly, as in the adult leaf, to fuse (*5 — 3*). This
indicates pretty clearly that the place where the two sides of the
nectar roll meet is a site of concrescence in the fully elaborated leaf.
As in all these forms of juvenile leaves there are nectar glands, which
are confined to a broad band along the inside of the hood and apex
but not elsewhere on the inner surface (*6 — 18*). The epidermis is
all of tesselated umbonate cells above, becoming longer pointed further
down. The glands are not quite so elaborate here as in the adult
leaf. Those on the outer surface are typical in appearance.

A single juvenile leaf was found in which there was a closure of
the mouth for only a short distance above the base. What might
have been the tube was laid quite open, and formed no trap at all.
Glands were present on the apical appendage and along a midband,
as usual. The epidermis was tesselated. That is, the leaf was a normal juvenile leaf in all respects except that the edges remained free
(*5 — 6*).

Cases of this kind might be used as evidence that the pitcher
arises by fusion of the leaf margins (MACFARLANE) but can as well
be explained as resulting from disharmony of growth. On various
grounds another explanation is to be preferred. (*See beyond*).

It may be noted in the juvenile leaves that the margins of the
"total stipule" (TROLL) run far up the petiolar region. In a juvenile

leaf about 30 mm. long, the ends of the stipular margins were encountered about half the way up (ca. 15 mm.). This very gradual running out of the stipular margins conveys the impression that the edge of the wing is doubled throughout its length, and inasmuch as in the adult leaf the edge of the wing in its upper reaches is, as a matter of fact, also double, this doubling seems continuous with that of the stipular wings. We shall, however, see elsewhere that the one had nothing to do with the other. In the juvenile leaf, however, the wing is single above so that the end of the stipulation is clear. This involves the study of transverse sections ($5 — 4$).

At the same time it can be seen that the outgrowth to form the wing had already started its growth beneath the stipular margins. A study of the development of the leaf shows why this takes place.

The adult leaves have been described a number of times, by Torrey, Hooker, Macfarlane, Kurtz, Goebel and others, but despite this, the precise morphological relations of the parts about the mouth of the pitchers remain only vaguely comprehended.

Adult leaves are produced both on short shoots, when they may be quite small (1.5 cm. to 10 cm.) and on large vigorous rhizomes when they attain a stature of a meter more or less. When seen in its native habitat, growing thickly in large clumps, with its tall leaves standing straight up, it affords a spectacular sight. The picture which is seen reproduced ($4 — 1$) was taken in an open glade on a steepish wet hillside in the mountains east of Crescent City, Calif. in August 1938, when many of the leaves were just approaching maturity. The seeds were already fully ripe, since the flowers ($4 — 2, 3$) are produced in early spring, before the leaves start to grow.

The pitcher arises from a clasping base, the wings of which appear concurrent with the ventral wing, the edge of which is doubled as in *Sarracenia* ($6 — 15$). The tube is tapering, widening upward. At the top the tube spreads suddenly and at the same time is bent sharply forward to form a dome, bringing the mouth into a horizontal position underneath. From the front of the mouth a prominent forked appendage, of "swallow-tail" (Lemmon) or fishtail form, hangs down with a forward curve. In the largest leaves the dome may be 10 cm. long, 6 broad and 5 deep, while in a very small, but still perfectly formed pitcher 1.5 cm. long, the dome measures only 2.5 mm. in length. A feature peculiar to *Darlingtonia* is the twisting of the tube either to the right or left so that the helmet-shaped dome is turned about 180 degrees from the axis of the plant. All the leaves then are turned outwardly, a position conceivably of advantage in attracting prey. The small leaves often lie more or less prostrate and the fishtail appendage lies on the surface of the ground forming a ramp leading small creeping things to the opening ($6 — 14$).

When the leaf is yet immature, but of full extent, the tissues of the dome are still soft, and the two sides lie against one another. In attaining their final shape the sides expand, the dome is inflated, and then becomes indurated, so that, supported by the sclerotic cell walls and other mechanical tissues, the dome attains a marked firmness, like a hard hat. The wings of the appendage spread to form a platform leading to the opening, its ventral surface secreting much nectar as a lure. Light green at first, the color gradually deepens and at last becomes splashed with red. The roof of the dome and the back of the upper part of the tube are mottled with numerous white flecks, devoid of chlorophyll, glands and hairs, and, to an insect at the mouth, form a visual lure ($4 — 4$, 5). Such fenestrations or areolae are found in *Sarracenia minor*, *S. psittacina*, and *S. Drummondii* and perhaps some others. The transparency of an areole is traceable to the entire absence of chlorophyll-bearing tissues and of intercellular spaces. Each areole lies in a mesh of the vascular tissue surrounded by an irregular edging of chlorophyllous tissue with, inside, stomata, glands and blunt curved downward pointing hairs, the latter encroaching a little more on the clear tissue, which is composed of wavy walled epidermis on both surfaces, with three or four courses of thick-walled, perfectly clear cells. There is no pigment of any kind, except in old leaves, when a yellow tinge may be detected. So complete is the absence of air-spaces and pigment, that the areole is quite glassy. A few coarse starch grains occur especially toward the margins.

We will now consider the structures about the mouth. We note in the first place that the ventral wing just below the mouth as in all the *Sarraceniae* has a doubled edge, less conspicuous in some species (*S. purpurea*) than in others (*S. minor*). This is most conspicuous in *Darlingtonia*, in which the double margin may be traced down a long way and appears, as it did to TORREY and to KURTZ, to be continuous with the edges of the basal stipular wings. The embryology shows, however, that this is not the case (*See beyond*). If it were not so, then we should have to explain a condition in *Darlingtonia* which is not common to the *Sarraceniae*. As the evidence indicates, the ventral wing or keel originates in the same way in both these genera. The condition in *Heliamphora*, which has a pair of independent wings, cannot in the absence of embryological evidence be brought into comparison, as TROLL also remarked.

Now these two admittedly shallow free edges of the keel mark the margins of the mouth. In *Darlingtonia* they may be traced along the nectar roll and marking its outer limb. The wing edges are accompanied by the major wing veins, and these run forward to the base of the fishtail, and enter it, one on each side, where they branch. The appendage receives the end of the midvein also, but this immediately branches. The fishtail is evidently due to deep emargination, as GOEBEL maintained, and is not a pair of pinnae, as MAC-FARLANE believed. The condition in *Darlingtonia* is not parallel to that in *S. psittacina*, in which the inrolled edges of the flap lobes form valves with a weal along the edge of each representing the nectar roll, but not of the same form. This receives only a minor branch of the keel veins, which continues along the margins of the flap lobes. In *Darlingtonia* the nectar roll results from hypertrophy of the leaf edge in a lateral direction. The strong venation is correlated with the supply necessary to the fishtail with its large number of active glands and its large size. As already remarked, the veins running along the outer limb of the nectar roll ($5 — 7$-10) pass forward to enter the fishtail near its outer margins, there branch and furnish the main supply lines. One readily infers that the outer marginal zone of each lobe of the fishtail is a continuation of the nectar roll on its own side. Its position and topographical relations in the definitive pitcher leaf show that it gets these as a result of torsion and contraction of the tissues at its base. I have been prompted to make a guess as to what a primitive condition of the *Darlingtonia* leaf might have been. PLATE *6* — 13 represents such a hypothetical condition. In order to get B, which with a little more forward curvature would represent the modern pitcher, all that need occur is the transverse contraction of the base of the flap accompanied by bending forward. It should be noted that there is no fusion of the two sides of the nectar roll in front, so that the inner superficies of the hood are continuous through the gap between the forward ends of the two sides of the nectar roll with the ventral (upper) surface of the fishtail. That a change of this nature has occurred in the process of evolution is indicated by the case above mentioned of a juvenile leaf with a nectar roll and an emarginate apex, but not contracted transversely at its base (*5* — 3). In this case the edge of the nectar roll is clearly continuous with the edge of the apical appendage. This is an objective example of the hypothetical primitive condition presented in *6* — 11.

The fishtail appendage on its outer (dorsal) surface has stomata and simple glands in great numbers. The inner or ventral surface has no stomata, but there are numerous glands, and a good many stiff, thick, blunt hairs turned morphologically downwards, but, because of the upsidedownness of the hanging appendage, point upward and furnish a rough surface which assists, rather than impedes, a climbing insect, lured by the abundant nectar. To the presence of this there is abundant evidence in the living plant. The converging folds of the appendage, as an insect crawls upward, (*4* — 5; *5* — 9), guide it toward the entrance into the hood, where it meets the inturned nectar roll. Once inside, the insect has to face the dangers of the inner surface. It is not to be supposed that insects will insist on using the appendage. Nectar glands occur everywhere on the outer surface. The ventral wing, as well as the appendage, may act as a wing-fence to guide them to the opening. Meeting the heavy exudation of nectar on the nectar roll is an added spur to entrance, however they may have been attracted thus far.

To turn to the conditions found in the interior of the pitcher. The forward (upper) portion, the dome, is lined with many stiff, coarse hairs so directed as to urge insects toward the depths of the tube. These are largely absent from the areolae, though small ones may occur. They are most plentiful on the floor, where there are no areolae. Intermingled with the hairs are many nectar glands, so that the whole forward portion of the floor of the dome serves as a feeding ground, from which also insects can feed with great convenience on the nectar roll, as from a table. The rear of the dome, however, the surface of which extends down into the tube, has no glands, but the imbricated epidermal cells are elongated, each into a sharp downwardly pointed hair, which offers no foothold. This continues far into the tube, as far as a point where there are no more fenestrations in the wall. Here the character of the hairs gradually changes, and they become fewer and longer. In the extreme depth of the tube the hairs are absent, and there are no glands. If the absence of glands indicates anything it is that in *Darlingtonia* the only digestion which may occur is that induced by bacteria, and that this at least takes place has been testified by J. G. LEMMON in a letter to CANBY who mentions the observation in a paper in 1875. LEMMON remarked that he detected a strong smell of decay at some distance, as did JONES and others later.

The structure of the nectar glands is quite unique, though they evidently may be regarded as conforming to the *Sarracenia* type. On the surface a gland appears as one of the epidermal cells, or if compound from two to five or six such cells (6 — 18, 19, 22). It appears filled with cytoplasm and a nucleus is always distinctly visible, sometimes two or three (in the thin superimposed cells). Focussing more deeply the gland cells become larger and rounded in outline. The reason for this is understood when a section is examined (6 — 20, 21, 23). It is then seen that the diameter of the glands increases with depth and is composed of a row of flat cells, evidently derived by periclinal division of an original epidermal cell. Underlying each gland (if simple) is usually a single parenchyma cell, which in the glands of the outer surface is quite deep, suggesting to MACFARLANE the adjective "globoid" (6 — 20, 21).

When the gland is compound there will be seen in section two (rarely more because of the unfavorable chances of such a section) tiers of flat cells. These glands are not only compound but are much larger than those on the outer surface, where they are invariably small (about the size of the stomata) and simple. Compound glands occur in great numbers on the nectar roll, and, to a less extent, on the forward interior face of the dome.

When a pitcher is allowed to lie in a weak solution of methylene blue, the glands of the outer surface become stained throughout, though the surrounding epidermal cells remain colorless. There is evidently ease of diffusion through the external cells. MACFARLANE explained this by the absence of cuticle from the outer gland cell, saying that he could observe the torn edges of the cuticle in a surface view, but I have been unable to verify this. By the evidence of exposure to methylene blue it also appears that the walls of the gland are cutinized (GOEBEL) except at the base, as is the case with the glands of other genera of the *Sarraceniaceae*.

In the absence of digestive glands, but on the presumptive nutrition of the plant from the decaying insects which are caught in great numbers (EDWARDS counted 33 spp.), the question as to what part, if any, of the interior surface of the tube can absorb the products of such decay, is pertinent. We have seen that zone 4 in *S. purpurea* is devoid of cuticle. In *Darlingtonia* it is surprising to note that the whole of the surface from the lower limit of zone 1, that is, below about two-thirds of the dome, is capable of absorption. When a leaf is plunged into a weak methylene blue solution for 20 hours the tissues, as far as and including the outer part of the third layer of parenchyma, become dyed, while no dye enters through the outer surface epidermis, except through the nectar glands. There can hardly be any question, therefore, that the inner surface of the pitcher is capable of absorbing solutes which result from the decay of insects within it. This is due, probably in a large part, to the absence of cuticle from the whole area occupied by the long detentive hairs, according to BATALIN (1880) who observed the loosening of the cuticle from the free surface of the cells by the formation of blisters (in *Sarracenia flava*). BATALIN even suggests that this non-cuticularized epidermis takes over in the absence of glands, their function, not only of absorption but also of digestion, since throwing off the cuticle seems to be indicative of the excretion of some substance, possibly digestive. The condition in *Darlingtonia* does not seem to be wholly parallel to that described by BATALIN for *Sarracenia*. I placed a pitcher in methylene blue overnight and found the whole inner surface stained deeply in the morning. On sectioning, the whole inner epidermis was found deeply colored. On staining with Sudan III there was distinct evidence of cuticularization, especially in the radial walls. The outer walls were thinly stained, sometimes not at all, while the cuticle of the outer epidermis was obviously thick and richly stained. I could not, however, find clear evidence that the matter stands as BATALIN describes it.

Development of the leaf. — Material for the study of the development of the leaf in *Darlingtonia* was obtained on May 22, 1938, growing in a sphagnum swamp 6 miles N. of Florence, on the coast of Oregon at a few feet above sea level. At that time the plant was in full flower, and in some plants very young leaves were beginning to make their appearance. New leafage would be achieved in the course of a month, the present leaves having persisted since the previous season. In the depths of the pitchers were to be found merely the chitinous remains of insects long since caught, and no odor, such as has been detected by others during the active season, was noticed.

The morphology of the leaf is easily the most complicated of all the pitcher plants of the *Sarracenia* type. This is because of the torsion of tissues which occurs at the outer (distal) extremities of the two sides of the nectar roll, and the edges of the fishtail flap. The nectar roll appears to be extended as an infold of the outer edges of the fishtail flap, which hangs down from the distal sector of the opening, its ventral face being that one which faces the tube of the pitcher. We may follow the development of the leaf in examining the following series of stages, chosen conveniently.

Case 1. A very early stage of development (6 — 1) in which the whole leaf consists of a flat cone 0.3 mm. high. This may be regarded as identical with the corresponding early stage of *Sarracenia purpurea* as represented by TROLL (1932) and earlier by GOEBEL (1891), though in GOEBEL's figure the mouth of the beginning pitcher is too wide, and the leaf-base is not shown. The mouth is not set so nearly horizontal as in *Sarracenia*. The margins of the leaf-base wings are continuous transversely from one side to the other. A small stretch of tissue separates this from the edges of the mouth, already well marked. The rim of the mouth is continuous all around, making peltation complete.

Case 2. Leaf 0.7 mm. tall (6 — 2). The mouth and its continuous rim form a definite papilla, the upper margin taking the lead in upward growth. The tissues between the lower transverse rim of the mouth are somewhat raised to form a low ridge. The twisting, characteristic of the *Darlingtonia* leaf, has already begun.

Case 3. A leaf 1.5 mm. long (*6 — 3*). The leaf base has elongated, carrying the margins of its wings up some distance. Above, the rim of the mouth has been extended down as a low double ridge and the lateral reaches of the rim now begin to form the two sides of the terminal fishtail of the mature leaf (*6 — 6*). The ascidium reaches well down into the leaf base.

Case 4. Leaf 2.6 mm. long (*6 — 7*). The wings of the leaf base have now developed so that the distinction between this and the leaf-blade is sharp. The double ridge, continuous with the two sides of the mouth is longer and is raised up on the edge of the *ala ventralis*. The close apposition of this with the apex of the leaf-base wings shown by TROLL for *Sarracenia* does not occur here. It has now become clear that the double character of the edge of the *ala ventralis* is derived from the rim of the mouth. If not so extended in *Sarracenia*, yet the origin of the double edge is the same. In this case the twist of the leaf is to the right.

Case 5. A trifle older than case 2, not so old as case 3, in sagittal section (*6 — 4*). Here can be clearly seen the identity of the side lip of the mouth and the edge of the keel. The pore of the mouth is still small. The section being truly sagittal, the other keel edge is not seen. No indication of the nectar roll is yet visible. Advance beyond this stage consists of the enlargement of the lateral reaches of the lips of the mouth concomitant with the laying down of the nectar roll and its continuation along the outer margins of the fishtail.

Cases 6, 7 and *8* (*6 — 5, 6, 10*). Successive stages following on case 5, showing the development of the fishtail from the sides of the mouth, the apex being now arrested and of slower growth. In cases 7 and 8, the outer marginal roll of the one side of the fishtail is seen, and that it is continuous with the nectar roll which has also appeared. The fold between the distal ends of the nectar roll has begun development.

Case 9 (*6 — 16*). Surface view of a somewhat later stage, about like that shown by GOEBEL. The difficulty of interpretation is obvious.

Case 10 (*6 — 8*). The dome has begun development and the tube is twisted through 90 degrees. The distinction between the edges of the wings of the leaf base has become obscure, except in transverse sections (*5 — 5*). Seen in sagittal section the dome is represented in *6 — 9*. The fold (*6 — 10*) has now come into a vertical position as the dome has enlarged fore and aft, and the outer marginal roll of the one side of the fishtail is seen continuous with the nectar roll, which has pushed forward. The ventral surface of the fishtail is continuous with the inside surface of the dome.

In a word, all parts are now clearly defined, and the glands have appeared. The final condition may be seen in various figures illustrating the mature leaf. At the time growth is complete, the leaf has twisted through an angle of 180 degrees, though it may be as small as 90 degrees or as large as 270 degrees. The torsion does not involve the dome. It is either to the right or left in any given plant (antidromy of McCLOSKY).

Digestion and Absorption. — EDWARDS (1876) and GOEBEL were of the opinion that true digestion, that is, by means of a secreted enzyme, does not take place in *Darlingtonia*. More recently HEPBURN and his collaborators ST. JOHN and JONES (1920, 1927) examined the fluid of unopened, cotton-plugged and open pitchers with regard to its effect chiefly on carmine fibrin and fibrin in the presence of a bactericide (0.2 % trikresol). Of a total of 57 experiments in the laboratory and field, none gave a definitely positive result, occasional, very slight aberrancies being due probably to the presence of bacterial ferments. On anatomical grounds this is to be expected, though as above noted, BATALIN made a suggestion that the non-cuticularized cells of the depths of the pitcher might take over the function of the glands. But that the function of the secretion of a protease could be one seems, in view of the above cited results, to be out of the question. That insects are disintegrated by bacteria is obvious, and that their products are available as nutriment to the plant is indicated by the fact that absorption of various substances can and does take place as shown also by HEPBURN and his colleagues, and as would appear to be the case in view of the non-cutinized tissues of the pitcher through which methylene blue readily passes. HEPBURN, ST. JOHN and JONES showed that water is absorbed, and dissolved lithium was found to have been taken up by the tissues. When various nitrogenous substances were introduced, both these and the solvent were absorbed, but in the presence of a phosphate buffer the water might increase though the compounds were absorbed. Mrs. AUSTIN had found (1876) that when stimulated by the introduction of bits of meat, the amount of fluid increased in the pitchers. Her results were quoted by ASA GRAY (1876). Though the experiments were done in the field, there is assurance of the exclusion of rain which, if any fell, which is quite unlikely, could gain no entrance into the hooded pitchers. HEPBURN *et al.* investigated this point, also in the field (Plumas Co., Calif.) and found that when milk was introduced into the pitchers, there was invariably an increase in the amount of fluid ranging from 20 to 1242 per cent in periods of 1–7 days. They studied 77 pitchers, and the amount of increase of volume varied independently of the time, so that some pitchers were much more active than others. When beef broth was used, there was an increase of from 302 to 387 per cent in fluid content in five days. When bits of meat were used the results depended on whether the meat was cooked or raw. If cooked there was little if any increase, because only small patches of the surface were affected. If raw, an increase of volume of from 48 to 157 per cent was observed. No results were obtained with raw or coagulated egg-white, nor with cheese, casein or fibrin "possibly for the same reason as with meat." When acids and alkalis in very dilute solutions were introduced, there was no very "marked tendency" for the volume of fluid to "increase or decrease", but it was noted that, as in the human stomach, the fluid returned to neutrality whatever the nature of the introduced reagent.

Has the fluid of pitchers the power of wetting insects, when immersed, more than pure water? While positive evidence was obtained for other species of *Sarraceniaceae*, that from *Darlingtonia*, from experiments done in the field, was purely negative.

Experiments done by the same authors to determine if other enzymes than protease might be detected in *Darlingtonia* gave negative results except for diastase, of which, however, only a trace could be detected. Maltase, invertase, emulsin and urease were absent. It seems, therefore, indisputable that this plant depends solely upon the activity of bacteria to provide the absorbable protein and other nutrients, if any, through the pitcher walls. EDWARDS' opinion, expressed in 1876, turned out to be correct.

The presence of bacteria and their activities were observed by HEPBURN *et al.* A chemical study of the pitcher fluid was made by these authors who found that in closed, plugged and open pitchers, a small amount of nitrogen could be recovered, *viz.* 0.027% from closed pitchers, 0.015% to 0.009% from plugged pitchers and 0.034% to 0.049% from open pitchers. The fluid studied has a specific gravity of 1.003 at 15 degrees C. and contained 0.213% solids, 0.104% ash, and 0.046% calcium oxide (lime) forming 44.23% of the ash. Chlorides were present. No reducing sugars could be found, though it is quite probable that such may sometimes be present by contamination with the nectar found elsewhere on the walls of the pitcher.

Literature Cited:

AMES, MARY E. P., Calif. Horticulturalist and Floral Magazine 10:225–229, 1880. Quotes a letter from Mrs. AUSTIN *re* increase of fluid in pitchers of *Darlingtonia*.

ARBER (*see* under *Cephalotus*).

AUSTIN, R. M. L., Brief an Dr. K. KECK, über *Darlingtonia*. Oester. Bot. Zeitschr. 1876: 170–171.

BARNHART, J. H., BRACKENRIDGE and his book on Ferns. Journ. N. Y. Bot. Gard. 23:117–124, 1919.

BATALIN, A., Über die Function der Epidermis in den Schläuchen von *Sarracenia* und *Darlingtonia*. Acta Hort. Petropolitani 7:346–359, 1880.

BRAUN, A., Über *Darlingtonia californica* Torrey. Sitzungsber. d. Gesellsch. naturf. Freunde, Berlin 1873:73–75.

CANBY, WM. M., *Darlingtonia californica*, an insectivorous plant. Proc. A. A. A. Sci. 1874:64–72, Salem, Mass. 1878. Reprinted in Oester. Bot. Zeitschr. 1875:287–293.

DARWIN, C., Insectivorous Plants. London 1875.

EDWARDS, HENRY, *Darlingtonia californica* Torrey. Proc. Calif. Acad. Sci. 6:161–166, 1875 (published in 1876).

GOEBEL, K., Pflanzenbiologische Schilderungen. Part 2, V. Insectivoren. Marburg, 1891.

GRAY, ASA, (Description of the seed of *Darlingtonia*). Amer. Journ. of Science and Arts, 2 ser. 35:136–7, 1863.

GRAY, ASA, Darwiniana. Appleton, New York 1876, 330 pp. (Cites AUSTIN'S Observations on fluid in pitchers of *Darlingtonia*).

HEPBURN, J. S., F. M. JONES & ELIZ. Q. ST. JOHN, Biochemical studies of North American *Sarraceniaceae*. Trans. Wagner Free Inst. Phila. 11:1–95, 1927. A very full bibliography.

HOOKER, J. D., On the carnivorous habits of some of our brother organisms — plants. Rep. Brit. Assoc. Adv. Sci., Belfast 1874.

KURTZ, F., Zur Kenntnis der *Darlingtonia californica* Torrey. Verhandl. Bot. Vereins Brandenburg, meeting June 2, 1878, 24 pp.

LEMMON, J. G., Brief an Dr. K. KECK über *Darlingtonia*. Oester. Bot. Zeitschr. 1876:35.

MACBRIDE, J., On the power of *Sarracenia adunca* to entrap insects. Trans. Linn. Soc. London 12:48–52, 1817 (read in 1815).

MACFARLANE, J. M., Observations on the pitchered insectivorous plants, I. Ann. Bot. 3:253–266, 1889, 1890.

MACFARLANE, J. M., Observations on the pitchered insectivorous plants, II. Ann. Bot. 7:403–458, 1893.

MELLICHAMP, J. H., Letter to Dr. HOOKER on the California pitcher plant. Gard. Chron. 1871:46.

MELLICHAMP, J. H., Notes on *Sarracenia variolaris*. Proc. A. A. A. S. 23 meeting, 1874. 1875:113–133. An earlier communication appeared in Gard. Chron. 1874:818–819, earlier published in the N. Y. Tribune by ASA GRAY.

TORREY, JOHN, On *Darlingtonia californica*, a new pitcher plant from Northern California. Smithsonian Contrib. to Knowledge 5:1, 1853. (Year of discovery given as 1842. According to BARNHART, 1919, the year must have been 1841).

TROLL, W., Morphologie der schildförmigen Blätter. Planta 17:153–314, 1932.

VOGL, A., Die Blätter der *Sarracenia purpurea*. Sitzungsber. Wien. Akad. Wiss. 50, Oct. 1864.

Chapter IV

NEPENTHES

Geographical distribution. — Habitat. — General character. — Morphology of the leaf and the seedling. — Development of the leaf and adventive shoots. — The pitcher (Morphology; Variety of form, color etc.; The mouth; The lid; Spur; Special anatomy). — The rim or peristome. — Histology of the peristome. — The glands: their histology. — Anatomy of the pitcher-wall (Vascular system; The interior surface; Wax zone; Digestive zone; Rim). — Digestion. — The animal life of the pitchers. — Folklore, uses. — Antisepsis of pitcher fluid.

The species of *Nepenthes* are found scattered throughout the tropics of the Old World with the center of distribution in the region of Borneo, being found as far East as N. Australia and New Guinea, and to the West in Ceylon and in Madagascar, its extreme outpost (DANSER). Madagascar, indeed, was the scene of its first discovery by the Governor, FLACOURT, in the middle of the 17th century, and it was reported from Ceylon a little later by PAUL HERMANN, a physician, who sent the specimens to COMMELIN in Amsterdam. (WUNSCHMANN 1872).

They grow with rare exceptions only in moist or very moist situations, and they are successfully cultivated in greenhouses only if the relative humidity is kept very high; in particular, a slightly reduced humidity inhibits the development of pitchers. In their vertical distribution they occur from near sea-level to 9000 ft. altitude (*Nepenthes Rajah* and *villosa*, on Kina Balu, Borneo). They are chiefly jungle plants, though one species at least (*N. destillatoria* in Ceylon) grows in wet savannahs where it climbs on scattered shrubs. *N. gracilis* was found by KORTHALS (1839) in "dry sandy, stony ground" though it was found to prosper better in other, moister situations. The demands of the plant are for wet soil and hot to cool temperatures accompanied by a high humidity of the air.

It is most rarely that they can be successfully cultivated outdoors in temperate regions but it was reported some years ago at a meeting of the Naturalists Club of Sydney, N. S. W. that two unidentified species were grown out of doors on a trellis, at Parramatta, not far from Sydney. This is a region where staghorn ferns are grown out of doors by everybody, and the *Nepenthes* species above mentioned may be especially hardy.

In general appearance the species of this genus are pretty uniform, the more striking differences being found in the size and shape of the pitchers. The plant consists of a creeping rhizome from which spring coarse, clambering vines with thick, glossy leaves of frequently considerable length (1 meter) arranged in a ⅖ phyllotaxy, though one species (*N. Veitchii*) is wholly distichous (TROLL 1939). The leaf consists of a spreading winged base narrowing into a short isthmus beyond which it spreads into a ligulate to orbicular blade beyond which extends a short or long tendril which can twine about a support and ending in a pitcher with a lid overhanging the mouth, behind which is a small or larger spur. The pitcher is always held in an upright position. When young the various parts are clothed with a tight rusty pubescence of curiously branched hairs. In climbing, often to the crowns of tall trees (16 to 20 meters: *N. bicalcarata, Rafflesiana*, etc. according to MACFARLANE), the plant supports itself by means of the stout tendrils. It sometimes grows epiphytically, as in the case of *N. Veitchii* (BURBIDGE, 1880). Such species may have climbing stems 3 cm. in diameter. TROLL (1932) has given us an excellent word picture of the appearance of *N. ampullaria* (4 — 9) in its habitat.

"I came across *N. ampullaria* among the massive vegetations of a swamp-forest on the island of Siburut, off the west coast of Sumatra. It was a fabulous, unforgettable sight. Everywhere, through the network of lianas the peculiarly formed pitchers of this species gleamed forth, often in tight clusters; and, most remarkably, the muddy, moss overgrown soil was spotted with the pitchers of this plant, so that one got the impression of a carpet. How is this peculiar behavior to be explained?

"*N. ampullaria* develops a rhizome which creeps in the earth or between clumps of moss. This sends out one or more liana-like shoots which climb high into the trees, and at their ends, where they can enjoy bright illumination, they become leafy. The leaves of these long shoots are of the usual type — they possess a well developed lamina and a functional tendril. Elsewhere the lianas are bare or have remains of dead leaves clinging to them.

"Of quite a different appearance are the pitcher leaves which are found on the ground. True, the pitchers are well developed, but the tendrils are always short and serve only to hold them in an upright position.

"If one searches for the attachments of these simplified leaves, they will be found to occur on short branches, just as GOEBEL described them. It has been overlooked, however, that they are not confined to the main rhizome but spring also from numerous prostrate stems which attain a considerable thickness. Such branches may be followed for a distance of several meters along the soil surface quite easily because of the numerous dense clusters of pitchers which are strung along them." (*Translated*).

Earlier observers in some cases thought that the lid of the pitcher is capable of motion, and so to close and open its mouth. LOUREIRO is mentioned by SIMS (1826) to have held this view. But this of course is not the case — the lid attains a quite fixed posture, usually overhanging the mouth of the pitcher, but sometimes turned quite back.

The morphology of the very highly specialized leaf of *Nepenthes* can best be considered by a comparison of the mature condition with that met with in the leaves of seedlings and of adventitious shoots on cuttings. The former have been studied by DICKSON, J. D. HOOKER, GOEBEL, MACFARLANE and STERN. In spite of a general uniformity of evidence, with exceptions to be noted, there is a wide divergence of opinion as to the homology of the parts, MACFARLANE regarding the leaf as a p'nnate structure and GOEBEL as a simple leaf with a highly specialized region forming the ascidium or pitcher. These and other interpretations will be considered.

Seedlings. — The primary leaves of the seedling (first described by
BISCHOFF in 1834), the cotyledons, are elongate oval and present no
noteworthy features. The following leaves, which will for convenience
be called primary, consist of a short spreading and clasping base,
narrowing briefly to expand at once into a pitcher (KORTHALS) with the
edges of the leaf base extending up its ventral (adaxial) face as two
wings which either meet transversely somewhat beneath the rim of the
pitcher mouth (HOOKER, 1859, DICKSON, MACFARLANE), or end
abruptly without meeting (GOEBEL). STERN, restudying GOEBEL's
material, verified this but pointed out that he found a row of gland-
like tentacles $(7 - 5)$ and these might indicate a transverse connection.
TROLL strongly favored the view that there occurs actually or fundamentally a union of the wings below the rim to express "total stipulation." The edge of the mouth of the pitcher is armed with a transverse
rim usually well developed, and occupies about one-half to two-thirds
of the periphery, the rest being taken up by the base of a lid, that is,
in the primary leaves the lid base is very broad $(7 - 7, 9)$ while in
the adult leaf type it is narrow, with the consequence that the veins
are spread apart in the former and crowded together in the latter.
The venation of the lid appears quite evidently to be an extension of
the plan of that of the pitcher, and not secondary as is that of the rim,
if we may lean on juvenile leaf forms arising on small forced shoots.
The lid bears a number of tentacle-like emergencies at its edges and
upper surface, and behind it extends an appendage which is properly
regarded as the organic apex of the leaf, the "spur." With the advance
of age, the region between the leaf base and the pitcher elongates, so
that a blade now intervenes, with its margins continuous with the wings
of the pitcher. The intercalation of a tendril at this region is indicated
in the narrowing of the blade $(7 - 7, 11)$, and in the more mature
condition a tendril is realized. The leaf then consists of an expanded
base, a blade, generally of some length, a tendril which becomes
functional as such, supporting at its end the pitcher which is always
winged, though less obviously, it may be, than in the seedling $(4 - 7,$
$8)$. In some species the pitchers on the higher parts of the plant have
the wings reduced to mere ridges.

The early development of the pitcher leaf has been described by
J. D. HOOKER (1859), BOWER, STERN, who, as to the facts, agree.
In the very early condition, there is to be observed a depression just
below the apex of the yet merely low conical structure $(7 - 1)$. The
lid develops as a transverse ridge at the distal limb of the depression
and is independent of the true apex $(7 - 2)$. The lid is therefore not
the tip of the leaf, but an outgrowth on the ventral face of the leaf
near its apex (HOOKER). It grows downward over the opening, which
in the meantime becomes deeper to form the acidium. It has the
appearance of a two lobed affair $(7 - 4)$, and that it is really such
has been thought by BOWER and by MACFARLANE who cite in support
of their view the fact that the lid in the mature leaf is often emarginate. The conical apex continues its development into an expanded
leaf tip which may at length bear one to several expanded lobes
(*N. ampullaria*), "pinnae" as they have been called, and MACFARLANE
regards them as supporting evidence of his theory that the whole leaf

is a pinnate structure obscured by secondary changes. They are more or less conspicuous on mature leaves in some species (*N. ampullaria*) while on others the spur, as it is called, is a tapering simple conical projection often much displaced by the secondary growth of the tissues beneath it so that the lid is moved forward to occupy an apparently terminal position (*4* — 10; *7* — 23). Meanwhile the leaf blade develops more or less in front, *i.e.* on the ventral surface, of the enlarging ascidium in two usually deep ridges, the margins of which are continuous to the base. From their position it appears clear that the ascidium is formed by the expansion chiefly of the lower moiety of the midrib, so that at full growth the leaf margins mark the limits of the upper surface of the midrib.

In adventitious shoots produced by forcing cuttings, good material of which I obtained at Munich, various embryonic conditions of the leaf are preserved in the mature condition, which are always small and embryonic ("juvenile") in appearance as in fact. This is to be referred to the failure locally of the incidences of growth which would mold the leaf into the mature form, such as the failure of the leaf to elongate in the region giving rise to the tendril; or the continuation of growth where it is normally suppressed, such as in the narrowing of the blade at the base of the ascidium. The former is shown in Fig. *7* — 11 which is nearly mature, the leaf blade being here narrowed in the region which in a completely developed leaf would have become the tendril. The second condition is shown in Fig. *7* — 13 in which it is seen that the leaf blade has expanded, beginning to do so at the middle point of the ascidium instead of below the base. In both these, as in other early stages of development, the apparent "two-lobed" condition of the lid, seen by BOWER and others, stands out. That this is more than appearance may be doubted. It may be contended that the lobing may be an appearance due merely to the infolding of the middle longitudinal zone, the marginal zones resting on the rim of the pitcher, which during the earlier stages of development is laterally compressed so that the sides of the mouth, that is of the rim, are close together and parallel (*7* — 24; *8* — 19). The presence of emargination is not by any means general, and at best, as GOEBEL points out, its presence is not an indication of lobation. In any event emargination may easily occur when it does, from the manner of longitudinal folding by mutual pressure of the rim and lid apex.

The spur (we continue to treat of juvenile leaves of short shoots) is usually broad and lobed, and, being the organic leaf apex (HOOKER) receives the terminal part of the mid vein, which does not pass into the lid, so that this is devoid of a midvein (*7* — 7-10). Below the base of the spur, however, the midvein of the pitcher may send anastomoses joining it with lateral veins. The venation of the spur is made up almost wholly of lateral veins derived from far down at the base of the pitcher, swerving around from back to front, and then back again below the rim. In specimens resembling the more adult type of pitcher, veins appear in the lid which, though suggesting a midvein, are really branches and anastomoses between the laterals and the midvein (*7* — 9; TEXT FIG. 2, p. 63).

The mature leaf may in some species attain a length of one to three feet. It consists of an expanded base, sometimes connate about the supporting stem, and expands above into an elongate blade corresponding morphologically to the narrowed portion of the seedling leaf. At the apex it may sometimes be found to be peltate (*N. clipeata*), and this, as above said, is compared by MACFARLANE to the peltation observed by him of the two ventral ridges just below the mouth of the pitcher. Beyond this there occurs a tendril which is short and non-functional as such in soil rosettes (*e.g. N. ampullaria*), but which in the climbing forms becomes long, stout and twining. SACHS (1896, through GOEBEL) held that the tendril activity (the actual winding) acts as a stimulant to the growth of the pitcher, but the evidence is not convincing, for it is quite usual to find well developed pitchers when no winding has intervened (*4 — 7, 8*). Though the tendrils wind about supports, they may wind even when supports are not available; but it is not true, as OUDEMANS thought, that this winding is a means of bringing the pitchers into the proper position. The sensitive tissues which are responsible for this occur at the base of the pitcher and neighboring portion of the tendril (STERN).

The Pitcher. — It is with the structure and behavior of the mature pitcher that we are chiefly concerned. It shows a considerable variety of form, from that of a cylinder (*N. phyllamphora, N. gracilis*), a cylinder modified by a basal globular expansion (*N. ventricosa, N. Lowii*), an open funnel, narrowest at the base (*N. inermis, N. dubia*), to an oval sac slightly compressed laterally (*N. ampullaria*). All of these forms have been illustrated by DANSER (1928). In most species, and this is especially noticeable in the approximately cylindrical ones, the upper one-third, more or less, is somewhat constricted, corresponding in extent to the waxy zone within (to be described beyond). From some species this is absent (*N. ventricosa, N. bicalcarata, N. ampullaria*) or may be very narrow (*N. intermedia*). It is said to be exceptionally present in forms from which it is normally absent. The size of the pitcher may reach in some species the length of a foot, with a capacity great enough to accomodate small mammals, birds, etc., *e.g. N. rajah* 25–30 cm. by 12 cm. (HOOKER). The majority of species have pitchers which range from 5 to 15 cm. in length.

The pitchers produced even in a single individual, this being a character of the species, may be of two or even three different forms, that is, they may be mono-, di-, or tri-morphic (MACFARLANE). When this occurs, the rosette leaves in contact with the soil differ from the cauline, the uppermost of these being again different from those midway of the plant. Thus *N. ampullaria* has rosette leaves with goblet shaped pitchers, the cauline ones being cylindrical; while in *N. Boschiana, N. maxima* and *N. Vieillardii*, the lowermost pitchers are globose, the lower cauline tubular and the uppermost infundibuliform or cornucopioid. So different are they that different pieces of the same species have been described as different species. In some cases the internal structure differs, there being a wax zone in some pitchers and not in others. In color the pitchers are usually green with more or less splotchings of red, and when this occurs in the rim the color lies in very definitely regular transverse stripes, obviously connected with the regular, straight-rowed arrangement of the cells. Some species have, according to MACFARLANE, "porcellaneous white" pitchers marked with "deep crimson splotches" (*N. Rafflesiana* var. *nivea*, *N. Burbidgei*). Others have uniform deep red color, even when growing in the shade, or covered with a growth of moss, while the pitchers exposed to greater illumination are less deeply colored, (*N. Rajah*, *N. Edwardsiana*). These relations, in perhaps less striking fashion, are shown by *N. ampullaria* in which the soil pitchers are splotched with red while the cauline pitchers are almost or entirely free of color. Some species have pale green pitchers with no markings at all (*N. ventricosa*) (*4 — 7*). On account of the frequently brilliant coloring, believed by TROLL to be, in addition to the nectar, attractive to insects, the pitchers are regarded by Malayans as "bungabunga" (flowers) (TROLL 1939). The glossy rim may be entirely red or transversely striped with red, or devoid of color other than green. The outer surface of the pitcher is usually clothed with a rough pubescence of many branched hairs, each rising from a unicellular stalk with thin walls, those of the rest of the cells forming the branching complex being very thick (*8 — 4*). There are also low sessile stellate hairs which in some species (*N. intermedia*) stand in a pit (*8 — 1-3*). The four arms forming the star are each two-celled, but the whole may be composed of eight to sixteen cells. They are regarded as hydathodes by STERN (1916). These trichomes are by no means confined to the pitchers, however, the whole plant showing a marked degree of the rough hairiness, especially along the tendrils and the backs of the "phyllode."

Borne on a tendril, often hanging, the pitcher in order to function must stand upright. This is accomplished by tropisms resident in the region between the pitcher base and the end of the tendril. Since the tendril is positively geotropic, and the pitcher "geotropically conditioned," though not simply negatively geotropic (STERN), the usual position is a sharply upturned pitcher on the end of the vertically hanging tendril.

In one species at least (*N. bicalcarata*) the portion of the tendril near the pitcher is swollen and hollow to form a formicary, but the space is separated from that of the pitcher by a partition and it remains filled with air. Ants usually eat away an entrance into the interior, as they do *e.g.* into the stems of *Cecropia* and the thorns of *Acacia* sp. etc., and use the hollow as a nest.

The mouth of the pitcher is always more or less oblique, and during development is hermetically sealed by the lid, which opens only when the definitive size and shape of the pitcher is almost attained. It is well known that, until this happens, the contained fluid, of which there is a considerable amount, is kept in a bacteria-sterile condition. The method by which the edge of the lid is kept hermetically sealed during development is both interesting and unique. There is, it must be observed, no concrescence or fusion of tissues (*7 — 24; 8 — 19*). What happens is that the edge of the lid is in the first place tightly applied. Then, whatever chink there may be left is tightly sealed by a dense growth of branching hairs which clothe the outer face of the pitcher mouth and the edge of the lid (MACFARLANE 1908). These interweave so as to produce a firm wad of cottony stuff. As long as the growth of the two parts is synchronous the sealing remains effective. During the last phase of development differences in growth cause the lid and pitcher mouth to separate and the former, as the result of the growth of the isthmus of tissue between the lid and pitcher edge, is lifted in many cases a considerable height above the mouth (7 — 22, 23). In its final position the lid may overhang the mouth, becoming a more or less effective bar to the entrance of rain, especially in such forms as *N. Rajah* Hook. in which the lid continues to grow and attains a sufficiently large size to overshade the opening entirely. In other species it remains small and narrow and turns completely back, fully exposing the mouth of the pitcher (*N. ampullaria* Jack, *N. dubia* Dans.) (4 — 9), and though overhanging the mouth, is obviously quite ineffective as a roof (*N. inermis* Dans.). When the lid is large and overhanging in position, it is thin, more or less emarginate, indicating to BOWER and to MACFARLANE that the two halves of the lid represent paired pinnae. In some species there is a median ridge on the inner surface bearing numerous nectar glands (7 — 25), and in other species there is a shallow invagination near the apex, the function of which, if it has one, is not clear; or, as in *N. Ladenburgii*, there is a short clavate projection. In *N. Tiveyi* (and, says MACFARLANE, in *N. maxima*) there is a short, thick, glandular crest or ridge near the base and near the apex a sharp thorn-like projection, hollow on its forward surface (7 — 25).

The under surface of the lid is the seat of numerous nectar glands except in a few species (*N. ampullaria, N. inermis* probably). In *N. Lowii* Hook., it is supplied with many small appendages or bristles, as DANSER calls them, with nectar glands on the general surface between their bases.

At or below the base of the lid on the outside of the pitcher stands the spur. This, as may readily be ascertained by examining the young pitcher during development, is the apical portion of the leaf (HOOKER) and it appears that the lid is an outgrowth over the upper surface. The spur is very small in some species and stands just at the base of the lid (*N. inermis*). In *N. bicalcarata, e.g.*, it becomes considerably displaced downwardly, and stands out, quite suggesting a spur, from a neck of tissue which raises the lid far above the opening (*N. bicalcarata*) (7 — 23). Sometimes the spur is compound and bears pinnae-like laterals, suggesting lateral leaflets (MACFARLANE) (*N. ampullaria, N. phyllamphora*).

Special anatomy. — The edge of the mouth of the pitcher is of distinctly peculiar structure. It appears to be a parapet standing on the edge, sloping inwardly on the whole, but with the outer margin sometimes turned more or less down. In a section of it made transversely, it is T-shaped with the arms of the T of various lengths, according to the species. In the majority both arms are of some length, so that the parapet in such cases overhangs as much on the outside as on the inside, and with a general slope as much away as toward the opening of the pitcher. *N. ventricosa* may be cited as an example of this condition (7 — 16). In others (7 — 15, 17) the inner arm is short, the outer long, while in *N. inermis* (7 — 20) both are very short, the outer a trifle longer than the inner. In *N. Veitchii* the width of the rim towards the lid is so great (up to 60 mm, says DANSER) as to bear a likeness to a "Marie Stuart collar" (DE RUITER 1935). The greatest reduction of the inner arm is found in *N. Lowii* (7 — 18), which has been described as without a peristome (DANSER). There is, however, a row of glands embedded in tissues which project to form a slight, interrupted shelf while the outer arm is of some width relatively. At the other end of the series stand such forms as *N. bicalcarata, N. intermedia* and *N. ampullaria* (7 — 19), in which the outer arm is very short and tightly reflexed and the inner very long; in these species the peristome has a very pronounced funnel shape. In *N. ampullaria*, which forms rosettes of pitchered leaves on the forest floor, the pitchers partly buried on the humus, the whole constitutes a group of pitfalls, each with a broad overhanging edge which would prevent escape quite effectively in many cases.

Of the two arms of the T, one, the outer, represents the true pitcher mouth edge, outwardly reflexed. The inner arm is an outgrowth from the inner wall near the edge. This is easily seen to be the case in young pitchers during their development (HEIDE, 1910) (8 — 19). In any case it can be seen that the vascular tissues of the inner arm are derived by sharp branching from the main trunks which extend to and along the edge proper.

But although the peristome is composed as it were of two flanges, an outer, the edge of the pitcher mouth, and an inner, growing out as a ridge from the inner wall, the whole during late development is so moulded that the two flanges are amalgamated to constitute a single organ, the inner surface of the edging flange and the outer surface of the side flange becoming a continuous uninterrupted surface. The whole is mechanically very rigid, for it is strengthened by a very thick cuticle and the surface is broken up into minute striae and coarser corrugations (4 — 11). The latter give the peristome their ribbed appearance, and their most pronounced expression is reached in *N. villosa* Hook. On the inner edge of the peristome the corrugations end in minute teeth, and between each pair of teeth (7 — 21) there is an opening, the mouth of a large nectar gland which lies buried in the tissues. The nectar oozes in a drop held between a pair of teeth, of access to insects standing on the rim and reaching down. This arrangement together with the nectar glands on the under side of the lid constitute a lure, the "attractive zone" of HOOKER. The hard, glossy surface of the peristome is not, as it may seem to the eye, a smooth, slippery one, for as a matter of observation, small insects (ants, etc.) can walk freely on it, using their footpads. When the tissues below the base of the lid are considerably extended, as they are in *N. bicalcarata* and *N. intermedia* (7 — 22, 23), the peristome is extended likewise, and in these two cases, but only in these, there is, at its extreme upper ends which are separated by the base of the lid, a very strong development of the last dozen or so corrugations to form two long sharp thorns, resembling the canine teeth of a cat. In *N. bicalcarata*, these are long, solid, curved, very sharp and distinctly canine in appearance. A rather fanciful explanation of the use of these was advanced by BURBIDGE (1880) who pointed out that the *Tarsius spectrum*, a small, insectivorous, monkey-like mammal, "visits the pitchers of *N. Rafflesiana*" (which is similar to *N. bicalcarata* in all respects except that it lacks the canine-like thorns), "and empties them of their prey, but not those of *N. bicalcarata,* in which the very sharp spurs are so arranged that the tarsius is certainly held and pierced when he inserts his head to see what there is in the pitcher." GOEBEL remarks of this idea that more study of the matter in the habitat is required. In *N. intermedia* the spurs are interesting because they are broad, and are quite obviously made up of a group of corrugations; they are not sharp and tooth-like, and could not act in the manner described by BURBIDGE for *N. bicalcarata.* Yet so far as we know, the latter shows no superiority over the former or over *N. Rafflesiana* in the struggle for existence. *N. intermedia* is a hybrid of *borneensis* and *Rafflesiana* (the former parent is uncertain, MACFARLANE). If this occurred in nature it would be doubtful if the specialized tooth-like portion of the peristome could act adaptively as a beginning for the condition seen in *N. bicalcarata.*

The several interpretations of the morphology of the *Nepenthes* leaf, as resumed in part by TROLL (1932, 1939), are the following:

1. The lid is the lamina of the leaf, the rest is the petiole with highly specialized regions, phyllodial at the base. This view is traceable to A. P. DE CANDOLLE (1827). Among others GOEBEL took this position in his earlier writings (1884). The recognition by HOOKER that the spur is the true organic apex of the leaf threw this out of court. According to BOWER, GOEBEL regarded the lid as only a part of the lamina, the rest appearing in modified form as the pitcher, tendril, etc.

2. Instead of regarding the laminar portion of the leaf as petiolar, WUNSCHMANN (1872) preferred to see in it the "lower part of the leaf blade", and therefore that the leaf is non-petiolate. The evidence from development denies this.

3. The pitcher has arisen phylogenetically as an apical gland, which through enlargement and specialization became the complex of organs which we now know. This, HOOKER'S interpretation, was based in part on embryological observations and by comparison with such leaves as that of *Flagellaria, Gloriosa* which have a cirrhus, a terminal tenuous apex serving as a tendril. FAIVRE held a somewhat similar view that the pitcher arises in the elongated midrib. But the spur is, as said above, the organic apex of the leaf (HOOKER).

4. The leaf arises as a peltate one. According to this view the pitcher is a peltate leaf in which the margin is contracted so that the upper surface lines a hollow organ, the pitcher. Its outer surface is the lower leaf surface. DICKSON, receiving his impulse from BAILLON'S examination of the embryology of the *Sarracenia* leaf, and impressed by the analogy supplied by the interrupted leaf of *Codiaeum* sp., wrote "it seems highly probable that in *Nepenthes* we have to deal with a leaf, the lamina of which is interrupted in the middle of its course by becoming reduced to a midrib and that, while the proximal portion of the lamina retains its typical form of a flat expansion, the distal portion becomes peltately expanded into a funnel or pitcher." But TROLL, though conceding the outward resemblance, one which strikes anyone who has made the comparison, even to the peltation of the

lower moiety of the blade with a similar condition found in *N. clipeata*
Dans., points out that the resemblance is but superficial, since the
Codiaeum leaf is petioled while the "blade" of *Nepenthes* is more
probably an expansion of the leaf base (Blattgrund) to be compared
with the primary leaf of *Pothos*. GOEBEL also held the view that the
pitcher is a peltate leaf developed into a tubiform one, and compared
the pitcher of *Nepenthes* with that of *Utricularia*, which is also terminal either to a single "leaf" (*Polypompholyx, Utricularia Menziesii,*
etc.), and has a lid (door) which springs laterally from the true apex of
the trap visible as such in some species, *e.g. U. Welwitschii,* or to a leaf
segment.

5. The leaf of *Nepenthes* is not simple but compound. According
to BOWER the lid arises as a double organ, the two congenitally fused
(7— 4), and represents two leaflets. This was based on embryological
observations. MACFARLANE went still further and claimed to be able
to analyze the whole leaf into "3 to 4 or 5 pair of leaflets", the basal
lamina, the wings on the ventral surface of the pitcher, the lobes of the
lid (BOWER), and one or two pairs of lateral appendages sometimes
occurring on the spur, which itself terminates the leaf. This idea goes
back to CH. MORREN (1838) (GOEBEL 1891) who regarded the leaf as
having fused folioles and the lid as a terminal leaflet. GOEBEL (1923)
remarked that this view might have been entertained if, in the circle of
relationship, plants with compound leaves were known.

6. TROLL put forward the theory that the *Nepenthes* leaf is a complete parallel to the ordinary foliage leaf consisting of a basal zone
(Blattgrund), a petiole, and blade which is the pitcher (Oberblatt)
disturbed, however, by a modification of the petiole whereby it is at-
tended by a displacement upwards of the edges of the leaf base to
become the wings of the pitcher. Such a displacement occurs in *Syn-
gonium podophyllum*, and I have shown (1914) that it occurs in *Gos-
sypium* in which the flower peduncle normally suffers displacement up
the internode above, bringing the flower into an unusual position.
More specifically, TROLL sets forth that (*1*) the leaf base consists of a
clasping bottom leaf zone which is contracted briefly to reëxpand to
form the conspicuous lamina, and which in some species extends at its
apex across the base of the tendril in total stipulation (*N. clipeata,*
and others). (*2*) The blade is differentiated into the petiole and true
leaf blade. The former takes the form of a tendril, the latter the
pitcher, the blade in peltate form. But here the relation between the
petiolar structure and the peltation does not behave so simply as in
simple peltate leaves. (*3*) The spur is unifacial (as in *Pothos*). ARBER
(1941) questions this view. At its base, the edge of the blade grows
to form a transverse connection from which the lid arises. This again
is total stipulation.

The supporting evidence is now briefly stated. (*1*) In the first
place the tendril is of bifacial structure (TROLL) (*8 — 20*), and not, as
C. P. DE CANDOLLE (1898) thought, unifacial. The arrangement of the
fibrovascular bundles is not concentric with respect to phloem and
xylem, since the wood faces ventrally in the ventral moiety of the
organ. I can confirm this. (*2*) Reëxamining the embryology of the
leaf, it is clear that in the primary leaf (in seedlings) the thinned out

basal part is composed of two halves which separate above and now appear as the wings on the adaxial pitcher wall to form a transverse membrane below the rim (HOOKER, DICKSON, MACFARLANE). When the transverse connection is absent (which GOEBEL held to be the case), there is often an indication of it in the presence of a row of gland-like emergencies indicating such a connection (STERN observed such). MACFARLANE said that a transverse strand of the venation also is to be taken as an indication, but I cannot substantiate this $(7 — 7, 9)$. HOOKER's view that the pitcher is "the hollowed out upper half of the petiole" is discarded, and DICKSON's theory of contracted peltate leaf blade accepted. The earlier embryological condition is now examined. In an early stage, when the leaf appears as a low conical structure, there is a pit just below the apex on the adaxial side. Just below it is a transverse weal, the transverse connection of the edges of the leaf base. The leaf blade, it is important to note, arises on the abaxial side of the leaf base, the latter, as in *Iris*, presenting total stipulation. The blade cannot therefore be an extension of the apex of the stipule, but though near it must arise below, abaxially. If without further differentiation this embryonic stage passes into permanent form, a primary leaf results, in which the pitcher stands in a dorsal position. What authors have designated the blade is therefore only the leaf base showing total stipulation, of which the transverse sector, as already said, may be suppressed. In support of this I may point out that the extent of the pitcher wings is not commensurate with that of the veins beneath them, the wings often extending beyond the venation, which swerves away to pass around the mouth of the pitcher. This in the adult leaf. In intermediate forms, the development of the rudiments proceeds further, especially the tendril, by contraction below the pitcher. Nevertheless the wings of the pitcher pass down along the edges of the tendril. In purely adult forms the tendril becomes entirely wingless. TROLL now asks: (*1*) May the tendril be regarded as the petiole of the leaf between the pitcher as blade and the leaf base? (*2*) How are the wings of the pitcher to be understood? To answer these he analyzes the embryonic condition. In this a petiole is not recognizable as such, but assuming that it must be there, he postulates a zone of tissue, broad abaxially and narrow or absent adaxially, the narrow adaxial edge of this wedge of tissue impinging on the leaf base at its transverse weal (Wulst). The elongation of this petiolar zone meets, however, an impediment in the leaf base tissues, which converge below the mouth depression. In consequence, the leaf base is dragged out along with the petiole and adaxial side of the pitcher up to the edge of the mouth (but not quite, it may be added). The whole adaxial side of the young leaf from the leaf base to the mouth (I should say not quite) belongs to the leaf base and one may come to the view that the tendril is an extension of the leaf base as GOEBEL showed to be the case for the fan-palms. Nevertheless TROLL insists that the tendril is a petiole, though it may in some instances (such as *N. clipeata*) have an unifacial structure in the lower portion. But the leaf base is never unifacial, always bifacial. But where the tendril is bifacial it should be regarded not as entirely independent indeed, but concrescent with the leaf base.

As to the pitcher wings, which show a wide variety of definitive development, they may be considered as secondary outgrowths, like those of *Cephalotus* or, as GOEBEL held, like the keel of *Sarracenia*. Others have held them to be leaf margins. TROLL comes to the conclusion that they are the edges of the leaf base dragged out (verschleppte), while growing themselves, by the growing petiole and leaf beneath. Concerning the lid, its interpretation, before HOOKER recognized the spur as the true apex of the pitcher leaf, was easy, as being the true apex. STERN'S suggestion that it arises by a longitudinal splitting of the apical meristem is untenable in view of the anatomical facts. The views of BOWER, MACFARLANE and GOEBEL are also discarded. The key to the problem, says TROLL, is to be found in the structure of the spur, which is unifacial, from which it follows that the edges of the leaf blade at its base run together and unite (total stipulation). Important here is a fact, pointed out by HEIDE (1910) that the inner (lower) face of the lid is anatomically identical with that of the interior of the pitcher, and the upper (outer) with that of the outer pitcher surface. The lid cannot therefore be an "outgrowth of the upper surface" as GOEBEL held. It should here be noted that DICKSON stated (and truly) that the base of the lid in primary leaves (as also in other juvenile leaves) is very broad, extending "around fully one half of the orifice of the pitcher" (7 — 7). TROLL'S view as just stated is certainly supported by an examination of the venation of even old adult pitchers in which the isthmus between the orifice and the lid is very narrow. A macerated preparation of *N. formosa* demonstrates this, by which it is seen that, as already indicated in discussing primary leaves, the venation is but that of a totally stipulate leaf blade, sharply constricted below the apex. The apical portion, the lid, may in adult leaves be supplied with a midvein which is secondary since in primary leaves such a midvein does not exist. And when present, as it is in adult leaves, it is evidently smaller and is dominated by the lateral veins.

A novel interpretation of the rim, lid and spur has been advanced by Mrs. ARBER (1941). In doing this she rejects all earlier views, that of TROLL included, which hold that the lid is a transversal pinna. If TROLL is right, she says, the veins of the lid should have their wood upwards, not downwards. She questions also the statement of TROLL that the spur is unifacial, though admitting that the veins of the spur "tend toward a radial arrangement." Had TROLL selected *N. intermedia* and/or *N. bicalcarata* for study, his evidence would have been still more convincing. Having disposed of the spur as the leaf apex, Mrs. ARBER argues that "both the lid and the median point are merely localized expressions of collar-forming activity, which is responsible for the double curve-over of the aperture edge . . . . the lid, which is turned down in youth, corresponding to the inner curve-over, and the median point to the outer curve-over."

"The relative hypertrophy of the lid and median point may be correlated with the special character of the venation . . . . of the parallel type as in other pitchers. The midrib passes directly to the junction of the lid and median point, while the veins of the adaxial part of the pitcher also show a strong tendency to converge upon the apical region. The median point and the lid can thus draw upon a richer vascular supply than the rest of the collar, which is entered only by minor lateral veins, and thus overgrowth of the median region may be stimulated."

It may be answered (*1*) that the midrib vein enters and traverses the spur to its tip (7 — 9, 10; Text fig. 2). (*2*) The lid cannot be regarded as the inner "curve-over" since the surface of the rim would then be a part of the outer pitcher surface, which the histology of the rim denies. The "inner curve-over" would then have to be sought as an outgrowth of the under surface of the lid, and that does not exist. (*3*) The vascular system of the lid, assuming its origin as a transverse weal, along the pitcher edge (Troll), is as it should be. (*4*) The anatomy of the spur shows it to be the organic apex of the leaf

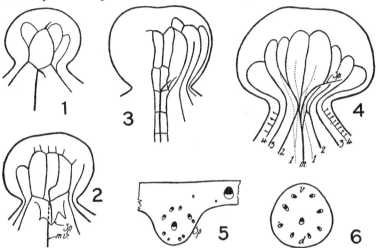

FIG. 2. — *Nepenthes* (various species). — 1, Venation of lid and spur of a pitcher 1 cm long; 2, of a pitcher 2 cm long; 3, of a pitcher 2.5 cm long; 4, of a full sized pitcher; the veins (dotted lines) lie at a different level and more ventral to the rest (solid lines); 5, Section of pitcher wall just below the insertion of the spur in *N. intermedia;* 6, Section through the spur of *N. bicalcarata.*

(Hooker), this being supported by additional evidence here from *N. intermedia* and *N. bicalcarata* (Text fig. 2). (*5*) The wide displacement of lid and spur in these and other species is not accounted for.

Histology of the peristome or rim. — If we examine into the minute anatomy of the hard, glossy surface tissue of the peristome we find that it is composed of straight rows of cells, running across following the transverse curve. In each row the cells overlap very much, in one direction, the tapering tail of one cell overlapping the next and forming a sharp ridge along it (*8 — 7*). The rows being straight, the cells not imbricated as in the other pitcher plants, the ridges of successive cells overlap the one over the other, to form a single sharp ridge, about 0.017 mm. from its parallel neighbor. The general surface is also formed into sulci separated by sharp secondary ridges about 0.17 mm.

apart, there being about 10-12 rows of cells to each sulcus (*N. ampullaria*) ($8 - 17$). Whether the very large ridges that occur in *N. villosa* are secondary, or of the third order I cannot say, as I have had no opportunity of examining the plant. The published drawing of HOOKER (1859) suggests the former.

The epidermis seen in a transverse section is complicated and requires elucidation. One may see a row of cells equal in size or larger cells separated by a pair of smaller ones ($8 - 18$). The latter are the backward extensions of two cells which straddle the large one between them. Two small cells, one *on each side* of the larger one, are therefore really the backward extensions of a single cell. Atop each large cell there is a central projection of various dimensions. This is the overlapping point of another neighbor cell, and appears as a solid mass of cellulose, or with a lumen, according to the position of the section. It is evident that the ridge is composed of the continuity of overlaps (HEIDE 1910). *N. Lowii* presents a different appearance ($8 - 12$). The overlapping spur is not lengthened so that no sharp ridge can be seen in transverse sections. Only where the secondary ridges occur do the cells give indication of striae; these not as well marked as in *N. ampullaria*. With regard to these details MACFARLANE'S account (1908) is inadequate.

The ridges of the second order of magnitude, those readily seen by the naked eye, end at the inner edge of the peristome in more or less prominent teeth. When these are definite and prominent there can be seen between them re-entrant bays marking the marginal pits, at the bottom of which lie the flask-shaped glands first observed by HUNT (1874), further studied by DICKSON (1883) and called by him "marginal glands." The conformation of the bays is such as to afford a seat for sustaining a large drop of nectar in position to attract insects to the peril of falling into the pitcher.

The secondary ridges of *N. Lowii* are very low and not conspicuous enough to catch the unaided eye except where, at their inner extremities, they become more elevated and end in a tooth beneath which rests the large nectar gland. In *N. inermis* a few low ridges converging on the broad tooth overhanging the gland may be seen. That it is true that the general surface of the peristome affords a precarious foothold for insects, ants at least, is as I have already said, doubtful. KNOLL found that they can use their footpads, for which, in spite of the minute ridges, the surface is sufficiently smooth.

Histology of the glands. — BRONGNIART (1824) was the first to notice the glandular character of the inner surface of the *Nepenthes* pitcher. TREVIRANUS, MEYEN (1837) and KORTHALS (1839) recognized the glands but thought that they were subepidermal, an error corrected by OUDEMANS (1864).

The pitchers of *Nepenthes* are conspicuously supplied with glands, those which serve to attract prey, the alluring glands, and those which secrete the fluid of the pitcher, which is digestive. The alluring glands are to be found on the under surface of the lid ($8 - 8$) and between the teeth of the inner edge of the peristome ($8 - 13$). The former are usually dished, biscuit-shaped, sessile glands resting in deepish depressions. Some of these glands, in shallower depressions, are to be found in the invagination near the apex of the lid in *N. Tiveyi*, suggesting that the pocket may serve to hold a drop of nectar when the pitcher is in active condition. In this species also, and in others perhaps, in which a strong ridge stands on the median line on the under surface of the lid, there occur on this ridge a number of nectar glands, deeply enough sunken so that the surrounding rim makes a distinct duct ($8 — 16$). The gland tissues are limited by a course of cells with suberized radial walls. The most strikingly developed alluring glands are to be found, as MACFARLANE showed, distributed here and there on the other leaf parts (midrib, tendril) serving to attract a wandering population of ants which sooner or later find their way to the pitcher. These glands are among the most highly developed structurally in the plant kingdom, notably because of the deep duct ($8 —15$).

Digestive glands occur on the inner surface of the pitcher wall in great numbers — as many as 6000 per cm. in *N. stenophylla*, as few as 100 in *N. gracillima* (DANSER).

Both nectar and digestive glands have the same structure. They consist of a single course of deep columnar cells resting on two courses of rounded cells, these lying in turn on a single course of cells having their radial walls suberized, called by MACFARLANE the "limiting" layer, and being in strict continuity with the surrounding epidermis. This indicates their origin which, according to OUDEMANS, MACFARLANE and STERN, is wholly epidermal, though FENNER has asserted that they involve also the underlying parenchyma. His drawing is not convincing. As to the origin of the marginal nectar glands, these too have been regarded by MACFARLANE as of epidermal origin, but STERN has maintained that they have two centers of origin, the deeper portion of the gland being of mesophyll, and only the upper portion of epidermal origin. I have examined *N. ampullaria* ($8 — 13$), the species that STERN worked with, and the evidence favors a doctrine of uniformity, that they are of wholly epidermal origin. The presence of the limiting layer seems to be decisive evidence.

Anatomy of the pitcher wall. — The wall of the pitcher is thin but of great strength, attributable chiefly to the thick-walled epidermis both within and without, supported by the veins which have a generous supply of sclerenchyma. The most interesting feature of the wall anatomy is the occurrence of large idioblasts with spirally thickened walls first seen by UNGER in *Nepenthes* (according to MANGIN 1882). These are very large spindle- or rod-shaped cells with clear contents, apparently merely sap, and multispiral wall thickenings. These, when the tissues are cut or torn, are drawn out as long cottony conspicuous thread. The natural expectation that these peculiar cells are connected with the vascular tissue system is not realized (GILBURT 1881) as they do not stand in any relation to, and are not at any point in contact with it.

Similar cells occur in some if not all species of *Crinum* (MANGIN); also in some orchids (*Pleurothallus, Bulbophyllum*) (TRÉCUL, through MANGIN); and in *Salicornia* (DUVAL-JOUVE 1868). MANGIN considered them as organs of support; and it is quite possible that they contribute to the walls of the pitcher a considerable degree of mechanical strength which they certainly display. In *Dischidia* the walls of the pitchers have in analogous situations sclerenchyma fibers. DUVAL-

JOUVE thought them to be organs of aeration, and that they were always in contact with sub-stomatal cavities, which is surely not the case. I have satisfied myself that they are quite independent of all other cells than those of the parenchyma in which they lie. They occur elsewhere than in the pitchers. It is probable that they are more properly to be regarded as water-reservoirs (KNY and ZIMMERMANN 1885).

The vascular system. — The course of the vascular strands is such as to indicate that the pitcher is produced by the expansion chiefly of the abaxial moiety of the leaf, and this is also indicated by the mutual approximation of the wings along the edges of the ventral surface (MAC-FARLANE). The finer endings of the vascular tissue often but not always (MACFARLANE) abut on the under side of the surface glands found on the interior surface of the pitcher and of the lid. The fact that unopened pitchers which have been removed from the plant soon lose their juice (invariably found in young pitchers before opening) observed by DE ZEEUW (1934) seems to be related to this fact.

Surface anatomy. — By this we mean the anatomy of the epidermis, that of the interior surface of the pitcher being of primary interest to us. Examination of the interior of the pitcher (*4 — 6*) will show that, with some exceptions (*N. ampullaria, bicalcarata, ventricosa, inermis*) there is a broad zone, beginning just beneath the rim, having a glaucous, opalescent appearance caused by an ample waxy secretion with a pebbly surface. The epidermal cells here are simply polygonal with the exception of a large number of slightly projecting lunate ones, so placed that their concave edges are turned downwards (*8 — 5*). They have the appearance, at once perceived, of half stomata, each in itself looking like a guard cell. OUDEMANS (1864) thought them to be wax-secreting glands. WUNSCHMANN would have none of this (1872) and pronounced them to be squat hairs, broader than long. DICKSON (1883) was the first to arrive at the correct interpretation: "I have here to note that each crescentic ledge consists of a semilunar cell which overlaps a lower and smaller one. Occasionally these two cells puzzlingly resemble deformed stomata," he wrote. His sometime associate MACFARLANE confirmed this, as did HABERLANDT, independently, and later BOBISUT (1910) showed that they are completely non-functional stomata, having no pore, though MACFARLANE had thought otherwise. MACFARLANE thought, too, that they exude water; and GOEBEL that they might serve for gas exchange (1891), neither of which can be true in the absence of a pore. I (1933*b*) have confirmed BOBISUT's observations. The lunate cell is one guard cell, projecting somewhat above the general level of the surface, hiding beneath itself the second guard cell (*8 — 6*), the whole having been rotated on the longer axis. The whole waxy zone is a "conductive" (HOOKER) or slippery surface (Gleitzone, GOEBEL) on which insects such as ants can find no foothold.

It is interesting to note in this connection that MACBRIDE, in 1817, made the suggestion that the inability of insects to cling to the surface of the pitcher of *Sarracenia adunca* might be due to the presence of an impalpable powder, or to the breaking away of fine hairs. To this question in relation to *Nepenthes* KNOLL (1914) has directed some painstaking experimentation.

KNOLL found that if he placed an ant on a cleaned surface of an iris leaf (*Iris pallida*), the waxy secretion thus being locally removed, and then placed the leaf in a vertical position, the ant could not get away from the smooth, clean part. It seems that the ant clings to smooth surfaces by means of its foot-pads, not by its claws, since there is no roughness available. It cannot cling to the glaucous surface of the *Iris* leaf, however, because the waxy secretion is loose and pulls off, cumbering the foot-pads so that the ant must stop to clean them before they are again useful. This KNOLL proved experimentally by seeing if an ant can walk on a smooth surface as of glass when it has been coated with a thin layer of a powder such as talc or carbon and found that it cannot do so. Since the ant can walk on clean glass or a smooth wax surface (beeswax melted onto a glass plate) it is quite evident that the difficulty for the ant lies in the particles which come off on his pads and prevent him from clinging. Experiments with the loose waxy covering of the iris leaf first removing it and then applying it again, showed the same result. Coming to the waxy zone of most *Nepenthes* pitchers, BOBISUT had already experimented and believed to have found that ants could not climb the surface when in the vertical position; even after he had (as he thought) removed the waxy surface. Believing that he had failed to remove the waxy covering perfectly, KNOLL continued his experiments in the same sense as before with *Iris*, etc. He removed the wax thoroughly with chloroform, *rubbing downwards* to avoid breaking the lunate cells and produced a smooth green surface showing clearly the red markings, and upon this he found that the insects could climb and run in any direction. When now he scattered talc powder or wax powder obtained from the pitchers themselves, they failed, showing that their ability to climb on the smooth surface was due to the absence of a deterrent to the use of their pads. He observed, however, that ants could readily negotiate the gliding zone of older pitchers in greenhouses, and thought that this is due to the removal of the wax by the vigorous sprinkling with water which the plants usually receive, just as rain is known to remove the waxy covering from plants like *Cotyledon*, etc. KNOLL'S observations on the walking behavior of ants and the effectiveness of the waxy zone as a precipitating mechanism have been repeated by my friend Prof. W. KUPPER and myself. The plant was a vigorously growing one of *N. gracillima* (aff.?), one which is evidently very attractive to ants as they are always to be seen in numbers rapidly walking hither and yon especially about the tops of the pitchers. We observed that they persistently visit the lid and the rim. They run no risk of capture on the lid. On the rim, however, it is supposed that they do. As a matter of fact, however, they do not, for they can walk on it in any direction with rapidity, and they frequently stop to take the nectar from the marginal glands. They even passed underneath the rim and back several times in one excursion without danger. If, however, they venture on to the waxy zone they at once display a quite different behavior. They cannot then by any chance move rapidly forward. If they progress at all, it is very slowly and with much groping with the legs as if searching for a hold. Usually this ends in a complete loss of foothold, and the ant falls into the abyss. One pitcher I examined held a collection of ants which must have run into the thousands. With regard to the ability of flies (houseflies and blue-bottles) to retain a foothold on the rim, my friend Professor A. H. REGINALD BULLER repeatedly observed many years ago that, in trying to straddle the rim, they promptly fell into the pitcher, in *N. Mastersiana*.

BOBISUT further thought that the curious deformed stomata could furnish a foothold for the claws of the ants, etc. but KNOLL showed that the conformation, position and size of the ant's claws and of the apparently available points for grasping with claws make them unavailable. From the ant's point of view the projecting guard cells should have been turned the other way. HABERLANDT thought that they helped an insect to crawl downward but not upward, since they afforded no foothold for the claws, but since the claws are not used, but the pads only (KNOLL), and since ants cannot climb downwards any better than upwards on the surface, KNOLL, not being able to avoid the impression that the stomata are in some way connected with trapping of insects, has advanced the following suggestion, namely, that the numerous projecting guard cells serve, when the waxy surface has more or less been removed by various means (rain, much traffic of insects), as a means of joggling the body of the ant by the slipping of a foot over them, somewhat as when, on climbing on a steep, precarious rocky surface, a hand should slip from its hold of a ledge and slap the rock surface just below. "Rütteleinrichtungen" KNOLL calls the projecting half-moon shaped cells, and regards them, briefly, as an arrangement for hindering the climbing of the walls of the slipping zone (HOOKER's conducting zone). It must be remembered that an ant uses its footpads and not the claws in trying to climb a smooth surface. The frequent irregularities in form of the surface make it the more perilous, according to KNOLL. The theory is ingenious and may very well represent the facts, which to KNOLL are such in view of his observations.

Below the slide or conducting zone, when present, the whole of the remaining surface constitutes the detentive or digestive zone ($4 — 6$). It is a glossy green or red (*N. ventricosa*) in color, and stands out in sharp contrast with the glaucous color of the waxy zone above. The surface is richly supplied with glands. Each gland stands in a slight depression, the upper edge of which projects and overhangs the gland like an eave, sometimes slightly, more often covering at least half the gland ($8 — 10, 11$), or in the case of *N. Pervillei* ($7 — 14$) forming a deep pit. In the depths of the pitcher, the glands often become more or less irregular in shape and are devoid of any overhang (MACFARLANE, STERN).

There seems to be every reason to regard these glands as both digestive (or peptic as MACFARLANE called them) and absorptive. Their activity becomes evident long before the pitcher reaches its maturity, young unopened pitchers always having the cavity half-filled with fluid. Later a plentiful additional secretion occurs when organic, but not so plentiful if inorganic materials are placed in the pitcher (HOOKER). That they are capable of reabsorbing the fluid is evident in the fact that in a rather short time (24 hours or so) the fluid may entirely disappear from unopened pitchers (DE ZEEUW), and GOEBEL showed that nitrogen, as ammonia and peptone, is rapidly reabsorbed (1891).

Concerning the overhanging eave-like coverings of the glands, KNOLL argued that they serve to prevent the use of the gland for foothold by insects, but incidentally prevent also damage by their claws to the glands themselves.

Digestion. — The students of digestion in *Nepenthes* (as in other insectivorous plants) have been divided into two camps (*a*) of those who argued that it is a function of the plant itself carried out by the secretion of an appropriate enzyme and (*b*) of those who have believed it to be the result of bacterial action (decay or rotting, DUBOIS). If the latter only takes place (as seems to be true in *Darlingtonia, Heliamphora,* and perhaps some spp. of *Sarracenia*) this fact does not disqualify these as carnivorous; bacterial action is an invariable accompaniment of some animal digestion (*e.g.* of cellulose in herbivores). Bacterial action is often unavoidable in open pitchers and it has not always been possible to separate the different digestive processes. *Nepenthes* offers a special condition in that the pitchers secrete a quantity of fluid before they open. The nature of this fluid was investigated by VOELKER (1849). He described it as limpid and colorless, with a slight agreeable odor and taste, and containing a non-volatile acid. The total solids in percentage of the fluid ranged from 0.27 to 0.92 of which 63.94 % to 74.14 % was non-volatile substances. Potassium, sodium, magnesium, calcium, chlorine (as hydrochloric acid) and organic acids were found, chiefly malic, with a little citric. TAIT found that pitcher fluid from unopened pitchers was sometimes acid, but frequently not. When flies had found their way into open pitchers the fluid became much more acid as well as more viscid. According to VON GORUP and WILL (1876) the fluid is colorless, clear or slightly opalescent, odorless, tasteless and of various consistency. After stimulation the fluid changes from being neutral or only slightly acid, to decidedly acid. "Miss R. BOK found that carefully washed beakers of *Nepenthes* filled with distilled water did not show any acid production while the addition of 20/mgr./liter NH_4Cl would cause prompt acid production. The pH went down to about 3.0 in 24 hours". (BAAS BECKING, *in ep.*).

It is an important and well attested fact that the fluid of unopened pitchers is above all free of bacteria, owing in part to the tight sealing around the edge of the lid by interwoven branching hairs, a precursor in Nature of the cotton plug used in bacteriological technique.

The pioneer work, constituting a prime stimulus to the investigation of digestion in carnivorous plants, was done by J. D. HOOKER, announced in his address before the Biological Section of the British Association for the Advancement of Science in August 1874. HOOKER was in touch with CHARLES DARWIN, and his interest was a natural outcome of this contact; for DARWIN was finishing his book on carnivorous plants at the time. HOOKER found that bits of egg-white, meat, fibrin and cartilage, when placed in the pitchers, showed unmistakable evidence in 24 hours of disintegration, but that this action was by no means so pronounced in fluid placed in test tubes. From this HOOKER inferred that the digestion depends not on the first fluid secreted by the glands, but that there is a direct response to the presence of the material to be digested. He saw evidence also of antiseptic action in that odor was not developed so rapidly in the pitcher fluid as in water. His general conclusion may be stated in his own words: "..... it would appear probable that a substance acting as a pepsine does is given off from the inner wall of the pitcher, but chiefly after placing the animal matter in the acid fluid; ....." In the following year (1875) LAWSON TATE announced that he had succeeded in separating a substance "closely resembling pepsin" from the secretion of *Drosera dichotoma* and a little later he obtained a similar substance from the fluid taken from the pitchers of several species of *Nepenthes*, but did not subject these extracts to the appropriate tests. The preparations seem to have been glycerin extracts, in which both were soluble. At the same time REES and WILL of Erlangen (1875) made preparations of *Drosera*, drying the leaves with absolute alcohol and extracting the ground material with glycerin. Such extracts, but only when slightly acidified with HCl (.2%), caused the disappearance of swollen fibrin at 40 degrees in 18 hours, peptones being produced, thus confirming the work of DARWIN on *Drosera*. At about the same time VON GORUP–BESANEZ (1874) studied the fluid of *Nepenthes* pitchers, and found that when he subjected shreds of fibrin to the naturally acid secretion, they were nearly digested in an hour at 40 degrees, peptones then being present. Additional acid as above accelerated the action.

VON GORUP and WILL (1876) investigated further. They compared the behavior of the fluid from stimulated pitchers (to which insects had had access) with that from unstimulated pitchers. The former was filtered and tested with acidulated fibrin, raw meat, coagulated egg-white, legumin and gelatin, obtaining positive evidence in all cases with the Biuret reaction, the gelatin excepted. This yielded a non-jelling gelatin-peptone. The fluid of unstimulated pitchers was found to fail to act unless acidified, but responded in the presence of HCl, formic, malic, citric, acetic and propionic acids. The efficiency of these was various, formic acid being very active ("fast momentan"), followed by malic, citric, acetic and propionic in the order named. The length of time in which positive results were obtained, as indicated by the Biuret reaction, varied from 10 minutes to three hours or more according to the activity of the acid and the temperature.

VINES was busy at the same time. Following the method of REES and WILL, he (1877) alcohol-dried pitcher walls bearing the glands of *Nepenthes* and ground and extracted them with glycerin. In testing his extracts he used the following method. In each of three test tubes he placed (*1*) extract acidified; (*2*) extract only and (*3*) acid only, and added a bit of swollen fibrin and kept the tubes at 40 degrees. Only the first of the preparations gave a positive result and a peptone reaction could be detected; the other two were negative. VINES noticed that the pitcher fluid in VON GORUP–BESANEZ' experiments appeared to be more active than his own extracts. Following the lead of EBSTEIN and GRUETZNER and of HAIDENHAIN (through VINES), who had obtained more active extracts of animal glands by previous treatment with acid, VINES then treated the pitcher walls bearing glands with 1% acetic acid for 24 hours, before extracting with glycerin, and found that this extract was more powerful than that of the control prepared without previous acid treatment. This indicated that, as in the case of animal glands (HAIDENHAIN), the ferment exists in the glands as a zymogen, a basic substance from which the ferment is derived by acidification. The facts seemed to bring the whole phenomenon of plant digestion into line with that in animals. This was the beginning of a sustained investigation on the part of VINES on this subject. DUBOIS and TISCHUTKIN held that there is no digestion proper to the *Nepenthes* pitcher, and that such digestion as takes place is bacterial. GOEBEL'S examination of the matter, however, afforded experimental evidence in agreement with that of VINES (1877), who now, however, repeated and extended his earlier work and drew the conclusion that settled the matter to all appearances. For instance, he showed that digestion goes on in the fluid of (unopened) pitchers in the presence of poisons deadly to bacteria (HCN, thymol, KCN, chloroform); but as opened pitchers were used the possibility is not excluded that a bacterial ferment had already accumulated. VINES concluded that the ferment present in the pitchers is secreted by the pitcher glands, is not a product of bacteria, but is tryptic in nature, like that of certain seeds (GREEN 1899) not producing peptones, or if it does, these are broken down at once into other bodies (leucine, etc.). It is remarkably stable and has an antiseptic action. The pitcher liquid is usually distinctly acid, contrary to the prevailing views, the acidity therefore not depending on the supposed stimulation by foreign bodies. In his third paper (1898) VINES showed more in detail that the enzyme is unusually stable towards heat and alkalis, for while exposure to these agencies does reduce its activity, "it retains a sort of residual digestive power which asserts itself in a very slow and prolonged digestion, and which can only be destroyed by very strong measures." The enzyme exists in the tissues as a zymogen, is essentially tryptic in character, and among its products of digestion true peptones are present. In his last paper published in 1901, VINES proposed the name "nepenthin" for the proteolytic ferment which he had previously studied and made further tests of the action of the pitcher fluid on fibrin and on Witte peptone, exposing them to action for several days at 38.5 degrees C. with the addition of HCl or citric acid. The results showed the presence of tryptophane, characteristic of tryptic digestion.

The detail of VINES' general conclusions, that the digestion is rather of the tryptic kind, was later called in question by ABDERHALDEN and TERUUCHI (1906). From data obtained by experiments in which glycyl-l-tyrosin was used, which gave negative results, they concluded that the *Nepenthes* protease is not a trypsin, though they did not assert certainty in view of the lack of sufficient material for further work (*See* STERN *and* STERN, *beyond*).

Quite opposite conclusions were drawn by TISCHUTKIN (1891), DUBOIS (1890) and COUVREUR (1900). TISCHUTKIN placed small cubes of egg-albumin in unopened pitchers by passing them through a small window cut in the wall under sterile conditions, and saw no digestion. When the test material was placed in pitcher fluid *in vitro*, digestion occurred after some days during which bacteria had accumulated. DuBois (1890) found the sterile fluid from unopened pitchers without action, but that from recently opened pitchers, while still clear, acted vigorously on egg-albumin. DuBois voted for the bacterial action theory. Couvreur (1900) argued that Vines' results were due to the interaction of the reagents on one another. This totally negative attitude had been combatted by Goebel (1893). In a preliminary experiment, he took a pitcher of *N. paradisiaca* (a hybrid) which contains a "clear, odorless and tasteless fluid" and in it placed a bit of fibrin, with one in water as control. In six days the fibrin was broken up and bacteria were plentiful, and the fluid showed a neutral or slightly alkaline reaction. A yellow reaction was obtained in the water but not in the pitcher, by which the products had been resorbed. No peptone had been produced. Cultures showed the presence of *Bacterium fluorescens liquefaciens*. This result admittedly agreed with those of DuBois and Tischutkin. But Goebel pointed out that the plant was not normal. When he took a strong, well grown plant he found otherwise. It had three pitchers, an old one, a strong vigorous one and an unopened one. In the old one, a wasp was attacked and digested. In three days the fluid was alkaline and bacteria and infusoria were plentiful. In the open but vigorous pitcher a fly had been caught. A bit of fibrin was introduced and was attacked in one hour. In 3 hours peptone was demonstrable. Another bit of fibrin together with 0.2% HCl were introduced, and this was digested in 40 minutes, and no bacteria could be found. The fluid of the unopened pitcher was neutral. In its fluid fibrin accompanied by 1% formic acid was digested in 12 hours, and no bacteria were detected after 8 days. He concluded therefore that a peptone forming ferment was present in the fully normal pitchers. He further showed that normal pitchers, when stimulated by the presence of an insect, secrete formic acid. By way of further control he tried to see if fibrin might be digested by the secretions of the lid, with negative results. To do this he fastened a bit of fibrin on the under side of the lid with moist filter paper. Thus Goebel confirmed Vines' conclusions. In general support of the view that the bacteria of decay have nothing to do with the digestion of insects in normal plants in their native habitats Goebel quoted Wallace who wrote in *The Malay Archipelago* as follows: "We had been told that we should find water at Padangbatu, but we looked for it in vain, as we were exceedingly thirsty. At last we turned to the pitcher plants, but the water contained in the pitchers (about half a pint in each) was full of insects and otherwise uninviting. On tasting it, however, we found it very palatable, though rather warm, and we all quenched our thirst from these natural jugs." And still earlier Hermann Nicolaus Grimm recorded (in 1682) the discovery of "aqua dulcis, limpida, amabilis, confortans et frigida" in the pitchers, and the fluid from six to eight of them was sufficient to satisfy a thirsty person.

That our greenhouse cultivated plants, because of their comparatively feeble vitality as compared with plants in their native habitats, may often behave abnormally, is indicated by the observation of Mohnike, whom Goebel cites, who said that the pitcher almost always contains a mass of dead insects including even large beetles.

The larvae of *Apogonia spherica* were found entire but quite digested internally. Insects die in the pitcher fluid much more quickly than in distilled water. In 48 hours or so, insects are disintegrated, only their chitinous skeletons remaining. Such statements, encountered in other writings, indicate a very vigorous action. GOEBEL ventured the statement that of all the pitchered carnivorous plants *Nepenthes* is the most vigorous in these matters.

CLAUTRIAU (1899-1900) took the opportunity of studying *Nepenthes* in its habitat in Java. His results fully corroborate in general GOEBEL and VINES. He observes:

While the fluid in unstimulated pitchers is neutral, it becomes acid on the introduction of foreign bodies. Even shaking has this effect, the strongest acidity obtained being equal to that of a liter of water acidified with 2 cc. of fuming HCl. In the fluid there is a thermolabile substance which acts as a wetting agent, so that insects are quickly drowned but are not killed by any poison. Insects are digested without any putrefaction. Antiseptics such as formaldehyde, chloroform, etc. inhibit both the secretion of acid and digestion, and the pitchers presently die. On the introduction of egg-white, both digestion and absorption occurred. If a small quantity was used absorption equalled digestion in rate; if a too large quantity was used, the products remained in quantity sufficient to afford a culture medium for bacteria. Quantitative experiments showed that 5 cc. of egg-white (10 cc. to 90 cc. water) is completely digested in vigorous pitchers in 2 days. If a pitcher were separated from the plant, digestion was inhibited, and CLAUTRIAU usually found that *in vitro* experiments gave negative results. At home in Brussels he showed by refined methods that albumin is completely digested to peptone. This is readily absorbed by the pitcher walls, so that he was able to give successive doses of food (albumin) and see that they were digested perfectly by the pitchers of *N. Mastersiana*.

CLAUTRIAU concluded that the enzyme is a true pepsin as it acts only in an acid medium and produces true peptone as an end result. No other products could be found. No amylase was detected. The evidence indicated that an ample secretion of both enzyme and acids required stimulation, and, on microchemical evidence, that peptone is absorbed by the glands and stored as protein. A superabundance of food may allow the play of bacteria, and the products of their activity (amino acids and ammonia) may be used by the plant. These do not necessarily damage the pitcher itself.

FENNER has (1904) advanced an interesting presentation of what he believes goes on in natural conditions. The original pitcher fluid is slightly acid (formic acid, GOEBEL). If a few gnats are introduced, they float on top of the fluid. If alive they endeavor to escape by climbing up the wall, and in this way they come in contact with the glands below their overhanging eaves, which, HABERLANDT has suggested, serve the purpose of retaining fluid by capillarity. The body of an insect wet with pitcher fluid thus applied serves to stimulate the glands to action, when they secrete a highly viscid, active fluid which attacks the insect so vigorously that it is digested in 5-8 hours. FENNER tested this view experimentally by taking an opened pitcher and placing an insect (a gnat) on an area of the wall which had been dried. A slight amount of secretion then occurs which is insufficient to act and readily dries up. But if an insect wet with pitcher fluid is used, an ample secretion from the gland ensues and the insect is digested in the time indicated above. It would appear according to FENNER's interpretation that the pitcher fluid acts as a stimulant to secretion. In this way the body of a small insect comes into contact with a more vigorous secretion. The greater activity, therefore, is not within the depths of the pitcher fluid but in the films of fluid by which the bodies of the insect adhere to the glands. Into this position they come naturally enough since they float towards the walls, and the fluid level, by shaking (as by the wind), is moved so that insects stick on the walls above it.

The collection of *Nepenthes* accumulated at the University of Pennsylvania by Professor MACFARLANE, furnished an abundant amount of material for the study of proteolysis by HEPBURN (1919), who carried out his experiments with unopened pitchers, and opened pitchers from which insects were excluded by means of cotton wool plugs. Some of these were stimulated by the introduction of glass beads after shaking. A distinction between "stimulated" and "unstimulated" pitchers became evident: Their fluid was found to differ in its activity. Bacteria were carefully excluded by means of active bactericides, and all experiments were controlled. With various substrates (ovalbumin, fibrin, ovomucoid, Heyden's nutrient and Witte peptone) and by means of formol titration (SÖRENSEN) he found that the fluid from stimulated pitchers digested all of them; but not that of unstimulated. In the presence of very dilute HCl edestin was also acted upon by fluid of stimulated but not by that of unstimulated pitchers. Carmine fibrin in the presence of acid was digested by both, but not by that of unstimulated pitchers in the absence of acid. Protean (from the globulin of the seed of castor bean, *Ricinus communis*) and ricin were attacked by the fluid of both stimulated and unstimulated pitchers if in the presence of very dilute acid. With sufficiently long exposure, glycyltryptophane was "apparently" hydrolysed by the fluid of stimulated pitchers. It appeared that the fluid of stimulated pitchers possessed proteolytic power in the absence of acid (as well as with acid) while that of unstimulated pitchers always required the addition of acid. It is not clear how the stimulation acts: whether by a change of acidity creating a favorable medium for an enzyme already present, or by the activation of a zymogen already present or by an increase in the secretion of the protease of the glands.

In 1932 STERN and STERN reopened the question. They chose a series of substrates (gelatin, casein, edestin, ovalbumin and serum protein), and tested the effect of the pitcher secretion on them throughout the whole physiological range of pH, and found that they obtained two maxima, one at pH 4.7 and 7.0 for gelatin, pH 3 and 8 for edestin, pH 4 and 8 for ovalbumin. Serum protein was not measurably attacked between pH 1.5 and 8.4. The behavior of casein is anomalous. The curve shows two maxima, at pH 3 and 5.5, with a deep dip between, due probably to the flocking of the protein at the isoelectric point and the binding of the enzyme. The tryptic optimum was not evident, due possibly to the inhibiting effect of the glycerine present. These results were obtained on pitcher secretion preserved with 50% glycerine, from *N. Hibberdii* and *N. mixta*. The secretion from open pitchers containing insects, mostly ants, was used. In order to exclude the effect of microbes and the enzymes of insect bodies, the authors also took the glandular walls, comminuted and extracted them with acetic-glycerine. The extract they found active on gelatine at pH 8, and on ovalbumin only in the region of pH 3–3.5, thus supplying evidence that a tryptic ferment is secreted by the glands of the *Nepenthes* pitcher. In order to compare the enzymes of *Nepenthes* with those of animals they made tests of the effect on them of certain activators, known to affect other proteinases, with negative results. Neither HCN, H_2S or cystein have any effect on the proteinase, nor does enterokinase on the tryptase; the latter STERN had shown for the proteinase of white blood cells.

The conclusions of STERN and STERN, that there are two enzymes present, a catheptic and a tryptic, and that the latter is not attributable to the presence of bacteria, led W. DE KRAMER (1932) in BAAS BECKING's laboratory at Leiden to re-examine the question. He came to the conclusion that the opinion that the tryptic action is due to bacteria is justified. DE ZEEUW, who quotes DE KRAMER's unpublished results, attacked this question. Both catheptic and tryptic action was found by them. DE ZEEUW experimented with unopened pitchers which were allowed to open under sterile conditions, using bromine water and sterile cotton for insurance against bacterial infection, and with unopened ones, which were always found sterile.

The fluid of unopened pitchers does not digest fibrin until an acid is added, an enzyme is therefore present. It becomes active within the pH range of 3.4 to 4.4, phosphoric, malic and citric acid having been used, and a phosphate buffer. That from an aseptically opened pitcher acted at pH 3.6 in phosphoric acid, while that from normally opened pitchers was active at pH 3.2 with phosphoric acid and from 7.2 and 8.6 with phosphate buffer. The last named was not sterile. *Bacterium fluorescens liquefaciens, B. prodigiosum* and two others were present, and all of these were found to exert tryptic action. By way of control the fluid of a pitcher, opened under sterile conditions, of *N. Morganiana*, was tested and found to digest fibrin at pH 4.4 to 5.5, the pH increasing steadily during 15 days. An acetic acid-glycerine extract was found to digest fibrin at pH 2.3 to 4.2, in direct contradiction to the results of STERN and STERN (1932) who also believed their extract to be bacteria-free.

Open pitchers display a wide range of pH (3.0–7.2), 33% reacting neutral or basic, 36 pitchers being examined. When completely digested insect cadavers were present, the fluid was neutral or weakly basic; when digestion was in its early stages, acid. Into a pitcher which showed an acid reaction (pH 3.0) the acid was neutralized by means of lime water, and a pH of 8.2 established. Since digestion was proceeding, the next morning the fluid was found to be at pH 3.0 again. Pitchers after being washed out thoroughly with distilled water were then supplied with distilled water (pH 7). When fibrin was added, the pH dropped to 3.5, as also when egg-albumin (such as used by CLAUTRIAU) was used. This is interpreted as demonstrating that the addition of a protein to the fluid stimulates the secretion of acid; but DE ZEEUW was unable to bring this about by mechanical stimulation, the contrary having been reported by HEPBURN (*see above*). The secretion of un-opened pitchers had been found by DE KRAMER to be always neutral, and this was re-examined by DE ZEEUW who found the pH ranging from 4.2 to 7 (ave. 6.6 ± 1.2) in October and from 4.2 to 4.8 (ave. 4.5 ± 0.3) in November and December, a difference possibly attribut-able to the time of year, with a lower temperature prevailing (in the greenhouse?). The fluid of pitchers opened under sterile conditions, therefore without chemical stimulation, always reacted acid (pH 4.2 to 5.8) but required additional acid to secure digestion. When acidified to pH 3.0 to 3.5 with certain acids (phosphoric, HCl, formic, malic, and succinic acid), and kept sterile with toluene, digestion proceeded, but not with the others tried, which probably destroyed the enzyme. What kind of acid is secreted by the pitcher, aside from the fact that it is not a volatile one, was not determined. But the acid reaction of the glands indicated that these are responsible. DE ZEEUW therefore reached the conclusion that the enzymes present are catheptic and tryptic, but that the former only is present in sterile pitcher fluid, the latter occurring only in opened pitchers to which bacteria had had access. Acid is secreted by the gland when stimulated by chemical but not by mechanical means.

As the matter stands at the present, therefore, the positive evidence that a catheptic proteinase is secreted by the pitchers of *Nepenthes* is conclusive. That tryptic digestion in the absence of bacteria takes place there seems little doubt, but this cannot yet be said to be com-pletely proven.

Antisepsis of pitcher fluid. — Reference has been made to the fact, usually accepted as such, that the pitcher fluid of normal actively di-gesting pitchers is free of bacterial action. WALLACE has already been quoted as testifying to this in the natural habitat in Borneo. GOEBEL atributed this, in the experiments he conducted, to the presence of for-mic acid secreted by the pitcher glands. ROBINSON (1908) observed that meat extract might remain in the pitchers of *N. destillatoria* for two weeks without the odor of foulness. Although they confirmed the generally accepted belief that the fluid of unopened pitchers is sterile, HEPBURN *et al.* (1919, 1927) found that opened pitchers, whether containing insects or not, invariably contained bacteria in large num-bers, whose activity in digesting proteins they found was low, and that they play only a secondary rôle in the digestion of insects, the leading rôle being played by the protease proper to the pitcher itself. They argued that the bacteria live in symbiosis with the plant, assisting some-what in the digestion of insects, thereby drawing nutrition therefrom. Since the plants they experimented with were under cultivation, the argument that their results do not reflect the conditions found in nature, as indicated by such experiences as WALLACE, seems justified. Testimony is, however, not uniform on this point. JENSEN (1910) speaks twice of the horrible stench arising from pitchers loaded with centi-pedes, cockroaches, butterflies and a huge scorpion found in pitchers near Tjibodas, Java. This may mean merely that the pitchers were overloaded beyond the limits at which the antiseptic effect could be expected to work. On the basis of experiments, JENSEN regards it as sure that certain larvae which live on the debris in pitchers have an antiferment which is not possessed by the same kind of larvae when inhabiting water in pools.

Under the title, "*The animal world of Nepenthes pitchers*", AUGUST THIENEMANN (1932) brought together all that at the time of publication was known about the fauna to be found in the pitchers of *Nepenthes*. Long ago, as early as 1747, G. E. RUMPHIUS, the renowned explorer, remarked in his *Herbarium Amboinense* (pt. 5, p. 122): —

"In aperto varii repunt vermiculi et insecta, quae in hoc moriuntur, excepta parva quadam squilla gibba, quae aliquando in hoc reperitur et vivit . . . . . " Since that time innumerable observations have been made and it would scarcely be profitable to detail them.

The first question which will occur to one interested in this fact is one which JENSEN (1910) asked, namely, how can animals live in the digestive fluids of the pitchers. In answer he said that he believed there was indicated the presence of an antipepsin formed by the animals in question. DOVER (1928) agreed with him, but did not go so far as to assert the presence of an antipepsin, though he believed that mosquito larvae do possess such, and suggested that the "presence of neutral salts in the tissues of the larvae might possibly retard peptic digestion;" THIENEMANN, however, maintained that there is no binding evidence that there is an antipepsin and goes further in saying that he sees no special problem to be involved. The numerous internal parasites of the animal body live in body fluids rich in ferments. DOVER, himself, observed that the larvae of *Megarhinus acaudatus* can remain alive in a very weak iodine and in a strong pepsin solution and in the latter lived some days, pupated and hatched out. Are we then to expect if an antipepsin is present that there is also an antiiodine? We may recall here that HEPBURN and JONES (1919) believe that they demonstrated the presence of antiproteases in the larvae of *Sarcophaga* which inhabit the pitchers of *Sarracenia flava*.

The inhabitants of the pitchers are divided by THIENEMANN into three classes, (*a*) those which are occasionally found, but which belong properly in other places (nepenthexene); (*b*) those which occur, find in the pitcher suitable conditions and can pass their watery lives there but which are not confined to them (nepenthephile) and thirdly those which live only in the pitchers and are not found elsewhere (nepenthebionts). Since the pitchers are commonly only partly filled with fluid, namely, *ca*. up to the waxy zone, there is a "terrestrial fauna" as well as an aquatic fauna.

Of the former, aside from 2 species of leaf miners (which, however, have been claimed to behave in relation to the water level) which are questionably peculiar to *Nepenthes* pitchers, there are four spiders, three of which are claimed to be nepenthebiont. The 4 species are *Misumenops nepenthicola*, *M. Thienemannii*, *Thomisus callidus* and *Th. nepenthephilus*. *Th. callidus* is nepenthephile; the others have been found up till the present only in pitchers of *Nepenthes*, but are not confined to any one species. But they are excluded from *N. ampullaria* because there is no waxy zone, states THIENEMANN; they should also be absent from *N. ventricosa*. Since the spiders above named find their food in insects attracted to the pitchers, they may be regarded as commensal. The case is somewhat if not quite the same as that of the spider-plant combination of *Roridula* (LLOYD, 1934).

The "aquatic fauna" nepenthexene forms include protozoa, myxophyceae, desmids and diatoms, rotatoria, Oligochaetes, crustaceae and also larvae of various Diptera and a very occasional tadpole. Such forms occur relatively infrequently, but are most abundant in those pitchers of *N. ampullaria* which stand half buried in the substratum, as would be expected. The nepenthephile animals occur in only very small numbers; only three known in fact. It is interesting to know that of these one is represented by two races, one of which lives in hollows of bamboos. The nepenthebionts include the remarkable number of 26 species; of the *Phoridae* 6, *Chironomidae* 1, and of the *Culicidae* 19. All these are Diptera, 19 of which are mosquitos. It is admitted that further research may reduce or enlarge this number somewhat, but it can hardly alter the general weight of the evidence that there is a strikingly large number of animals which habitually live in the pitchers of *Nepenthes* and nowhere else. They feed on the animal detritus found there. To account for this large number of forms adapted only to *Nepenthes* as commensals, THIENEMANN points out that DANSER refers the origin of the genus to a time earlier than the beginning of the Tertiary, in the Chalk, but DANSER thinks of the genus as a young one.

Folklore, uses. — It is inevitable that such an unusual and curious plant as *Nepenthes* should figure in the folklore of the peoples in contact with it. In this connection I quote an interesting passage from RUMPHIUS (*Herbarium Amboinense* 5:123) containing notes made about 1660 in the Far East. This was kindly translated for me by Prof. BAAS BECKING, who indeed drew my attention to it.

"Uses. This remarkable plant mostly serves as a curiosity, to keep its pitchers amongst other strange objects which are worth keeping to show the nice playfulness of nature. To this end open pitchers are preferred. They are emptied and wind-dried, filled with cotton or other fine material in order that the natural form may be preserved. Or the dried pitchers are placed in a book and pressed flat. However, to show the curiosity more completely, one should have the leaf still attached.

"The natives are unwilling to bring them to us from the mountains, because of an old superstition according to which if one cuts off the pitchers and pours out the water one will meet with a heavy rain before reaching home. As this happened a few times when I had ordered them to fetch me the largest species from the mountains of Mamalo, they were strengthened in their superstition, notwithstanding the fact that I convinced them that it had rained on the two days previous to this expedition. Others go to the mountains when the rain has not fallen for a long time, and empty all pitchers which they can reach with a stupid zeal as they want to bring rain to the land in this way; but the converted natives do not dare to perform such tricks, out of respect to our and to the Mohammedan priests.

"Now listen to the contrary effect. If children often wet the bed, the native goes to the mountains and fetches a few of the filled and still unopened (*sic*) pitchers, the water of which he pours over the head of the children and makes them drink of it, as they also do to adults who are unable to keep their water.

"As it seems, one or the other must be a lie or a great miracle, if one could by means of this little pitcher draw the water from the heavens and also keep it in the children's bellies."

At a guess, the virtue attributed by the natives to the open pitchers, out of which water can be poured, and the unopened pitcher, lies fundamentally in the fact that the latter holds its water. The symbolism appears evident.

B. H. DANSER (1927) remarks that no trace of these superstitions is to be found nowadays, but that the Malayans from Malacca and the Riouw Archipelago use the fluid from the unopened pitchers to wash their eyes or put it on inflamed skin until the new skin is formed. He points out also that the long viney stems (lianas) of *N. ampullaria* are used as ropes for slinging foot-bridges. Possibly other species are similarly used.

Literature Cited:

ABDERHALDEN & TERUUCHI, Zeitschr. f. Physiol. Chem. 49:21–25, 1906.
ARBER (see under *Cephalotus*).
BISCHOFF, G. W., Lehrbuch der allgemeinen Botanik. Berlin, 1834 (*through* TROLL).
BOBISUT, O., Über den Functionswechsel der Spaltöffnungen in der Gleitzone der *Nepenthes*-Kannen. Sitzungsber. d. K. Akad. d. Wiss., Math.-Naturwiss. Klasse 119:3–10, 1910.
BOWER, F. O., On the pitcher of *Nepenthes*. Ann. Bot. 3:239–252, 1889.
BOWER, F. O., On Dr. MACFARLANE's observations on pitchered insectivorous plants. Ann. Bot. 4:165, 1889.
BRONGNIART, AD., Ann. Sci. Nat. 1:29, 1824.
BURBIDGE, F. W. T., Gard. Chron. 1880:201.
DE CANDOLLE, A. P., Organographie végétale. Paris, 1827. (*through* GOEBEL and TROLL).
DE CANDOLLE, C. P., Sur les feuilles peltées. Bull. Trav. Soc. Bot. Genève. 9:1, 1898/9.
CLAUTRIAU, G., Mémoires couronnés . . . . . Acad. R. d. Sci. etc. Belg. 59:1–55, 1900.
COUVREUR, C. R. 130:848–849, 1900.
CURTIS, W., Botanical Magazine 53 (no. 2629), 1826.
CZAPEK, F., Biochemie der Pflanzen, 3 vols., 825 pp., Jena, 1925.
DANSER, B. H., Indische bekerplanten. De Tropische Natuur 1927:197–205.
DANSER, B. H., The *Nepenthaceae* of the Netherlands Indies. Bull. Jard. bot. Buit. sér. 3, 9:249–438, 1928.
DICKSON, A., On the structure of the pitcher in the seedling of *Nepenthes* as compared with that of the adult plant. Proc. R. Soc. Edin. 1883/4:381–385.
DICKSON, A., Gard. Chron. n. s. 20:812, 1883.
DOVER, CEDRIC, Fauna of pitcher plants. Journ. Malayan Br. R. As. Soc. 6:1–27, 1928.
DUBOIS, R., Sur le prétendu pouvoir digestif du liquide de l'urne des *Nepenthes*. C. R. 111: 315–317, 1890.
DUVAL–JOUVE, J., (re Spirally thickened cells in *Salicornia*). Bull. Soc. Bot. France 15, 1868 (through MANGIN).
FAIVRE, E., Recherches sur la structure . . . . . des urnes chez *Nepenthes*. Mém. de l'acad. d. sci., belles lettres et arts de Lyon 22:173–211, 1877.
FENNER, C. A., Beitrag zur Kenntnis der Anatomie, Entwickelungsgeschichte und Biologie der Laubblätter und Drüsen einiger Insectivoren. Flora 93:335–434, 1904.
GILBURT, W. H., Notes on the histology of pitcher plants. Quekett Micr. Journ. 6:151–164, 1881.
GOEBEL, K., Pflanzenbiologische Schilderungen II. Marburg 1891. (*Nepenthes:* pp. 93, 186).
GOEBEL, K., Organographie, 2d. ed., pt. 3, Jena 1923.
GORUP–BESANEZ E. VON, Über das Vorkommen eines diastatischen und peptonbildenden Ferments in den Wickensamen. Ber. d. deutsch. Chem. Gesellsch. 7:1478–1480, 1874 (Not directly concerned with carnivorous plants).
GORUP–BESANEZ, E. VON, Weitere Beobachtungen über diastatische und peptonbildende Fermente im Pflanzenreiche. Ber. d. deutsch. Chem. Gesellsch. 8:1510–1514, 1875 (Not directly concerned with carnivorous plants).
GORUP–BESANEZ, E. VON & H. WILL, Fortgesetzte Beobachtungen über peptonbildende Fermente im Pflanzenreiche. Ber. d. deutsch. Chem. Gesellsch. 9:673–678, 1876.
GREEN, J. R., The soluble ferments and fermentation, 1899.
GRIMM, H. N., De planta mirabili destillatoria *in* Miscell. nat. curios. Dec. II, ann. I, 1682 (through WUNSCHMANN).
GUENTHER, Die lebenden Bewohner der Kannen der insectenfressenden Pflanzen, *N. destillatoria* auf Ceylon. Zeitschr. wiss. Insectenbiologie 9:123, 1913.
HABERLANDT, G., Physiologische Pflanzenanatomie, 2. Aufl., Leipzig 1924 (*Nepenthes*, p. 442).
HEIDE, F., Observations on the corrugated rim of *Nepenthes*. Bot. Tidskrift 30:133–147, 1910 (The cover is dated 1909).
HEINRICHER, E., Zur Biologie von *Nepenthes*, etc. Ann. Jard. Buit. 20:277–298, 1906.
HEPBURN, J. S., Biochemical studies of the pitcher liquor of *Nepenthes*. Proc. Am. Phil. Soc. 57:112–129, 1918.
HEPBURN, J. S., E. Q. ST. JOHN & F. M. JONES, Biochemical studies of insectivorous plants. Contr. Bot. Lab. U. of Penna. 4:419–463, 1919. — *See* also p. 39.
HOOKER, J. D., On the origin and development of the pitcher of *Nepenthes*, with an account of some new Bornean plants of the genus. Trans. Linn. Soc. 22:415–424, 1859.
HOOKER, J. D., Address to the Department of Zoology and Botany, B. A. A. S. Report of the forty-fourth meeting, 1874:102–116, 1875.

HUNT, J. GIBBONS, (A minute in) Proc. Acad. Nat. Sci. Phila. 26:144, 1874.
JENSEN, H., *Nepenthes*-Tiere, II. Biologische Notizen. Ann. du Jard. Buitenzorg, Sup. III: 941–946, 1910.
KNOLL, F., Über die Ursache des Ausgleitens der Insektenbeine an Wachsbedeckten Pflanzentheilen. Jahrb. wiss. Botan. 54:448–497, 1914.
KNY, L. and A. ZIMMERMANN, Die Bedeutung der Spiralzellen von *Nepenthes*. Ber. d. d. bot. Gesellsch. 3, 1885.
KORTHALS, P. W., *Nepenthes. in* Verh. d. nat. Geschiedenis der Nederl. Overzeesche Bezittingen (Botanie), Leiden, 1839/1842, Ed. by C. J. TEMMINCK.
LLOYD, F. E., Abscission. Ottawa Naturalist 38:41–52; 61–75, 1914.
LLOYD, 1933*b, see* p. 269; 1934, *see* p. 8.
MACBRIDE, J. M., On the power of *Sarracenia adunca* to entrap insects. (Read in 1815) Trans. Linn. Soc. London 12:48–52, 1817.
MACFARLANE, J. M., Nature, Dec. 25, 1884.
MACFARLANE, J. M., Observations on the pitchered insectivorous plants, I. Ann. Bot. 3:253–266, 1889/90; II. 7:403–458, 1893.
MACFARLANE, J. M., *Nepenthaceae.* Das Pflanzenreich, Leipzig, 1908.
MANGIN, L., Sur le développement des cellules spiralées. Bull. Soc. bot. France 29:14–17, 1882.
MENZEL, R., Beiträge zur Kenntnis der Mikroflora vom Niederländischen Ost-Indien; II. Über den tierischen Inhalt der Kannen von *N. melamphora* Reinw. mit bes. Berücksichtigung der Nematoden. Treubia 3:116–122 (Doubts that the pitchers are a mere "Luxus-Anpassung"). Harpacticiden als Bromeliaceen-Bewohner. *Ibid.* 3:122–126, 1923.
MEYEN, F. J. F., Über die Sekretionsorganen der Pflanzen. Berlin, 1837.
MOHNIKE, Blicke auf das Pflanzen- und Thierleben in den niederländischen Malaienländern. 1883 (p. 148).
MORREN, CH., Morphologie des acidies. Bull. R. Acad. Brux. 5:430, 1838.
MORREN, CH., Criticism of BOWER'S Review of above. Ann. Bot. 7:420, 1893.
OUDEMANS, C. A. J. A., De Bekerplanten. Amsterdam 1864.
OYE, P. VAN, Zur Biologie der Kanne von *Nepenthes melamphora.* Biol. Zentralblatt 41: 529–534, 1921.
REES, M. & H. WILL, Einige Bemerkungen über "fleischfressende" Pflanzen. Bot. Zeit. 33:713–718, 1875 (*also see* Sitzungsber. d. phys.-med. Soz. Erlangen 8:13, 1875).
ROBINSON, W. J., Torreya 8:181–194, 1908.
RUITER, C. DE, Op zoek naar de bekerplant met de "Marie-Stuart kraag", *Nepenthes Veitchii* Hook. f. De Trop. Natuur 24:195, 1935. (*through* TROLL).
SCHMITZ, P. H. S. J. & J. V. DE JANTI, Contribution à l'étude de la faune népenthicole. Natuurhist. Maanblad I, 21 (9):116–117, 1932; II, 21 (12), 1932; III (by A. STÄRKE), 22 (3):29–31, 1933; IV (by E. O. ENGEL, Beitrag zur Morphologie der Larva von *Wilhelmina nepenthicola* Villeneuve), 22 (4):46–48, 1933; V (by SCHMITZ), 23 (3):26, 1934; VI (by S. L. BRUG, Culicidae collected from *Nepenthes* in Borneo), 23 (11):149–150, 1934.
SIMS, JOHN, *Nepenthes phyllamphora*, Ventricose Pitcher Plant. Curtis's Botanical Magazine, 53: plate 2629, 1826.
STERN, K., Beiträge zur Kenntnis der Nepenthaceen. Diss., Jena 1916, Flora 109:213–283, 1917.
STERN, K. G. and E. STERN, Ueber die Proteinasen insektivorer Pflanzen. Bioch. Zeitschr. 252:81–96, 1932.
TATE, LAWSON, Nature 12:251–252, 1875.
THIENEMANN, A., Die Tierwelt der *Nepenthes*-Kannen. Archiv f. Hydrobiologie, Suppl. 11, 1932. Tropische Binnengewässer 3:1–54.
TISCHUTKIN, N., Über die Rolle der Mikroorganismen bei der Ernährung der insectenfressenden Pflanzen. Arbeiten d. St. Petersb. Naturfor. Gesellsch., Abt. f. Bot., 1891:33–37. (*Digest* in Bot. Centralbl. 50:304–305, 1892).
TRÉCUL (*through* MANGIN).
TREVIRANUS, Zeitschr. f. Physiologie 3:78, 1829.
TROLL, W., Morphologie der schildförmigen Blätter. Planta 17:153–314, 1932.
TROLL, W., Vergleichende Morphologie der höheren Pflanzen. Berlin, 1939 (A rich source of literature citations.).
VINES, S. H., On the digestive ferment of *Nepenthes*. Journ. Linn. Soc. 15:427–431, 1877. The proteolytic enzyme of *Nepenthes* I: Ann. Bot. 11:563–584, 1897; II: Ann. Bot. 12:545–555, 1898; III: Ann. Bot. 15:563–573, 1901.
VINES, S. H., Jour. Anat. a. Physiol. 11: 124–127, 1876/1877.
VOELKER, A., On the chemical composition of the fluid in the ascidia of *Nepenthes*. Ann. and Mag. Nat. Hist. II, 4:128–136, 1849.
VOUK, V., Physiologischer Beitrag zur Kenntnis die Entwickelung des *Nepenthes*-Blattes. Bot.-Physiol. Inst. d. K. Univ. Zagreb, 22 Jan. 1918 (In support of the GOEBEL interpretation of the leaf morphology, based on growth localization).
WALLACE, A. R., The Malay Archipelago. 10th ed., p. 24, London, 1913.
WUNSCHMANN, E., Über die Gattung *Nepenthes*. Diss. Berlin, 1872, 46 S.
ZACHARIAS, E., Über die Anatomie des Stammes der Gattung *Nepenthes*. Inaug. Diss. Strassburg, 1877.
ZEEUW, J. DE, Versuche über die Verdauung der *Nepenthes*kannen. Biochem. Zeitschr. 269:187–195, 1934.

Chapter V

CEPHALOTUS FOLLICULARIS

Distribution. — Habit. — Habitat. — Foliage leaf. — Pitcher leaf. — Development of pitcher leaf. — Morphology. — Anatomy. — Digestion.

The West Australian Pitcher Plant is a unique form and, though related to *Sarracenia* and *Nepenthes*, diverges from them in many details of form and structure. It occurs in a lunate area, in extreme S. W. Australia, one horn of the crescent lying about 150 miles S. of Perth, the other at the Fitzgerald River, the southern rim of the area passing through Albany. Its first collector was probably ARCHIBALD MENZIES, naturalist of the Vancouver's Expedition of 1791. MENZIES "landed at King George's Sound and made large collections." But as these were not studied till much later by ROBERT BROWN, the plant, if actually found, did not become known. In the following year, 1792, came the expedition under D'ENTRECASTEAU (*"Voyage à la recherche de la Pérouse"*). The naturalist was LA BILLARDIÈRE. He landed first "on one of the islands of Esperance Bay and then on the mainland" (GARDNER 1926). Here the naturalist of the expedition found the plant which he later (1806) described under the name *Cephalotus follicularis*.

The plant is of rosette habit, the rosette, where primary, surmounting a tap-root (LA BILLARDIÈRE), and in older plants ending branches of a freely forking rootstock. These branches when small produce for some time only minute leaves and pitchers; more massive branches produce at once larger or even normal sized organs. The flowers, in a short panicle, and borne on a very long slender scape, triangular at its base, are small, apetalous, have a six-parted calyx and twelve stamens $(9 — 5)$.

The habitat is the drier parts of peaty swamps. The leaves are, as has been known since the publication of LA BILLARDIÈRE'S description, of two very distinct kinds: the foliage leaves, or "non-ascidiform" (DICKSON 1878) $(9 — 6)$ and the pitcher or ascidiform leaves $(9 — 1\text{-}3)$. The foliage leaves attain a length of about 13 or 14 cm. when of large size. The blade is ovate and acute, about the length of the petiole, which, as TROLL has shown, is of unifacial structure. Two of the vascular strands, dorsal and ventral, facing each other wood to wood, enter and extend up into the blade, thus indicating, according to TROLL, the peltate structure of the leaf. The ventral strand enters and supplies vascular tissues to the lid of the pitcher when this develops in place of a flat leaf. The blade is furthermore inclined to transverse thickening above the petiole $(9 — 6$ at left$)$. This becomes very pronounced in intergrade forms between pitchers and foliage leaves which in this plant occur very frequently, and will be described below.

The leaf is thick, coriaceous and supplied with nectar glands, and its surface smooth and glassy. The margins are ciliated with the peculiar hairs mentioned by DICKSON (1878). Their peculiarity consists in the secondary filling in of the lumen by callus (or callus-like substance), the protoplast withdrawing toward the base. A central thread-like core of protoplasmic substance with more or less continuity can be traced through the otherwise solid mass of callus.

Foliage leaves are produced in seasonal rhythm. Of this A. G. HAMILTON (1904) wrote, "I believe that the ordinary leaves develop in the autumn, reaching their full maturity in the spring, and then gradually going off, while the pitchers grow in winter and spring and are fully formed and functional in summer when the insects which they capture are most plentiful." This seems to be a true account. I can only add that at the time of my visit to the classical ground of Albany in the spring (Oct. 1936), the pitchers were in full representation, and foliage leaves much less conspicuous.

The pitchers when full sized measure in length about 5 cm. or slightly more. The majority measure less, say about 3 cm. in length, and about 2 cm. in transverse measurement, somewhat compressed from front to back. The orifice is oval in form, wider transversely than from back to front, measuring in a pitcher 5 cm. long, 1 × 1.5 cm. (inside measurement). HAMILTON well compares the form of the pitcher with that of a loose slipper, with the heel turned over to form a lid. Its stalk (the petiole) stands approximately at right angles with the axis of the pitcher, and in this at once we see a marked divergence from the morphology of *Sarracenia* and *Nepenthes*, in that the mouth of the pitcher faces the base of the petiole in *Cephalotus*, while the opposite occurs in the other two genera.

This is best understood by examining the development, as did EICHLER (1881) and GOEBEL, or by comparing the various aberrant pitchers which in this species are rather common and have been remarked by DICKSON, GOEBEL, and HAMILTON. The true orientation is clearly seen in a pitcher only 1 to 3 mm. long. Such a one in longitudinal section is seen in the figure (*10 — 6*), in which it is evident that the lid does not terminate the leaf (DICKSON), but is an outgrowth from the upper surface of the petiole below the pitcher proper while the pitcher has been produced by a ventro-dorsal invagination of the upper, more distal region. Abnormal leaves, which occur in sizes between 1 mm. to a few cm., bear out the above interpretation, and further show that the lid represents the transverse extension of the leaf margins across the basal zone of the blade, that therefore the pitcher is a peltate leaf highly differentiated into the complicated apparatus that it is (*10 — 13–18*). The orientation and course of the vascular bundles are in accord with this interpretation, though ARBER argues that the absence of a median ventral vein in the petiole does not agree with TROLL's description, and that this raises doubt as to the truly peltate condition. With ARBER, I find no median ventral bundle (*10 — 2*).

The mouth of the pitcher is surrounded by a corrugated rim, each corrugation forming a claw-like tooth extending inward and downward, much as in *Nepenthes*, except here the teeth are coarser and are not provided with glands. There are about 24 such teeth, the numbers on each side not being always symmetrical. I counted 12 on one side and 11 on the other in a particular specimen. They are largest in front (the ventral aspect of the opening) and are smaller and smaller as one swings around the curve towards the lid, and are longitudinally ridged. The largest teeth, however, are opposite the median and lateral ridges ($10 - 2$). The purse of the pitcher externally has three strong ridges, one a ventral one, T-shaped in transverse section, extending along the front of the pitcher along its whole length, along and below the midrib of the pouched leaf, the other two lateral and obliquely placed. These, too, are T-shaped though less obviously so. The lateral and median wings are connected by a low ridge, readily discernible only in strongly developed pitchers. From each lateral wing there runs a similar but more vague ridge toward the petiole ($10 - 1$, 11). All three bear strong cilia, chiefly on the edges of the lateral wings ($10 - 7$). These cilia develop early, so that a young pitcher looks, as HAMILTON put it, like a "vegetable hedgehog." These ridges must be regarded as enations from the ventral and subventral surfaces of the leaf (GOEBEL 1891, TROLL 1932). In addition to these there are low but quite evident ridges between them, especially evident near the toothed rim, and which may pass for mere rugosities, but which are probably more than that. The rest of the frontal (appearing ventral but really dorsal) surface presents low rugosities. The lid overhangs the opening more or less closely according to age, and is nicely arched, but is not, as once believed (WOOLLS), moveable. It is traversed radially by narrow patches of green ciliated tissue, often forking once or twice toward the margin of the lid; and lying between them are clear patches devoid of chlorophyll, which present window-like areas framed in green, or in nature usually bright red mullions. Whatever their purpose is, they are evidently analogous to the fenestrations in *Sarracenia* and *Darlingtonia:* they are to insects apparently open spaces and the insects are thus tempted to escape through them, to rebound into the depths of the pitcher. The lid is emarginate, a feature which can be seen in abnormal intergrade forms, in which the transverse pad at the base of the blade betrays itself as a bilobed structure ($10 - 11$, etc.). In the unopened pitcher the apical notch of the lid lies beneath the end of the median enation and straddles its wing, the lid margin inclosing the teeth. The edge of the lid is ciliated, the hairs becoming reduced and more or less contorted along the frontal region. It is devoid of a midvein, being supplied by two pairs of veins from the ventral moiety of the petiole bundles ($10 - 4$, 8). The veins traverse the green strips of the lid between the white patches. From each of the angles of the lid and mouth edge runs a low ridge (scarcely "wings" as ARBER puts it) demarking, according to DICKSON, the ventral aspect of the pitcher ($10 - 1$, 11).

Mrs. ARBER (1941) has advanced the suggestion that "the lid . . . . may be interpreted as a hypertrophy of the collar region", that it is "essentially of the same nature as the collar" being "indicated by the fact that the cornice continues unaltered below both the collar and the lid. It is possible that the thickened ribs of the expanded lid are equivalent to the hooks of the collar". To this it may be replied that the teeth of the rim are developed from the margin of the abaxial, distal part of the leaf and that the lid is the whole adaxial, basal part of the leaf which, as the teratological evidence shows ($10 - 13$–18), arises as two lobular extensions that fuse (concrescence), the indication of this fusion being found in the emargination of the lid, and in its "dual" structure, to be expected in peltate leaves.

The whole of the pitcher, "slipper" shaped as already said, has a gentle forwardly concave curvature. The under side is the thinnest region, and rests, in nature, on the surface of the soil, in such a manner that the pitcher stands more or less obliquely (9 — 1, 2).

The interior of the pitcher is divisible into two distinct zones, the upper of which forms a collar with, at its lower edge, an overhanging eave. The epidermis of this collar ("conducting shelf", DICKSON) forms a surface of low pointed trichomes which are downwardly directed, supplying a smooth, glistening, chalk-white face. This surface is continuous with that of the lid, where the trichomes point in the same sense but here they are very low and appear as imbricated. Among them are numerous nectar glands.

The jutting eave overhangs, like the entrance of a lobster pot, the far interior of the pitcher. Here the surface is smooth, and the epidermal cells are wavy-walled, the radial synclinal walls supported by numerous buttresses from the angles of the undulations. There are in the upper region (ca. one half of the surface) extending further down in front than behind, many glands, which are smaller above, becoming larger below. These are, it may be fairly argued, digestive in function. In the lower half there is on each side an obliquely placed kidney-shaped mass, in reality a thickened bolster of tissue, called by DICKSON the "lateral coloured patch," since it is usually deeply red colored, and which HAMILTON preferred to call the "lateral gland mass." The upper zone of this bolster is the seat of a number of very large glands though they are not wholly confined to it (9 — 4). Its lower half has a very peculiar feature in the presence of numerous immobile stomata with widely open mouths first observed but not properly understood by DICKSON (10 — 23). The function of the glands also is d'gestive, the general evidence for which was offered by DAKIN (see below). The lower portion of the general surface of the pitcher interior is entirely free of glands. HAMILTON thinks that normally only the lower portion of the pitcher holds fluid and the obliquity of the distribution of the glands in the upper zone is correlated therewith, since the pitchers usually lie somewhat obliquely on the ground. My own observations lead me to doubt this as a matter of fact; particularly it is difficult to agree that the quantity of fluid is so definitely restricted. While it is a curious enough fact that the distribution of the glands is as described above, there may very well be another explanation, for the glands of the lateral patches in any event would, according to the HAMILTON view, be submersed.

Slender rhizomes produce very small pitchers, having a slightly different aspect in detail from that of the normally larger pitchers. They attain a size in general of about 1 cm. in length, often less, with tissues correspondingly thinner and more delicate. A major difference is in the development of the teeth surrounding the mouth: there are fewer of them and all arise from an external low ridge, and stand freely independent of the actual edge of the mouth (10 — 9-12), one opposite each of the three wings, and two further back on each side. A further important difference is the relatively greater width of the collar, as will be clear in the figures. Correlated with size are the simpler venation and small number of glands. HAMILTON drew attention to this condition (1904). In the large pitchers the teeth are concrescent with the rim and overhang it inwardly. Another feature of juvenile pitchers is the large size of the lid, which is strongly arched and widely overhangs the opening, so that it more effectually prevents the entrance of rain water, or appears to. As I have observed these small pitchers are efficient in catching correspondingly small insects.

Transition forms between the large and small pitchers have not been observed. When a relatively large pitcher appears after a number of small ones have been produced, the passage from the small to the large form is made at once in a jump.

We turn to the anatomy of the pitcher ($10 — 3$, 6, 12). The venation is derived from two systems of bundles in the petiole, a dorsal, of three veins, and a ventral of two, these splitting near the pitcher into four, then six and branching further in spreading. Referring to the figures in which the veins are numbered, we see that of the ventral system, V_1, (median ventral pair) passes into the lid, right and left of the midline; V_2 sends veins into the sides of the lid and into the collar; V_3 goes entirely to the upper part of the digestive cavity, anastomosing with the dorsal veins. It seems quite doubtful that ARBER'S statement about "the relatively high development of the ventral system of the pitcher's venation" corresponds with the facts, since one third of it is not connected with the lid at all, and only a small part of it with the collar. Of the three dorsal veins of the petiole, the median is the midvein of the pitcher, passing entirely around it, and ending, not in the point of the median ridge, as DICKSON claimed, who therefore regarded it as the leaf apex, but in the collar, opposite the middle tooth, there branching. Of the laterals (D_2) each runs obliquely down the side of the pitcher toward the upper end of the glandular patch, having just before reaching it sent a branch into a lateral ridge, whence it emerges in the collar. Traversing the glandular patch obliquely it leaves it near the middle point and then runs up the wall parallel to the midvein, and ending in the collar. The midvein (D_1) sends branches right and left into the lower part of the pitcher. This basic arrangement of the vascular system of the pitcher can be most clearly seen in a very young one, 3 mm. long ($10 — 5$).

The external surface of the pitcher is covered with an epidermis of isodiametric cells with thick walls, and is supplied with stomata and nectar glands. On the lid the epidermis of the green patches is of more or less wavy-walled cells, with glands and stomata interspersed, while in the fenestrations the cells are isodiametric and straight walled, with glands but no stomata.

The epidermis of the interior surface of the lid and collar has been already described above. That of the far interior is of wavy-walled cells, the walls thick and buttressed at the angles. Scattered throughout the surface, except along a narrow strip beneath the eave of the collar, and the deeper portion of the pitcher demarked by an oblique line running downward and forward from about the middle point of the back surface across the top of the glandular bolster, there are numerous glands. These are smaller above and become increasingly larger below. In the bolster itself the glands attain the maximum size, and occupy chiefly the upper half of it, though not entirely excluded from the lower half ($9 — 4$). This latter is covered with a wavy-walled epidermis supplied with extremely numerous stomata.

The small glands which occur on the outer surface and on the inner surface of the lid, have, as GOEBEL (1891) pointed out, essentially the same structure as those of *Sarracenia*, but are directly comparable rather to those of the outer surface of the pitcher in that genus. In these there is only one course of cells, six in number, surmounting a single parenchyma cell ($2 — 16$). The same is true of *Cephalotus*, with the difference that, while in *Sarracenia* the "cover" cells are inwardly drawn out to a point, those in the *Cephalotus* gland reach inwardly as far as do the four surrounding cells ($10 — 21$). The glands are very small, indeed no bigger in transverse section than the stomata with which they are interspersed, and are no deeper than the surrounding epidermal cells. The outer walls are all suberized, except both outer and inner walls of the basal cell, derived from the parenchyma. The inner wall of this cell, in contact with the six other cells, is not, as in *Sarracenia*, reticulated. Whether more than one cell at the base of the gland may be regarded as part of the gland is questionable but possible. I have seen some indications that such is the case, as GOEBEL (1891) seems to have thought. As he did not afford a drawing (nor has any-one else since) of this particular gland, it is difficult to decide what precisely was GOEBEL's meaning.

These glands are found on all green parts, and appear to have the same function as analogous glands in *Nepenthes, Sarracenia*. HAMIL-TON observed insects feeding on the outer surface of the pitcher, but could not satisfy himself that nectar was present. It is possible as GOEBEL suggested that they secrete something else attractive to in-sects.

The glands of the inner surface of the lid have the same structure as those above described.

In the far interior of the pitcher the glands are of various sizes, smaller above and increasingly larger the deeper they are placed till the maximum size is reached in the glandular patches. They are flask-shaped, with a broad neck lying in the plane of the epidermis, made up of a greater or smaller number of columnar cells (neck cells) whose outer walls are very much thickened and pitted. The walls lying against the epidermis around the neck of the gland are also thickened and suberized, and, forming an investment of the whole gland there is a single layer of flattish cells (similar to the flat cell below the small gland of the outer pitcher surface) which are strongly cuticularized in their radial walls only, not, as GOEBEL thought, wholly. Each of these sheathing cells is therefore a window, or better a double cellulose window framed in mullions of suberized walls. The body of the gland is made up of rounded thin-walled cells, evidently the active glandular secreting cells, as indicated by the richness of the protoplasmic con-tent ($10 — 20$).

When the neck cells are examined as part of the epidermis in face view, the outer walls, in the case of the smallest glands, are arranged in the typical manner — two cover cells surrounded by four others. In slightly larger glands additional cells are intercalated. Their outer walls are seen now to be thick and pitted. The surrounding epidermal cells overlap the shoulder of the flask, and the strong buttress thickenings of their radial cell walls stand out ($10 — 20$).

The largest glands are to be found in the areas in the "colored patches" as DICKSON called them, on account of their deep red coloring. They differ in no respect beyond that of size from the others. They are spherical in form, with a thick neck and the central mass of something like 150 to 200 cells is surrounded as seen above by a single layer of flat cells with their radial walls suberized, the periclinal walls being of cellulose, thus ensuring a path of diffusion ($10 — 19$).

The colored or glandular patches, of which there are two, one on each side of the pitcher, are the most remarkable feature of this species. They are reniform, thickened regions of the wall, the outline being sharp and well marked below and more or less crenate along the upper edge ($9 — 4$). It is a "bolster" (GOEBEL) of tissue in which the mesophyll is more developed than otherwise, and projecting inwardly, showing no sign of its presence on the outer surface. The glands just mentioned are more numerous on the upper moiety, but are by no means confined to it. The epidermis between the glands offers the most remarkable appearance of all in that it is supplied with innumerable stomata. DICKSON (1878) described them as small oval bodies surrounded by two to four other cells. HAMILTON remarked that they are "remarkably like stomates" but that there is always a wide opening between the guard cells. DAKIN (1918), at that time a member of the staff of the University of Western Australia, visited Albany and there obtained material for study. He saw clearly that these structures are stomata, confirming GOEBEL'S earlier description (1891). It is clear that the guard cells are immobile and that these stomata do not function as such. GOEBEL called them water pores, pointing out that the pore is plugged by the cellulose membrane of a parenchyma cell underlying it, which would not, of course, prevent the excretion of water. DAKIN found that the membrane closing the pore is locally thickened to form a "pad" which he thought acted as a torus that, with changing turgidity of the cell, would open and close the pore, the whole acting as a regulating mechanism. He further thought that the function of the stomata is absorption and suggested that the glandular patches be called lateral absorbing areas ($10 — 12$).

I found ($1933b$) that DAKIN is correct in his claim that the wall of the underlying parenchyma cell is thickened beneath the pore; but that the thickening is so definitely torus-like as he showed in his figure (1918, Fig. 11), and especially his interpretations are certainly to be doubted. There is some evidence that the plugging membrane is the result of hydrolysis of the occluding wall and that there is given off a mucilage-like secretion (LLOYD $1933b$), but further study on fresh material obtained at Albany does not strengthen this idea of the matter. The more ready staining of the torus-like thickening is due to the fact that it is not cuticularized as are the guard cells and the epidermis in general, so that cellulose stain (such as methylene blue) attacks the thickening quickly. That, however, these structures are important physiologically is hard to resist in view of their number and general relations. GOEBEL'S idea that they are water pores seems the most acceptable, that is, that they pour a fluid into the pitcher cavity; but this fluid may contain substances in solution, more likely enzymes, possibly one or more enzymes different from those of the glands. I did a simple experiment with living pitchers to test GOEBEL'S idea. Halving a pitcher longitudinally, and cleaning it out thoroughly, I placed it in contact, by its outer surface, with water in a closed damp chamber. In the course of some hours beads of moisture appeared from the mouths of the glands, larger ones from the larger glands but none from the stomata, at least in appreciable quantities. This seems to indicate that water excretion by the "water pores" plays a minor rôle, if any, and that DAKIN'S suggestion that their function is that of absorption cannot be dismissed without further examination. Any interpretation of the activity of these stomata must take into account the constant presence of a large amount of starch in large grains in the mesophyll of the glandular patches.

The problem of digestion by the pitchers has been examined in any thoroughgoing way only by DAKIN (1918), who spent a vacation at Albany, W. A., making as careful a study as he could, under laboratory conditions. To be sure, DICKSON (1878) had reported that LAWSON TATE had examined into the matter somewhat and had found that "fluid taken from virgin or unopened pitchers" showed "that it exerted a similar digestive action on animal substances to that exhibited by the *Nepenthes* pitcher, etc." DAKIN made use only of the fluid from opened pitchers, which did not surprise me when on careful examination of all the unopened pitchers which I could come by on my own visit to Albany, I found no one of them containing any sign of fluid, a matter of disappointment as I had intended to conduct experimentation on such fluid if it could be found. DAKIN'S results are as follows: He found that the pitchers capture many insects, notably ants, as others had found. They are represented usually by fragmentary remains of the chitinous parts. Even the very small pitchers, as I have previously said, catch small insects. That the soft parts undergo dissolution in some sort is at once evident. But, DAKIN asked, is this the result of digestion by enzymes secreted by the pitcher glands, or of bacterial action, or of both? Fibrin was his test substrate. The experiments were conducted with pitcher fluid with an antiseptic (HCN) and with and without weak acid (HCl) or alkali. The specific results which he records showed that pitcher fluid *in vitro* in the presence of added acid does digest fibrin, and that it contains a digestive ferment which will break up proteins into peptone-like bodies in the presence of acid. Since non-acidulated pitcher fluid does not act thus, it cannot be concluded that this process actually takes place in the pitchers under normal circumstances. Pitcher fluid alone procures dissolution of fibrin with the odor of putrefaction. DAKIN admits the possibility that digestion by pitcher fluid may, however, take place very slowly in the pitchers.

He raises, however, the question of the usefulness or necessity of this to the plant. He kept plants under his eye in the laboratory where they grew thriftily and flowered without having been supplied with insects. In view of the work of Büsgen (*Utricularia*) and of F. Darwin (*Drosera*) he does not exclude a "carnivorous tendency." On the whole, therefore, at the present moment, the evidence favors the view that both the secretions of the pitcher and the action of bacteria contribute to the breaking down of proteins making the products available to the plant. Experiments with starch showed no evidence of the presence of diastase.

Literature Cited:

Arber, Agnes, On the morphology of the pitcher-leaves in *Heliamphora, Sarracenia, Cephalotus*, and *Nepenthes*. Ann. Bot. n.s. 5:563–578, 1941.

Brown, Robert, General remarks on the botany of Terra Australis. Miscellaneous Botanical Works 1:76–78, 1866.

Dakin, W. J., The West Australian pitcher plant (*Cephalotus follicularis*), and its physiology. Journ. Roy. Soc. W. Austr. 4:37–53, 1917/1918.

Dickson, A., The structure of the pitcher of *Cephalotus follicularis*. Journ. of Bot. 16:1–5, 1878.

Dickson, A., On the morphology of the pitcher of *Cephalotus follicularis*. Trans. and Proc. Bot. Soc. Edin. 14:172–181, 1882.

Eichler, A. W., Über die Schlauchblätter von *Cephalotus*. Jahrb. des Berliner Bot. Gart. 1:193–197, 1881 (*through* Engler u. Prantl).

Gardner, C. A., The history of botanical investigation in Western Australia. Handbook for B. A. A. S. 18th meeting, Perth, W. A., 1926 (Pp. 40–52).

Gilburt, W. H., Notes on the histology of pitcher plants. Quekett Microscopic Journal 6:151–164, 1881.

Goebel, K., Pflanzenbiologische Schilderungen, Pt. 2. Marburg 1891. (*Cephalotus:* pp. 110–115; 170–173).

Hamilton, A. G., Notes on the West Australian pitcher plant (*Cephalotus follicularis* La Bill.). Proc. Linn. Soc. N. S. W. 29:36–53, 1904.

Lloyd, F. E., The carnivorous plants — a review with contributions (Presidential Address). Trans. Roy. Soc. Can. III, 27:1–67, 1933.

Maury, Paul, Note sur l'acidie du *Cephalotus follicularis* La Bill. Bull. Soc. Bot. France 34:164–168, 1887.

Tate, Lawson, Phil. Trans. Birmingham 1878 (*through* Hamilton).

Troll (*see* under *Nepenthes*).

Woolls, W., Lectures on the vegetable kingdom. p. 100 (*through* Hamilton).

Chapter VI

GENLISEA

Discovery. — Early studies. — Two kinds of leaves. — Anatomy of trap-leaf.

The specimens on which the genus *Genlisea* is based were discovered by AUGUSTE DE SAINT–HILAIRE in Brazil in 1833. Most of the species are found in the New World in Brazil, the Guianas and Cuba, while two are known from west tropical Africa. The Cuban species, found many years ago by C. WRIGHT at the time he found *Biovularia olivacea*, has never again been collected.

For our information about these plants we are indebted first of all to WARMING (1874) and to GOEBEL (1891). All the species are small plants which inhabit swampy places and apparently live mostly submersed in shallow water, only the inflorescence, as in *Utricularia*, projecting above the surface. This is to be inferred from the absence of stomata and from the fact that colonies of algae have been observed by me attached to the surfaces of the leaves. BENJAMIN in the *Flora Brasiliensis* says merely "herbae paludosae." The close relationship to *Utricularia* is shown by the fact that the structure of the flower is the same in the two genera, that of *Genlisea* differing in having a five-parted calyx instead of the two-parted calyx of *Utricularia*. All are rosette plants with two kinds of leaves, foliage and trapping, arising from a vertical or sometimes nearly prostrate rootstock. Like *Utricularia*, there are no roots, though the trap leaves look superficially much like them and have been mistakenly so regarded by some (*9 — 7*; *11 — 5*).

The first thorough description, though lacking in an important detail, was published by WARMING in 1874. This work was known to DARWIN, whose son FRANCIS repeated WARMING's observations and afforded the description given by DARWIN in his *Insectivorous Plants* (P. 360, 2nd ed. of 1875). GOEBEL's description of 1891, though incorrect in certain details, leaves otherwise little to be desired. The plant which these authors studied was *Genlisea ornata*, the largest known species. The present account is based on herbarium specimens (British Museum of Natural History and Kew) but more particularly on alcohol material kindly sent to me by Dr. F. C. HOEHNE, collected in Butantan, Brazil. As far as the anatomy is concerned the genus is very homogeneous. DARWIN, it is true, described *G. filiformis* as bearing bladders like those of *Utricularia* and being devoid of "utriculiferous leaves" characteristic of the other species. I examined all the specimens of *Genlisea filiformis* at Kew, which was the source of DARWIN's material, but could find no evidence to corroborate him. It seems quite certain that he examined a plant which had been growing with a *Utricularia* whose stolons had intermixed with the *Genlisea* leaves. Indeed, I saw a case of this.

There are two kinds of leaves, true foliage leaves, linear or spatulate in form, and trap leaves, all arising densely crowded and without trace-able order, from a slender rhizome, very much as the leaves and stolons arise from the radially symmetrical corm-like stem of the seedling of *Utricularia*. There are no axillary buds, again as in *Utricularia*, but the rhizome produces a few branches toward the apex, which is the widest part. The trap leaves arise like the stolons of *Utricularia* and at first look like them. At first cylindrical with a tapering grow-ing point, they grow out for some distance (1 cm. or more or less) be-fore any further differentation takes place. In structure this portion consists of epidermis inclosing a very extensive intercellular air space of lysigenous origin. In the dorsal sector lies a cord of relatively few parenchyma cells surrounding the vascular tissue, again quite like a *Utricularia* stolon. This portion may be called the foot stalk, but not petiole since this leaf region is produced by intercalary extension be-tween the leaf base and the apex, while, as GOEBEL pointed out, the base at the foot stalk is the oldest portion of the trap leaf, which ex-tends solely by apical growth. At length the end of the footstalk be-gins to widen and an invagination takes place just behind the tip and on the ventral (upper) side. The basal portion of the invagination be-comes a subspherical hollow bulb. The neck of this bulb extends for some distance to form a tube, which toward the mouth gradually widens to right and left, so that the opening becomes a transverse slit, with the lips dorsal and ventral, the latter being shorter, and the for-mer being more or less arched over the opening. The angles of the mouth develop into two long arms with circinate apices, the slit being on the outer curve of the crook ($11 - 3, 4, 7$). During elongation and resulting from rotatory growth, the arms become twisted, the one on the right, clockwise, the other counter clockwise ($11 - 8, 10$). In consequence one lip of the mouth of the arm, which extends through-out its length, becomes longer than the other, so that, if an arm be laid open it takes the form of a spiral ribbon ($11 - 9$). The arms may be likened to two ribbons folded longitudinally and twisted on the long axis so that the two edges form spirals roughly parallel to each other. One edge becomes the inner, and in the plant is the shorter. In the actual trap, the two edges are anchored to each other at short inter-vals. This is accomplished by large marginal cells, cystid-like in ap-pearance, which during growth become pressed into, and adherent to, the tissue of the apposed edge. These large cells we may with GOEBEL term prop-cells. They were first described by GOEBEL (1891) but not quite correctly. He wrote " ..... the funnel shaped entrances are formed by the occurrence at certain distances apart of two large clear cells which lie the one upon the other, and which may be called prop-cells. They are merely the end cells of the rows of trapping hairs in which, however, the hair itself is merely one-celled, while the cell be-neath is swollen to a giant size." By making a paper model it will be seen, continues GOEBEL, "that in order that the two prop-cells shall really meet each other it is necessary that the shorter edge of the arm shall be bent outwardly. One can see the two prop-cells ......" This passage is quoted to indicate that GOEBEL thought that there is a row of prop-cells along each margin of the arm entrance, and that during development these meet and adhere in pairs, the one prop-cell to the other. The facts are otherwise. There is a row of prop-cells on only one edge, and the prop-cell is only the middle cell of a three-celled hypertrophied trichome, the basal cell of which is much enlarged, while above it the middle cell is enormously large and ends in a small knob-shaped cell terminating the trichome ($12 — 15$). In structure they are, therefore, not at all different from the neighboring trapping hairs, except for relative sizes of the component cells. The size of the basal and middle cells is so large that, in sections which are bound to be pretty complicated to the eye, they appear as two apposed and ad-herent cells. GOEBEL represented them thus in his figures ($7a$ and $7b$, plate 16, 1891). It is significant that GOEBEL showed a terminal cell on only one of each pair of prop-cells, as he regarded them to be (Figs. 6 and $7b$). In this detail GOEBEL was correct. What he took for the prop-cells along the shorter border of the ribbon-like arm are the scar-like depressions, optically suggesting raised surfaces, which are really dished out surfaces against which the prop-cells of the longer border lay and to which they were attached ($11 — 6$). When the two margins of the arms are torn apart in dissection, it happens more frequently than otherwise that the whole of the prop-hair is torn away from its moorings, leaving bare the depressed surface to which it was attached. The depression so caused is spoon-shaped, the bottom being formed of cells which have been more or less distorted by the pressure of the prop-cell during growth ($12 — 18$). On the other hand, the prop-cell is sometimes torn away from its basal cell, and remains on the wrong margin, a perfidious witness whose evidence is hereby impeached.

A striking analog of the prop-cells is to be found in the cystidia in *Coprinus atramentarius* in which they serve to keep the slender gills at a certain distance apart, allowing the free dispersal of spores, as described by BULLER (1922), in his *Researches on Fungi*, where he in-troduces the engineering term "distance pieces" for the cystids. Protruding from one gill, from which they arise, their free ends are attached to the surface of the next gill.

The size of the trap leaf in *Genlisea repens*, one of the smallest species, is as follows. The footstalk is about 1 cm. in length support-ing the bulb-shaped flask which is about 1 mm. long and 0.7 mm. broad. The surmounting tube is about 1 cm. long, and 0.27 mm. in outside diameter. The arms extend 1 cm. beyond the transverse mouth and are little more than 0.5 mm. in width. In a large African species, the traps are about three to five times the foregoing dimensions, the tube being relatively shorter. The footstalk may be 5 cm. long, the tube two and the arms 3 to 5 cm. long. The bulb is about 4 mm. long and 2 mm. in diameter. The turns of the arms are looser and make a larger angle with a transverse plane.

The outer surface of the plant is supplied with a large number of sessile globular, glandular trichomes, similar to those of *Utricularia*, and which secrete mucilage ($12 — 11$). The trap, whose inner surface is most complicated, has excited the wonder of all who have busied themselves with this object. DARWIN referred to it as "a contrivance resembling an eel-trap though more complex." GOEBEL (1891) re-marked of it that "it is in the highest degree remarkable; one might say of it that it is constructed with over-weening care and anxiety so as

to allow only very small animals to enter and then to hold them ir-
revocably". This remarkable structure is as follows.

In form, the bulb and tubular neck (the tube) may be compared to
a chianti flask. Within the flask there are two ridges (if we were
speaking of an ovary they would be called placentae), one ventral and
one dorsal, extending from the base up the sides about two-thirds the
distance to the neck above ($12 — 10$). Within the tissue of the ridges
runs in each a branch of the single vascular strand arriving from the
footstalk, while the surface bears numerous glands, which may be pre-
sumed to be digestive and absorptive, either but probably both. A
few additional glands are to be found on the rest of the surface. The
two vascular strands, each of a single spiral vessel accompanied by a
thin strand of phloem, the one dorsal and the other ventral, pass upward from the bulb into the walls of the tube without change of direction. Near the mouth of the tube they divide, a branch from each
supplying each arm, which then has two vascular strands quite as if it
were a closed tube branched from the main tube. The inner surface
of the tube is broken up into a series of some forty transverse ridges
each formed of a transverse row of radially thickened cells, each of
which sends downward toward the flask a stiff curved trichome ($9 —$
8; $12 — 8, 9, 13$). Of these cells there are about 50, so that there are
that number of slender stiff bristles projecting inward and downward
from each ridge. Each section of the tube below and including a
transverse ridge is therefore of the form of the entrance to an eel trap,
or lobster pot, if you will. The whole tube, o.13 to o.42 mm. inside
diameter, is a series of such traps, some forty to fifty in number, each
with its funnel extending into the next below. In addition to these
downwardly directed hairs, and just below the ridges in each section
there are one or two transverse rows of glandular trichomes ($12 — 8$,
$9, 16$). The zone where these occur broadens toward the outer end
of the tube and is composed of wavy-walled cells, while the bristle
bearing cells are conspicuously straight and narrow, lengthwise the
tube.

On approaching the open end, the tube widens somewhat, and
spreads out to form the arms. The open end is formed of the upper
and lower sides to form two lips, the upper (ventral) somewhat shorter
than the lower, and fixed in a position a little distance apart by the
ballooned cells above mentioned (prop-cells) ($11 — 1$-4; $12 — 2, 3$).
These are closely enough placed so that in between, alternating with
them, a series of funnels, guarded by inward pointing hairs, is formed.
This is repeated along the open slit of the arm ($11 — 11$) quite to the
apex.

In passing up into the arms, the same general structure described
for the tube is repeated ($12 — 1, 4$), but the ridges are now curved
obliquely, comformably with the directions and amounts of growth
($11 — 6, 9$). Along the edges of the arm, as one inspects it if laid
open, the ridges run almost parallel thereto, each ridge beginning in a
prop-cell. Passing obliquely inward and forward they gradually approach the other edge in a harmonic curve. When past the middle of
the arm they bend rather sharply back and approach a direction again
parallel to the other edge and then end at the scar-like depression

formed by its prop-cell at the other end ($11 - 6$). In consequence of this development, the trapping hairs stand approximately at right angles to the edges of the funnel formed by the prop-cells, so that although oblique, the ridges with their trapping hairs function as in the straight tube, although no two hairs on the same ridge have precisely the same direction. The whole structure is one to arouse wonder in the observer.

The inner surface, except that occupied by the bristle ridges, is made up of wavy-walled cells with scattered glandular hairs, repeating again the structure of the tube ($11 - 6$). The funnel shaped mouths of the tube and arms are guarded, outside the level of the prop-cells, by shorter stiffer hairs, claw-like in shape ($12 - 12$), allowing some room for the entrance of prey, but nevertheless inveigling them toward the interior. The captures consist of copepods, and the like, small water spiders, nematodes and plenty of other forms, many of which I have seen in the Brazilian material studied.

In both species examined, the structure is the same, with the slight difference that the large African species structures are not so crowded and in consequence are easier to decipher.

The glands are all of the same type, that common to this genus and *Utricularia*, consisting of a basal cell anchored in the epidermis, a short neck cell, and the capital of two to eight cells. It is wholly a matter of speculation as to the function of these glands. They may supply only mucilage to lubricate the interior and facilitate the movements of prey downwards through the arms and neck, or they may secrete digestive enzymes or both. I have observed that prey only half way down the tubular neck shows signs of a far degree of disintegration, but, as bacterial action cannot at the moment be excluded, it boots nothing to do more than indicate the possibilities. The goal of prey is the flask at the bottom of the neck. Here one finds various remnants of the animals, copepods, spiders, nematodes, together with algae.

According to GOEBEL, the twisting growth of the arms facilitates their penetration of the substrate which, being filled with water, is quite loose. This explanation does not help for the trap leaf up till the time when the arms begin to form, which is a good deal more than half the time of its growth activity. If teleological interpretation be of any use, one might venture that the twisted form of the arms results in the presentation in all direction of entrances to the interior so that prey find openings in whatever direction they may approach.

Literature Cited:

BENJAMIN, L., Flora Brasiliensis, 10:252, 1847.
BULLER, A. H. REGINALD, Researches on Fungi, Vol. 2, 1922.
DARWIN, C., Insectivorous Plants. 2d. ed., London 1875.
GOEBEL, K., Pflanzenbiologische Schilderungen, 1891. Zur Biologie von *Genlisea*. Flora 77:208-212, 1893.
ST. HILAIRE, A. DE, Voyage au district des Diamans, II:428, 1833.
ST. HILAIRE & F. DE GIRARD, Monographie des Primulacées et des Lentibulariées du Brésil méridional et de la République Argentine. Mém. Soc. roy. des Sci. etc. d'Orléans 5, 1840.
TUTIN, T. G., New Species from British Guiana, Cambridge University Expedition, 1933. Journ. Bot. 1934:306-341.
WARMING, EUG., Contribution à la connaissance des *Lentibulariaceae*, I. *Genlisea ornata* Mart.; II. Germination des graines de l'*Utricularia vulgaris*. Vidensk. Medd. f. Naturhist. For. Kjøbenhavn 1874:33-58. Résumé in French (appendix 8).
WRIGHT, C., in GRISEBACH'S Catalogus plantarum Cubensium. Leipzig, 1866.

Chapter VII

BYBLIS

Occurrence. — Appearance and systematic position. — Habitat. — Structure. — Functions of the glands.

Byblis is a genus confined to western Australia, where it is endemic. There are two species, *B. linifolia* Salisb. and *B. gigantea* Lindl., the latter being much the larger plant, one about 50 cm. tall. It is a half-shrub in habit, consisting of a woody rhizome bearing in any one season the dying parts of the previous and the growing ones of the present season (*13* — 1). These consist usually of a single chief stem with one to three branches from near the base, all bearing long (1–2 dm.) linear leaves, clothed with numerous stalked mucilage glands. The color, a yellow-green, is characteristic, and the surface is charged with numerous glistening mucilage droplets. The flowers, raised on axillary peduncles, are violet or rose colored, have a deeply five lobed rotate corolla, which appears superficially as polypetalous, the lobes alternating with five oval attenuate sepals and with the five stamens. The systematic position of this plant has not been at all clear. PLANCHON (1848) and BENTHAM (Flora australiensis 2:469) believed that it is related to the *Pittosporaceae* rather than to the *Droseraceae*. Later LANG, stressing too much its sympetaly, advanced reasons for its relation to *Pinguicula* and its inclusion within the *Lentibulariaceae*, while more recently DOMIN (1922) has placed it in a new family, the *Byblidaceae*, of which *B. linifolia* is the type.

Byblis gigantea was found growing abundantly in sandy, swampy places in the Swan River district not far from Perth, where also are to be found very characteristic species of *Polypompholyx*, (*P. tenella* and *multifida*) and the peculiar Australian species of *Utricularia*, *U. Menziesii*, *Hookeri*, etc., and all, except *Polypompholyx tenella*, confined to W. Australia. *Byblis gigantea* is, however, to be found in drier and better drained parts of such swamps, as for example at Cannington where it grows around the base of a low hillock on which stood a house, and not, as ROSS suggests, in very wet places on the banks of streams. The substrate was a coarse quartz sand with some admixture of fine white or yellow clay, and little humus. Specimens of *Byblis linifolia* were received from N. E. Arnhem Land where it was found growing "around rocky pools in the bed of a river".

The stem arises from a slender rhizome with triarch (LANG) or, as I have observed, diarch roots often showing a considerable degree of secondary thickening with a thick cortex loaded with starch and tannin-emulsion-colloid (LLOYD 1911). Both of these may be regarded as storage material. From the perennating rootstock arises the new annual stem with its appendages, which are secondary branches, leaves and long peduncled flowers. All these parts are clothed with two kinds of glands, sessile and stalked. In all parts except the sepals, the epidermis is composed of elongated straight-walled cells, all of which in young organs lie at the same level. With maturity, the epidermis becomes ribbed with sunken furrows between the ribs. The floor of the furrow is composed of a double row of shorter cells, each pair bearing a sessile gland (14 — 10, 13). In scattered positions occur stalked glands which secrete abundant mucilage. In the sepals the epidermal cells are wavy-walled on both surfaces, less so on the outer (lower) surface toward the base. On the outer, dorsal face of the leaf occur both sessile and stalked glands, the latter very numerous, on the inner face only sessile glands occur (9 — 9). Stalked glands are to be found even on the ovary wall. Stomata occur on both faces of the sepals, and on the leaves and stem they are to be found interrupting the rows of sessile glands (14 — 13). They are somewhat raised and extend considerably above the ditch bottom. In this way according to FENNER the stomatal pore does not become clogged with the secretion of the sessile glands, which probably fills that reach of the ditch occupied by them.

The leaves are long, slender and linear in form, tapering toward the apex. When in the bud they display, in the case of B. *gigantea*, no circination, the apices showing only a very meagre outward curvature, if any. In B. *linifolia*, however, the leaves are outwardly circinate, as in *Drosophyllum*. This somewhat surprising fact was clearly seen in the material from Arnhem Land sent me by my friend Mr. CHARLES BARRETT, and figured in 14 — 7. B. *gigantea* is seen in 14 — 8. Of this DIELS (1930) says merely that the leaves are spirally *inrolled* at the tip.

In transverse section the leaves are triangular with round angles (14 — 11). Toward the tip they become nearly cylindrical and the tip itself is somewhat enlarged to form a knob, properly interpreted to be a hydathode (LANG, FENNER). Its interior is occupied by a large mass of tracheidal tissue in contact with and ending the vascular strand which reaches thereto. One or two protuberant stomata are to be found at the apical surface, not by any means always at the extreme apex, together with both stalked and sessile glands. The rigidity of the leaf, which is very slender for its length, is attained by the very thick-walled epidermis and the strands of mechanical tissue accompanying the vascular bundles. Beneath the epidermis on all sides there is a thick layer of chlorenchyma in which there is no sharp demarkation between palisade and spongy tissue. All of the cells are oval rather than columnar and lie in three courses. Beneath the epidermis the palisade cells have expanding ends in contact with it (14 — 9, 10). This, FENNER explains, ensures a contact for lively diffusion between the glands and the vascular system. The upper leaf surface is rather flat, with a very shallow depression along the middle. On this surface there are very few stalked glands, which on the lower surface are very numerous. Sessile glands are as numerous here as elsewhere (9 — 9).

The sessile gland (14 — 10, 13) stands upon a pair of epidermal cells, and consists of a capital of eight radially disposed cells, supported on a single very short stalk cell, this resting on two short epidermal cells, which according to FENNER originate from a single basal cell of the very young trichome. The furrow in which the sessile glands stand is sufficiently deep and narrow so that the sides of the glands lean against and are supported by the sides of the furrow.

The stalked gland ($14 — 12$-15) has a capital of usually 32 cells radiating from the centre and standing out like an umbrella top. These cells all abut on a central short cell resting on the top of the long stalk cell. This in turn stands on a group of basal cells which may be as many as eight in number, or as few as two in the case of a small stalked gland. The latter may also have as few as four cells in the capital, the mature glands showing no great degree of uniformity in this regard. The stalk cells of the larger glands have strongly striated thick cellulose walls, the striations reaching deeply, as far as the cuticle. These striations run obliquely (as in the cotton fiber) and when the gland dries (in air or alcohol), the stalk cells twist, as noted by DARWIN ($14 — 14$). FENNER regards this arrangement as one to allow bending of the trichome without collapse.

While the gland capitals are covered with a thin cuticle there is access by diffusion through pores, mentioned but not described by FENNER. I found them ($1933b$) to be rather large oval openings arranged in a circle about and some distance away from the centre of the capital. They become evident on treatment of the stalked glands with sulfuric acid ($14 — 12$). Both the sessile and stalked glands are readily penetrable by dyes (methylene blue).

Our earlier knowledge of the function of the glands bearing on the question of the carnivorous habit of the plant we have at the hands of A. NINIAN BRUCE (1905). Her work is clearly indicative of this, but the question needs further investigation, which in this type of plant is not easy. BRUCE placed minute cubes of coagulated egg-albumen in contact with the sessile glands, and after a period of some days (two to eight) the whiteness has completely disappeared. During the progress of digestion the round white core of the cube of albumen could be observed to suffer gradual reduction in size. This material placed in contact with the heads of stalked glands failed to show any evidence of digestion, but when removed and placed in contact with the sessile glands promptly did so. This seems to indicate that bacterial action does not supervene. Some observations by FENNER justify BRUCE's results. When insects are caught, he says, and come in contact with the sessile glands, a secretion is thrown out by them which is much less viscous than that of the stalked glands. After four to six hours, the group of glands affected again become dry and an examination of them shows that the contents of the gland cells and even of the stalk cells betray evidence of absorption in the presence of a greater density of the protoplasm and the presence of large rounded dark masses. These changes are not to be observed in the stalked glands, which do nothing else than secrete mucilage. I attempted to prove the matter for myself at Perth, W. Australia. *Byblis* appeared late in the season, during the latter part of my visit, so that I had only limited time at my disposal. My method consisted in placing minute fragments of carmine fibrin in contact with the glands of the living leaf, on the plant, and in a small vial with a dozen short pieces of leaf with and without a little added water, with and without added weak HCl, and with and without ammonium nitrate. The results were entirely negative, even after two weeks, though there was at length a distinct and unpleasant odor emitted.

I first learned from Mr. A. G. HAMILTON that *Byblis* harbours a small insect which he called a "buttner". In Perth I received the same information from Mr. H. STEDMAN, who kindly took me to a locality at some distance north of Perth where we found a lot of plants growing. All of these were infested with a small wingless capsid which turns out to be a new genus and will be described by Dr. W. R. CHINA of the British Museum (Natural History) (*13* — 1). While small insects in general are caught by the mucilage secreted by the stalked glands, this capsid moves about freely without difficulty, just as do similar insects, also capsids, over the surface of *Drosera* leaves in Australia, and of the African genus *Roridula*, once thought to be carnivorous. How the insect manages this is a bit puzzling. It is noticeable that it prefers to walk on the upper leaf surface where there are very few and usually smaller glands but when alarmed it progresses rapidly in any direction without becoming entangled with the mucilage. Full sized insects are perhaps too big to be readily encumbered, but the smaller ones move about just as freely. Their food consists of freshly captured flies, the juices of which they suck, the relation of insect and plant affording a sort of commensalism, but this term could hardly be used in the case of *Roridula* (non-carnivorous) the secretion from whose glands is resinous (LLOYD 1934).

Literature Cited:

BRUCE, A. NINIAN, On the activity of the glands of *Byblis gigantea*. Notes Roy. Bot. Garden Edin. 16:9–14, 1905, also 17:83, 1907.

DIELS, L., *Byblidaceae*, Nat. Pflanzenfamilien. 18a. 1930.

DOMIN, K., *Byblidaceae*, a new archichlamydeous family. Contr. to the Australian flora, undated, but about 1920. Extracted from MS. and published separately in Acta Bot. Bohem. 1:3–4, 1922.

FENNER, *see under Nepenthes*.

HAMILTON, A. G., Notes on *Byblis gigantea*. Proc. Linn. Soc. New South Wales 28:680–684, 1903.

LANG, F. X., Untersuchungen über Morphologie, Anatomie und Samenentwickelung von *Polypompholyx* und *Byblis gigantea*. Flora 88:3–60, 1901.

LLOYD, F. E., The tannin-colloid complexes in the fruit of the persimmon. Biochem. Journ. 1:7–41 (pl. 1–3), 1911.

LLOYD, 1933 (*see under Heliamphora*).

LLOYD, 1934 (*see under Introduction*).

PLANCHON, J. E., Sur la famille des Droséracées. Ann. sci. nat. bot., 3 sér., 9:79–99, 1848. (Contains also descriptions of *Drosera* carpels bearing tentacles, these being intergrades between normal leaves and carpels).

ROSS, H., *Byblis gigantea*. Gartenflora 51:337–339 (pl. 1500), 1902.

Chapter VIII

DROSOPHYLLUM LUSITANICUM

Drosophyllum lusitanicum Lk. (*13*—2) is a plant with much the appearance of *Byblis*, but it is larger and shrubbier (1–1.6 m. tall) and is unusual, for the carnivorous plants, in growing not in a wet, but in a very dry habitat in Morocco and nearby Portugal and Spain. HARSHBERGER visited a locality in Sra. de Valongo near Oporto, where he found *Drosophyllum* growing in open formations, scattered over the quartz-rocky soil. He observed its leaves to be crowded with small gnats. Its flowers are bright sulphur yellow, are 1–1½ inches in diameter, and have convolute aestivation. It is called locally "herba piniera orvalhada" (dewy pine) in allusion to its bedewed appearance due to the numerous glands carrying large droplets of clear mucilage. The base is strongly woody, and its abundant roots penetrate deeply into the dry soil. "Mr. W. C. TAIT informs me that it grows plentifully on the sides of dry hills near Oporto, and that vast numbers of flies adhere to the leaves. The latter fact is well known to the villagers, who call the plant the 'fly-catcher,' and hang it up in their cottages for this purpose" wrote DARWIN (1875). Inquiry by correspondence with Dr. QUINTANILHA has elicited doubt of the correctness of TAIT's statement as to the use by the paisanos of the plant as a fly-catcher, though it seems reasonable enough.

The leaf is linear with a deep furrow along the upper side. It is traversed by three vascular bundles, a median and two lateral, arising from a single bundle entering at the base (*14*—5).

A peculiar feature is found in the reverse circination (*14*—4) the rolled leaf-tip facing outwardly while in *Drosera* very generally the opposite holds. Although in *Byblis gigantea* the leaves are nearly straight, showing no evident circination, in *Byblis linifolia* the behavior is like that of *Drosophyllum*. FENNER expresses the opinion that this arrangement has its significance in permitting the free development of the stalked glands, but he overlooks the fact that the circination of *Drosera* is in the opposite sense without any prejudice to the development of the tentacles. The case of *Byblis linifolia* was not known to him. In any event, in the tight coils the dorsal and ventral leaf surfaces are mutually compressed; and assuming that the tentacles (hairs in the case of *Byblis*) develop after uncoiling, the ventral (upper) surface is freer than the dorsal, where the most of the tentacles or hairs are to be found.

Another characteristic behavior of the leaves is their marcescence. Instead of falling away as they die, they remain attached, forming a grass-skirt about the stem. FRANÇA (1922) regarded this as a symptom of a condition which he regarded as pathological, due to overnutrition and the inability, because of the absence of an excretory apparatus, to throw off waste. QUINTANILHA, however, disagrees with this and, in our opinion, justly.

In the seedling, the cotyledons withdraw from the seed during germination and develop into broadly linear tapering members, supplied with glands enabling them to capture prey (FRANÇA).

The leaf bears two kinds of glands, stalked mucilage glands and sessile digestive glands ($14 - 1$, 2, 6). Their position is determined if at all only to a slight extent by the three vascular bundles, from which, however, they receive branchlets ending at the bases of the glandular tissues. There are three double files of stalked glands, one along each leaf margin, roughly speaking, and two rows along the under leaf surface, one on each side of the midvein. The sessile glands are more scattered, and apparently only in some degree determined in position by the vascular tissues. Sessile glands occur on both upper and under leaf surface, stalked glands only on the under surface and along the margins.

Structure of the glands. — *Drosophyllum* differs from *Byblis* in that the glands, instead of being trichomes, are emergences, and, as DARWIN pointed out, have much the same structure as those of *Drosera*, without, however, being endowed with the power of movement. This refers of course to the stalked glands. These have a stout stalk surmounted by a large nearly hemispherical capital, and, as DARWIN put it, have the "appearance of miniature mushrooms."

The capital ($14 - 2$) consists of three courses of cells running parallel with the outer surface. The outer of these, the epidermis, is of rather thick, wavy-walled cells, with strong buttress thickenings, stiffening the angles of the radial walls ($14 - 3$). The dense protoplasmic contents and prominent nuclei speak for their glandular activity. These are covered with a cuticle, which according to FENNER is finely porous, thus permitting the exudation of the mucilaginous secretion. I have not succeeded in convincing myself that the pores are optically demonstrable, but it is certain that the cuticle offers no impediment to the diffusion of methylene blue, for less than a minute's exposure to a watery solution of this dye results in the deep staining of the whole capital while the dye does not penetrate the remaining epidermis at all. MEYER and DEWÈVRE also failed to see the pores but demonstrated on killing the escape through the cuticle of the pigment which renders the gland conspicuous. They found also that lithium nitrate taken up through the roots is found 12 hours later in the mucilaginous secretion. The cells of the second course underlying the epidermis are somewhat more irregular in form, but are likewise provided with buttress-thickenings in the radial walls, though they are not so numerous and prominent as in the epidermal cells. The general character of these two courses is the same; they were called, by PENZIG (1877), the secretion-layer. Underlying these two courses is a third, of flat cells, of greater size in the transverse direction (with reference to the axis of the gland) with their contiguous radial walls strongly cuticularized, so that in a cleared preparation when suitably stained, as with congo red, one sees a strong network lying within the capital. Contrary to an earlier view (SOLEREDER 1899, p. 367) not the entire but only the radial walls are cuticularized, thus (GOEBEL 1891) leaving a free diffusion passage. This feature is held in common with other glandular structures described elsewhere.

The third layer (limiting layer of PENZIG) caps a mass of short irregular tracheids constituting the expanded end of a strand of vascular tissue extending through the stalk and communicating with the vascular tissues of the leaf. This strand consists of both xylem and phloem elements (FENNER *contra* MEYER and DEWÈVRE) affording, according to FENNER, not only a pathway for water but, in the case of the phloem, for the transmission of stimuli to the neighboring sessile glands, which have been shown to show secretory activity in response to such stimulus received from the stalked glands. The stalk itself is made up of the epidermis and an underlying course of parenchyma, surrounding the vascular strand. The capping secreting cells contain brilliant red coloring matter, interpreted as an optical lure for insects, and when the capital bears its shining droplet of clear mucilage, which acts as a light collecting lens, the glands appear as brillliant red dots. The sessile glands have no such coloring matter. These (*14*—6) have the same structure as the stalked glands, differing only in the absence of the stalk. Occasionally an intergrading condition is met with; GOEBEL found one such, with a very short stalk. The sessile glands are usually oval, generally smaller, and have a less extensive contact with the vascular system. Each gland, however, is underlaid by a group of cavernous looking tracheidal cells, with no protoplasmic content, evidently an important part of the gland but with what function we do not know. If FENNER saw this feature, he regarded it as the end of the tracheidal system. For there is also to be found at the base of each gland the end of a branch of the vascular system. These glands are devoid of a mucilaginous secretion, as of coloring pigment and even of chlorophyll, for they appear whitish.

The mucilage secreted by the stalked glands is peculiar, in that it is not readily drawn out into slender viscous threads, but is easily pulled off the gland by a touch of even a needle point as DARWIN observed. "From this peculiarity, when a small insect alights on a leaf of *Drosophyllum*, the drops adhere to its wings, feet or body, and are drawn from the gland; the insect then crawls onward and other drops adhere to it; so that at last, bathed by the viscid secretion it sinks down and dies, resting on the small sessile glands with which the surface of the leaf is thickly covered" (DARWIN, 1875, 2nd ed., p. 271). The secretion of mucilage continues after removal and DARWIN found that when a plant is kept under a bell glass to prevent evaporation the secretion is produced in such quantities as to run down the leaf surface in droplets; and further that the secretion shows an acid reaction. GOEBEL found that among the possible acids present formic acid is one, and believed that this is effective in preventing bacterial action. Emanating from these glands, probably, is an odor which GOEBEL likened to that of honey, which would be attractive to insects and thus act as a lure.

In the case of many carnivorous plants "overfeeding" usually results in the damage and death of the leaf wholly or locally, notably in the pitcher plants. This has not been observed to occur in *Drosophyllum*, and may be accounted for by the inhibition of bacterial action as just indicated.

The sessile glands do not exude a secretion unless stimulated

(DARWIN, GOEBEL, FENNER, QUINTANILHA). The secretion appears normally when the mucilage glands are stimulated by the catching of prey, but not merely mechanically, as by placing on them sand grains, bits of paper, etc. FENNER showed in considerable detail by appropriate experiments that the maximum activity of the sessile glands is obtained when, after the stalk glands nearby have received prey, both prey and mucilage secretion are brought into contact with them. But in the presence of mucilage removed from the stalked glands and mixed with the juices of prey, leaving the stalked glands unstimulated, the sessile glands work only slightly if at all. FENNER concluded that the maximum activity of the sessile glands is called forth by something passing through the tissues by way of the vascular elements (phloem). The sessile and stalked glands must, therefore, be considered as a single mechanism in which one part is dependent on the other.

There is a general agreement on the part of the authors mentioned that *Drosophyllum* exercises its own proper power of digestion, and that this is not the result of bacterial activity. As mentioned already, GOEBEL regarded digestion as too rapid for bacterial action, and that the presence of formic acid excludes such activity, and though he was unable to state the concentration of acid present, he supports his inference by inoculating nutrient gelatine plates with negative results. The activity of formic acid may not, however, GOEBEL adds, be confined to that of an antiseptic, but it may consist in an initial dissolution of the proteins of the body of the prey, with the escape of materials which then affect the sessile glands and stimulate them to greater activity.

DARWIN found that fragments of egg albumen, fibrin, were acted upon rapidly when they came in contact with the sessile glands. If only in contact with the stalked glands, they were not attacked. If then placed on the sessile glands, there was a copious secretion, and the albumen was completely dissolved in 7 to 22 hours. "We may therefore conclude, either that the secretion from the tall glands has little power of digestion, though strongly acid, or that the amount poured forth from a single gland is insufficient to dissolve a particle of albumen which within the same time would have been dissolved by the secretion from several of the sessile glands." Fibrin likewise, when placed on the stalked glands, was not attacked, though, as in the case of albumen, the secretion was absorbed (together with whatever escaped into it from the fibrin). But when the fibrin was slipped onto the sessile glands, digestion proceeded rapidly (17 to 21 hours) with an abundant exudation of fluid from the glands. DARWIN thought the digestion more rapid than in *Drosera*. He had not excluded the action of bacteria, which, however, as above said, GOEBEL did by suitable culture experiments. He observed a more rapid action than did DARWIN. A fibrin flock 1 cm. long and one-fourth the width of the leaf was noticeably attacked in a half-hour on a warm summer day, and in an hour no trace could be seen, though the spot had been carefully marked by a bit of paper. With a lens small fragments could still be seen. A true digestion, he concluded, is therefore present. The enzyme is secreted in response to a special stimulus, and chiefly, if not exclusively, by the sessile glands. The stalked glands are chiefly a trapping apparatus (GOEBEL 1891).

In 1894 came MEYER and DEWÈVRE. They managed to collect 1.6 grams of mucilage and investigated it. It was stiff, clear, had the odor of honey and was strongly acid. It contained no free reducing sugar, but on heating with HCl it reduced Fehling, and gave a weak red color with thymol and H_2SO_4 (indicating polysaccharides). The presence of a sugar was indicated by a yellow coloration with chlor-zinc-iodide as also its precipitation by lead acetate, by barium hydroxide and by alcohol. No proteins were present. It was poor in salts, only Ca being present. No K, phosphates or nitrates were found. The acidity was due to a non-volatile acid, and not to formic acid, as GOEBEL had held. These authors verified DARWIN's observation that the sessile glands secrete only on stimulus by a protein. Insects are attracted both by the odor and by the glistening of the droplets of mucilage. They recorded observations also which indicate that there are two periods of activity in the plant. (1) From the beginning of vegetative activity to the beginning of seed ripening (from Jan. 15 to May 15, in the greenhouse). During fruit ripening the leaves begin dying from apex to base and the glands do not secrete vigorously. The soil must be kept "dry" during this period. (2) After fruit ripening is complete (Aug. 1 to Oct. 15) secretion and odor are both strong, especially in sunny weather. The experience of DARWIN was again substantiated in finding that coagulated egg albumen, meat and fibrin were acted upon, especially if well smeared with mucilage and placed on the sessile glands. The time necessary for complete digestion was about the same as in DARWIN's experience. GOEBEL's figures were criticised as being too low but an error of proofreading may have crept in, rather than, as is suggested, incorrect observation. It was found that very small fragments of albumen were attacked in the mucilage of a stalked gland and completely digested in 7 days. If large bits were imposed, they absorbed the mucilage, and damage might result to the gland in consequence. No diastase was found. Bacteria were never found and it was clear that the mucilage, as GOEBEL said, is antiseptic.

FRANÇA (1925) gave a general account of the plant, and studied especially the cytological changes which he observed in the glands during digestion and absorption, using both living material viewed microscopically, and fixed material stained with iron haematoxylin and fuchsine, etc. He found evidence that the two courses of the glandular cells (the outer and second) have different functions, that the outer course is secretory only, the inner both secretory and absorptive. The sessile glands have only the power of secretion. This evidence consists in the cytological appearances observed during digestion and absorption. Changes of the bright red color in the glands to a deeper, much darker shade, had been noted by DARWIN. When such glands are examined, the cells of the outer layer of the gland are seen to have remained unchanged, while those of the second layer are now charged with large black granules. These rise to a maximum some hours after the glands have been supplied with muscle fiber. Some similar granules are found also in the more distal short cells of the stalk of the gland and finally in approximate leaf tissues. Such dark granules are seen when an insect has been captured, but only in the deeper gland cells.

With neutral red the protoplasm displays a great number of small red granules, considered to be granules of secretion. On the other hand the deeper cells are filled with voluminous granulations of dark red color. In this way it is supposed that the power of absorption is demonstrated, for when prey has been captured, the superficial cells show only the small granules, while the deeper cells and the distal stalk cells are at the same time found crowded with grey or black granules *in addition to* the secretory granules seen also in the outer cell layer. The recounted facts are held to support FRANÇA's conclusion that the outer glandular layer of cells is secretory only and the inner layer both secretory and absorptive. Additional and supporting evidence is found by FRANÇA in the presence of canaliculi. Some occur "in the thickness" of the membranes between the cells of the two layers and open on the outside of the gland by means of minute oval mouths. It is these which permit the entrance of absorbed substances to the deeper cell layer. Others occur in "the thickness" of the buttresses of the epidermal cells (between which fingers of the protoplasm project, as described by HABERLANDT for *Drosera*), and these "without doubt" permit the escape of secretion. I have carefully examined preparations after treatment with H_2SO_4, followed by Sudan III and have been unable to find any evidence of pores. The evidence in the form of a drawing in his plate has little convincing effect.

A critical study of *Drosophyllum* was undertaken by QUINTANILHA at Coimbra. His results, published in 1926, briefly stated are as follows. *Drosophyllum* is indeed a carnivorous plant, acting by means of a proteolytic ferment of the type of animal pepsin. A mosquito can be completely digested in 24 hours. Bacterial digestion does not enter into the picture (in this agreeing with GOEBEL, whose experiments were repeated and verified). The stalked glands are essentially organs of capture but at the same time they are "signales d'alarme"; that is, on capture of an insect, they send a stimulus to the sessile glands and provoke their activity. These are exclusively organs of digestion and absorption, but they act only on stimulation. Experimentally and under favorable conditions, the stalked glands may digest very small amounts of albumen without the intervention of the sessile glands, but the proteolytic properties of the mucilage are always insignificant. Experimentally it was shown also that the sessile glands, when previously excited, can digest and absorb albumen without the intervention of the stalked glands which had been removed by amputation, and in this condition the absorption is as rapid, or even more rapid, than it would be in collaboration with the stalked glands because of dilution of the secretion. In the normal state the stalked glands act as traps and furnish stimuli to the sessile glands.

Excitation of the sessile glands can be procured directly by chemical but not by mechanical means and indirectly by both means. Simple pressure or friction of the stalked glands does not procure excitation of the sessile. However, the cutting off of the glands from the stalks can excite indirectly and mechanically the sessile glands. The excitation is slow of transmission and is limited to an area of about 1 cm. from the tentacle stimulated. On anatomical grounds QUINTANILHA inclines to believe with FENNER that the phloem of the vascular system serves to transmit the stimulus. The digestive capacity of the plant is reduced after fructification.

The same author studied the cytological concomitants of the digestive and absorptive activity, and his findings are of interest in connection with those of HOMÈS and others on aggregation in *Drosera* and with those of FRANÇA above given. He found that the state of aggregation can be procured independently of digestion. During digestion there occur "black concretions" in the inner course of cells of the stalked glands. These are not the "sphérules alimentaires" of FRANÇA, but intravacuolar precipitation of anthocyanin compounds. In the sessile glands, however, concretions appear in the cells derived from the absorption of albumins impregnated with melanin. The chondriome of the glandular cells does not act directly in the elaboration of proteolytic enzymes and it does not present alterations which allow us to attribute to them an important rôle in the phenomenon of digestion. Only in the internal secretory layer of the sessile gland the elements of the chondriome are considerably reduced in volume during intracellular digestion. The number of the chondrioconts is also reduced and that of the mitochondria is increased proportionally.

On the other hand, the vacuome appears to be the seat of the elaboration of ferments and certainly has an important rôle in the processes of digestion and secretion.

Pathological conditions in the plant due to overfeeding have not been observed. It is clear that *Drosophyllum* profits by food materials supplied by animals, and that this compensates for an insufficient mineral nutrition, QUINTANILHA says in general conclusion.

Literature Cited:

DARWIN, C., Insectivorous Plants. 2d. ed., London 1875. 1908 reprint.

FENNER, C. A., Beiträge zur Kenntnis der Anatomie, Entwickelungsgeschichte und Biologie der Laubblätter und Drüsen einiger Insektivoren. Flora 93:335–434, 1904.

FERNANDES, ABÍLIO, Morphologia e biologia das plantas carnívoras. Anuário da Sociedade Broteriana 6:14–46, 1940; 7:16–52, 1941. A third part appeared later in 1941; the whole was issued as a brochure, repaged, in 1941. Good photographs of *Drosophyllum* and of its habitat.

FRANÇA, C., La question des plantes carnivores dans le passé et dans le présent. Bol. Soc. Broteriana I (2 ser.):38–57, 1922.

FRANÇA, C., Recherches sur le "*Drosophyllum lusitanicum*" et remarques sur les plantes carnivores. Arch. portug. d. Sci. biol. 1:1–30, 1925.

GOEBEL, K., Pflanzenbiologische Schilderungen. Marburg 1889–1891.

HARSHBERGER, J. W., Notes on the Portuguese insectivorous plant, *Drosophyllum lusitanicum*. Proc. Amer. Philosoph. Soc. 64:51–54, 1925.

MEYER, A. & A. DEWÈVRE, Über *Drosophyllum lusitanicum*. Bot. Centralbl. 60:33–41, 1894.

PENZIG, O., Untersuchungen über *Drosophyllum lusitanicum*. Diss. Breslau, 1877.

QUINTANILHA, A., O problema das plantas carnívoras. Dissertation Coimbra, 1926, 88 pp (Contains a very full bibliography of the literature pertinent to carnivorous plants. French résumé). Extr. from Bol. Soc. Brot. 4.

SOLEREDER 1899 (*see* under *Dionaea*).

Chapter IX

PINGUICULA, BUTTERWORT

Distribution. — General appearance. — Habitat. — The leaves. — Two kinds of glands (Points of structure. Early work of DARWIN: movements. Secretion and digestion). — Popular uses.

The genus *Pinguicula* consists of about 30 species distributed throughout the northern hemisphere in temperate or cool temperate regions. Although making use of a far different mode of capture of prey, it is closely related to *Utricularia* and *Genlisea*, and is one of the three lentibulariaceous genera, as shown by the flower structure. The personate corolla is blue, purple or yellow, and differs from that of *Utricularia* principally in the five-parted calyx.

All the species are of very uniform character. The plant consists of a short vertical stem giving rise to a compact rosette of leaves which usually lie flat on the ground, or in some species (*P. gypsicola*) are directed obliquely upward also. They exhale a distinct fungus-like odor. The tissue tensions in the leaves are such that when a plant is uprooted from the soil they become at once strongly reflexed, as DARWIN observed; but this is a feature common to rosette plants. The leaves are entire, usually ovate (*P. vulgaris*) or broadly ovate (*P. cuneata*), with upcurled margins. In color they are a pale faded green, yellowish in bright light (BATALIN), deeper green in the shade, in *P. vulgaris* pale purple due to the presence of pigment in the lower epidermis. They are very soft and yielding, easily bruised and torn; and, being "greasy" to touch, the name, derived from the Latin *pinguis*, fat, was suggested, according to accounts. The dorsal surface is quite smooth and shiny, the ventral glistening with myriads of minute mucilage glands. In addition to their glands, both surfaces bear numerous stomata peculiar in having no chlorophyll, though there is present according to BATALIN a pale yellow pigment. The flowers are borne singly on slender, glandular, pubescent scapes, have a five-parted corolla, with a slender spur, so large and showy in some species of the genus that they are found in glasshouse cultivation. Although the peduncles also have glandular hairs, DARWIN thought them devoid of digestive function. The seedlings have a short taproot possessed of a few root hairs, but this does not persist and soon gives way to adventitious roots arising from the stem above. In possessing a taproot, even though fugacious, this genus differs from the others of the family, in which there is none. There is but one cotyledon, which arises as a semicircular ridge around the plumule, and when fully developed is strongly folded lengthwise and may in longitudinal sections be easily interpreted as two, as GOEBEL pointed out.

Pinguicula grows in wet places, with mosses, etc., in chinks of wet, dripping rocks, on hummocks in swamps (*13* —4) and similar situations, in general conformity with the majority of carnivorous plants. Towards the end of the growing season the plant produces very compact buds of various sizes (brood-buds) which can reproduce the plant in the following growing season (HOVELACQUE).

The entire leaves and peduncles are provided with two kinds of glands, stalked and sessile (13 — 10, 11), densely scattered on the upper surface, with a much smaller number of sessile glands with four-celled capitals on the lower dorsal surface (15 — 2–4). According to FENNER the latter are hydathodic in character for he observed a minute droplet of fluid water, presumably, on each gland. They may safely be excluded from taking part in the capture and digestion of prey. GOEBEL had thought their secretion to be mucilaginous but this seems not to be the case. All these glands are of epidermal origin (GRESSNER, 1877; FENNER, 1904). The stalked glands of the upper surface stand on an epidermal cell, the stalk cell displaying a marked entasis, ending in a single short domed cell supporting the capital composed of 16 radiating cells. This secretes and supports a globule of stiff mucilage which serves to entrap and smother the prey, which must be small — only small insects are effectively caught — such as aphides, minute flies of various kinds, etc. The sessile glands have a similar structure, but the stalk cell is not cut off from the foundation epidermis cell, and there is no elongation of it. The base of the gland, therefore, lies flush with the general surface. The capital has only eight cells. The sessile glands of the under surface have capitals with only four cells. All these have been described by FENNER. This investigator further adds that some four rows of cells along the very thin leaf margin are also glandular, and that these secrete mucilage. The margin is of only three cells in thickness, a single course of cells being embraced between the two epidermes (15 — 5). It is always curled upwards through about 180 degrees, and this has been interpreted as an adaptation for conserving the digestive fluids which escape from the glands on stimulation. FENNER believes also that the escape of secretions from the glands is made possible by the occurrence of pores in the cuticle. I have not been able to see them, but treatment with methylene blue proves the easy passage of solutes, for if a leaf is plunged into a solution of medium strength the capitals of the glands are almost immediately and deeply stained. The capitals of the stalked glands are also stained but not so quickly as those of the sessile glands, perhaps because of the presence of mucilage. With regard to the structure of the cells along the margin of the upper surface, I can see no cytological evidence, such as claimed by FENNER, that they are glandular, nor have I seen a band of mucilage as described by him. J. R. GREEN (1899, p. 214) cites DARWIN to the effect that *Pinguicula* secretes a digestive fluid on the edges of the upper surface of the leaf which folds over to enclose its captive. On perusing DARWIN'S account I am unable to subscribe to GREEN'S statement. True, DARWIN does use the expression "placed among one margin" or "on one margin" but this was not meant to indicate that when secretion occurred it was confined to the margin, but that the nearby stalked glands contributed. Drops of meat infusions could not be confined to the margin without coming into contact with nearby glands. DARWIN in his first set of experiments was concerned with the possibility of leaf movement which he demonstrated to his own satisfaction. In his experiment on digestion he invariably placed the substrate to be acted on "on the leaf", and I think it is quite evident from the context that DARWIN did not think of the margin of the leaf as having a localized digestive action.

Pinguicula was first studied and shown to be carnivorous by DARWIN. "I was led to investigate the habits of this plant by being told by Mr. W. MARSHALL that on the mountains of Cumberland many insects adhere to the leaves" (Insectivorous Plants, p. 297). He noted the presence of two kinds of glands, sessile and stalked, later studied carefully by FENNER. Having studied Drosera extensively DARWIN first looked for and discovered movements of the leaves. In a series of 17 experiments small flies, or portions of larger flies, smaller and larger fragments of meat, meat juice stabilized in small bits of sponge, even fragments of glass were placed in various positions in rows parallel to the margin, near the apex, and along the midrib, and he found curvatures of the leaf margin to occur within periods of a few (2–4) hours, to increase for some hours and finally to disappear. The apex of the leaf never shows motion, this being confined to the margins. He found evidence leading him to believe that the stimulus could be transmitted to a distance of about 6 mm. (his exp. 13). A weak solution of ammonium carbonate caused marked incurvation of the leaf margin in 3.5 hrs., a stronger solution (1 to 218 H$_2$O) causing no movement, probably due to damage. Mechanical irritation of the leaf surface either before or after the application of meat juice, thus imitating the actions of dying prey, did not hasten or increase the response. The effect produced by fragments of glass was as rapid as that following the application of nitrogenous substances, but the degree of curvature was less. The substances used other than glass incited a more or less copious flow of secretion.

DARWIN commented on the brevity of the response action, there being a complete restoration of form within 24 hours. He was thus prompted to doubt the usefulness of the behavior, but ventured the idea that the infolded margin could prevent the washing away of prey, as in fact was observed by a friend of DARWIN in Wales. If the prey is large the infolding leaf margin pushed it further toward the middle of the midrib, thus bringing it into contact with more glands, an effect comparable to the action of the tentacles in Drosera. The margins of the leaf are always curved up, and this DARWIN thought to help to conserve the fluids from loss, keeping them on the leaf surface to be absorbed. GOEBEL could not substantiate DARWIN's conclusions about the sensitivity of the Pinguicula leaf, his experimental results being mostly negative. On the other hand, FENNER, one of GOEBEL's students, did find slight movements on the application of fragments of glass, followed by quick recovery. The secretion of mucilage is thereby excited. When an insect falls on or near the leaf margin, an abundant secretion follows, overwhelming it. This escape of fluids from the leaf alters the tensions and this results in the inrolling of the leaf margin which does not occur in older mature leaves. When the insects sink down to the leaf surface and come into contact with the sessile glands (13 — 11), an acid secretion of greater viscosity and containing a digestive enzyme escapes from these. GOEBEL had shown that the abundant mucilaginous secretion following application of granules of sugar is without digestive power.

Having cultivated material of *P. vulgaris* collected in the mountains of California east of Crescent City, I repeated such experiments as done by DARWIN, GOEBEL and FENNER on about a dozen leaves, with definitely positive results. I cite only one as typical, this being illustrated in *15 — 1, see also 13 — 6.* The total activity extended over more than six days. Four minute flies were observed caught in a row parallel to one margin and two similarly placed with respect to the other margin. Already the one margin was slightly curved upwards on Oct. 2, the other showed no motion until the night of Oct. 3–4. On the morning of Oct. 4 both margins were well curved, enough to hide all the flies. On Oct. 6, the inward rolling of the margins was well developed, and next day it had begun to recede, again exposing the flies to one's vision. This behavior was typical of the whole series of cases. This and a number of other cases observed seem to throw doubt on the validity of DARWIN's statement that the time leaves remain incurved, even though the exciting objects remain in position, is but short, *i.e.*, not more than twenty-four hours. It is further well known that the contact of an insect with the leaf at a point removed from the margin, *i.e.*, near the midrib, results in the dishing of the leaf below the insect (DARWIN, BATALIN). This, as BATALIN suggests, is the same phenomenon as observed in *Drosera*, and must be attributed to growth and not to injury as DARWIN supposed. When flies are arranged along and more or less parallel to the leaf margin the growth results in the rolling of it. There is little doubt of the correctness of this explanation; and moreover it agrees with our knowledge of the procedure in *Drosera* and *Dionaea*.

Movement in *Pinguicula* is then an undoubted fact. How much significance may be attached to it is a question. GOEBEL attached little. DARWIN thought that the rolling of the leaf margin brings more glands into contact with the prey, and in some cases pushes it into new positions further away from the margin. DARWIN probably underestimated the persistence of the change in movement, and therefore its importance. The upward curved leaf margins help to hold the secretion in place. This is probably as much as we can say about the matter.

DARWIN then turned his attention to the question of secretion and digestion. He found that when he placed prey (small flies), fragments of meat, cartilage, fibrin, albumen (egg-white, coagulated), gluten and gelatin, etc., on the leaf surface, there was an increase of secretion, often copious, and that this was acid. Evidence of digestion was clear: insects fell apart readily, and other substances showed the expected signs of disintegration. Objects not containing soluble nitrogenous matter, or other soluble matter do not excite secretion. Non-nitrogenous fluids can cause free flow of the secretion, but this remains neutral (non-acid). Among the substances or objects which incite acid secretion were small leaves (*Erica tetralix*), pollen and various seeds, all often seen to adhere to leaves in the open, all, of course, containing nitrogen from which DARWIN argued that these objects also, as well as animal prey, help to nourish the plant. Since the peduncles are equally glandular with the leaf, and since the life of a peduncle is fully a month or more, whatever benefit may be derived from prey caught by leaves may also be said to accrue from that caught by the peduncles.

Cytological changes. — DARWIN examined the condition of the glandular cells after being in contact for some time with sources of matter which was plainly absorbed, and found evidence of change in structure and appearance of the protoplasm and its content, usually in the appearance of granular matter colored brownish, or in the cell contents, at first limpid, being aggregated into slowly moving masses of protoplasm. The difficulties of observation and inference are obviously great, a great deal more so than in the case of *Drosera*. DARWIN referred the appearances to the absorption of food materials.

NICOLOSI–RONCATI (1912) endeavored to relate cytoplasmic changes observed in fixed and stained material to secretive activity, in *P. hirtiflora*. In actively secreting glands (mucilage glands presumably), the cytoplasm is vacuolated and contains many fuchsinophile granules scattered toward the periphery of the cell with moniliform bodies in the vicinity of the nucleus. The nucleolus, large and intensely fuchsinophile at the beginning of secretion, diminishes notably in volume and in capacity for staining in evidently secreting cells. The author concluded that the first impulse to secretion comes from the nucleolus, the primary granules of secretion being formed by the chromatin. These diffuse throughout the body of the cell definitively elaborating secretory substance. This work, while affording a beginning, does not lead us very definitely forward, as at this time we are unable to distinguish the kind of secretion dealt with, whether of mucilage or enzymes.

TISCHUTKIN (1889) carried out experiments similar to those of DARWIN, and worked also with glycerin extracts of leaves and mixtures of leaf secretion, withdrawn by means of a pipette, with glycerin, acidified variously (HCl, formic, malic acids). Both glycerin extracts and mixtures gave only negative results. Albumen, gelatin and fibrin placed on the leaves gave results for him much the same as for DARWIN. TISCHUTKIN states then that in *Pinguicula* insects which are caught call forth a secretion of acid sap which can procure a certain alteration of their substance. Examining the work of REES, GORUP and WILL (later substantiated) he sees in its deficiencies evidence of bacterial action and he comes to the conviction that the rôle of the plant is the secretion of a medium which is suited to the life and activity of microorganisms (bacteria), and concludes without further experimental evidence that in *Pinguicula* we are dealing with bacterial action, in this agreeing with MORREN (1875).

Somewhat later GOEBEL also attacked the problem of digestion in *Pinguicula*. When he put particles of fibrin on the leaves, the secretion was intensified, and the smallest particles digested in 24 hours. The secretion was weakly acid. When insects (those, as already said, are always small, for *Pinguicula* is adapted to the capture and digestion of only small ones) are found in an advanced stage of digestion, the glands are found to contain droplets of fat. Large insects or fibrin fragments are overcome by decay. By *ad hoc* culture experiments GOEBEL showed that TISCHUTKIN'S views are not justified. He showed that when even small flies, partly digested, were transferred to nutrient gelatin plates, no evidence of bacterial activity was forthcoming. He convinced himself, on experimental evidence, that *Pinguicula* secretes an antiseptic substance which prevents bacterial action, and, while his procedure cannot be regarded as beyond criticism, yet it is to be noted that later LOEW and ASO (1907) claimed to have found benzoic acid in the leaves. Naturally the amount present is not sufficient to meet all conditions, since in nature the *Pinguicula* catches only minute flies, and only small amounts of the antiseptic agent are called for. In TISCHUTKIN's experiments, says GOEBEL, he used too large masses of material with erroneous results. The capacity of the stomach to digest cheese, he added, cannot fairly be judged by feeding a kilo of cheese at one time.

GOEBEL made an experiment which seems to distinguish between the action of the sessile and stalked glands, substantiating DARWIN's findings that "non-nitrogenous fluids if dense cause the glands to pour forth a large supply of viscid fluid, but this is not in the least acid. On the other hand the secretion from glands excited by contact with nitrogenous solids and fluids is invariably acid . . . . .". TISCHUTKIN had tried to extract leaves by placing them in glycerin, with negative results. By strewing granular cane sugar on the leaf surface of some 70 plants, GOEBEL collected about 1 cc. of secretion which was neutral and after the addition of 0.2 % formic acid a particle of fibrin remained in it undigested at 35° C. From this it appears that *an abundant secretion* (probably from the stalked glands) *is not necessarily correlated with digestive activity*. On the other hand if leaves are stimulated by strewing particles of fibrin, smeared with meat juice and finally placed in meat juice, with 1.5 % formic acid added and allowed to stand for 18 hours, a fluid was obtained which digested swollen fibrin in 25 hours. No bacteria were present, due to the hindering action of the formic acid. In any event, the amount of enzyme obtainable is small.

In the foregoing it will be seen that the conclusion that *Pinguicula* is a true carnivorous plant rests on the evidence that fragments of nitrogenous matters and insects are disintegrated by the secreted juices, and that this takes place in the absence of bacteria (GOEBEL). DERNBY (1917) pushed the matter further, and by means of glycerin extracts obtained a true tryptase, not observed elsewhere among plants. There is also a weak and incomplete pepsidase effect, as small amounts of amino-compounds are set free at pH 8. The tryptase attacked caseinogen at pH 8–9.

But this has not gone without further challenge. MIRIMANOFF (1938) found that the gland cells of both stalked and sessile glands, where an insect was attached, showed aggregation. His description of this agrees with that of DARWIN and others. He could not induce it, however, with other substances (egg-white, cheese, meat extract). It appeared to him that only certain products of deamination were responsible for disturbing the osmotic equilibrium of the cell, inducing the changes leading to aggregation. It is reversible, and different from those irreversible changes observed on the application of neutral red, though by some observers they have been regarded as similar or alike. Incidentally, pointing out the total contradiction between the results of TISCHUTKIN, who denied the rôle of other than bacterial digestion, and COLLA, who argued the opposite, he states his belief that digestion by the leaf is extraordinarily feeble, and it seemed to MIRIMANOFF that *Pinguicula* would better be regarded as a "semi-carnivore". Following up this hint OLIVET and MIRIMANOFF (1940) re-examined the matter by a new method. They applied (*a*) a sterilized insect (*Drosophila*) to a bacteria-sterile leaf, and (*b*) one to a non-sterile leaf; and (*c*) a non-sterile insect to a non-sterile leaf. In the first case there was no evidence of digestion, and none of aggregation and no discoloration of the glands. In the second there was an evident discoloration of the glands, and aggregation was observed. Tested, the fly now was swarming with bacteria among which were gelatin-liquifying motile forms. In the last case digestion of the insect proceeded with abundant evidence of aggregation and discoloration. It was tried to obtain the putative protease by diffusion into gelatin-sugar in the cold. On warming at ordinary temperatures there was no liquifaction. They concluded that the digestion of insects on *Pinguicula* is the result of bacterial activity, and while the authors do not deny the presence of a protease secreted by the plant, they hold its action to be negligible.

Thus the question has been reopened, and demands further critical examination.

Pinguicula has long been supposed to have the ability to curdle milk. LINNAEUS (Flora Lapponica, p. 10) tells us that the Lapps used it for the curdling of milk and that the peasants of the Italian Alps use it similarly (PFEFFER, through OPPENHEIMER). FRANCIS DARWIN also records the fact that the same use was made of it by the farmers of Wales "for the past 30 years" as previous to 1875. This probably means a very much longer time (F. DARWIN, in a footnote in DARWIN, 1888).

The fact that some plants can cause coagulation in milk (notably *Galium verum*) was known to the ancients, according to CZAPEK. It is not clear what precisely the function of a rennet on this plant would be, but it seems that it is not a substance *per se*, but that the proteolytic enzymes have the property of coagulation, as will be seen beyond. In relation to this question, the following quotations were sent me by Dr. OKE GUSTAFSSON, translated and transmitted by Dr. JENS CLAUSEN, to both of whom I owe thanks: —

"This 'tätört' (*Pinguicula vulgaris*) has long been used in some of the more northern provinces of Sweden, as for example Jämtland and Dalarne. It has been mixed with fresh milk by smearing either the milk-sieve or the container with the glutinous leaves. For a long time it has been a common view that the milk was changed to ropy- or long-milk by its tough and viscid slime similar to cheese-lep (The milk has been given this name because it is so thick and tough [viscid] that it can be pulled into long strands). Through experiments it has now been found that long-milk cannot always be produced with *Pinguicula* (the 'tätört'), if ever, but that on the contrary such milk can originate without this medium." (LINDMAN).

Properties and uses in Norway and Denmark. — "When the leaves are laid in milk it will curdle, although without separating from the whey, and this milk, in Norway called 'Tættemælk' (ropy milk) will make other milk curdle. From this the Norwegian name 'Tættegræs' (curdlegrass) and the Färöe name 'Undslæva Grêas' have their origin. Especially the milk of reindeer is supposed to curdle. However, it had been impossible for me to obtain information that at the present time this plant is used in Norway for production of ropy milk, because usually the left-overs of milk curdled in this manner are used to thicken fresh milk with.

"Previously this plant has been accused of producing liver sickness (rot) in sheep but we now know that this is an effect of the liver fluke, *Distomum hepaticum*, which lives in wet pastures (Note by J. CLAUSEN, *in ep.*). The bees seek this plant, but stock do not eat it. It is told that it will stain yellow. It is an indicator of moist, so-called sour soil. In places it is used mixed with linseed oil as a home-remedy against wounds." (HORNEMANN).

DERNBY considered this whole question fully, citing the popular belief in Scandinavia that both *Pinguicula* and *Drosera* procure when in contact with milk a "long", that is, a very viscous coagulum. Although the work of TROILI–PETERSSON and OLSEN–SOPP (Centralb. f. Bact. II 33: 1912) shows that these plants have nothing to do with "långmjölk", yet the expressed sap of *Pinguicula* leaves does have a definite effect on sweet milk, that is, on its casein. It produces a viscous fluid of alkaline reaction, but the casein is not coagulated, but broken down into simpler bodies. DERNBY states the following conclusions from experimental evidence: — (*1*) Dialysed expressed sap of *Pinguicula* cannot make milk "thick"; (*2*) On the other hand it splits casein of milk, but only partly, in a weakly alkaline field, just as it does Witte-peptone under the same conditions; (*3*) The enzyme is very similar to trypsin, working at an opt. pH of ca. 8; (*4*) No enzyme of pepsin-erepsin character could be found.

Therapeutic effects. — P. GEDDES pointed out that all alpine peasantry apply the leaves to the sores of cattle, and its healing effect, if such there is, might be referred to the antiseptic properties. More recently there have been more exact studies made of this property (McLEAN, 1919) indicating the truth of GEDDES' report.

Summarizing, we may conclude that *Pinguicula* is a carnivorous plant inasmuch as it catches small insects and digests them, at least in part, by means of its own ferments. The possible part played by bacteria is not excluded. Its leaves are very sensitive to too great "portions" of food as GOEBEL truly said. Only minute insects can be captured in nature, this being a matter of common observation. Large insects or bits of fibrin, unless very small, cause decay beneath with permanent injury to the tissues. A closer understanding of the chemical nature of the digestive ferments has been attained by DERNBY.

As to the power of the leaf to move, first observed by DARWIN, there can be no doubt of the fact, and that the stimulus, supplied by the application of various kinds of substances, organic and inorganic, is transmitted in some fashion, but only slowly. The shortest time in which DARWIN observed movement was 2 hours 17 minutes, the stimulus being transmitted over a very short distance, a matter probably of not more than 2 to 6 mm. Movements can be induced by substances which do not cause increased secretion, such as fine grains of sand, as I have also observed. Increased secretion follows the application of sugar and proteins among others. But that following sugar does not contain ferments, indicating the abeyance of activity on the part of the sessile glands in this case.

Literature Cited:

BATALIN, A., Mechanik der Bewegungen der insektenfressenden Pflanzen. Flora 60:33–39; 54–58; 65–73; 105–111; 129–144; 145–154, 1877 (*Pinguicula*, pp. 150–154).

COLLA, SILVIA, Sui fermenti secreti da *Pinguicula alpina* L. Annuario della Chanousia 3:144, 1937 (*through* MIRIMANOFF).

CZAPEK, F., Biochemie der Pflanzen. 3 vols. 825 pp. Jena, 1925.

DARWIN, C., Irritability of *Pinguicula*. Gard. Chron. II, 2:15 and 19, 4 July, 1874.

DARWIN, C., Insectivorous Plants. 2d Ed., 1875.

DERNBY, K. G., Die proteolitischen Enzyme der *Pinguicula vulgaris*. Bioch. Zeitschr. 80:152–158, 1917.

FENNER (*see* under *Nepenthes*).

GEDDES, P., Chapters in modern Botany. New York 1893, 201 pp.

GOEBEL, K., Pflanzenbiologische Schilderungen, II. 1891.

GORUP, (*see* under *Nepenthes*)

GREEN, J. R., (*see* under *Nepenthes*).

GRESSNER, H., Botanische Untersuchungen, 1. Beobachtungen über *Pinguicula vulgaris*. Jahresber. d. evangel. Fürstl. Bentheim'schen Gymn. Arnold. z. Burgsteinfurt. Iserlohn 1877.

HORNEMANN, J. W., Forsøg til en dansk oekonomisk Plantelære. Kjøbenhavn 1821, pp. 27–28.

HOVELACQUE, M., Sur les propagules de *Pinguicula vulgaris*. C. R. 106:310, Feb. 1888.

KLEIN, J., *Pinguicula alpina*, als insektenfressende Pflanze und in anatomischer Beziehung. Beitr. z. Biol. d. Pflanzen. 3:163–185, 1880.

LINDMAN, C. A. M., Bilder ur Nordens flora. p. 100. Stockholm, 1922.

LOEW, O. & A. ASO, Benzoesäure in *Pinguicula vulgaris*. Bull. Agri. Coll. Tokyo Imp. Univ. 7:411–412, 1907.

McLEAN, R. C., The anaerobic treatment of wounds in life and its maintenance. New York, 1919.

MIRIMANOFF, A., Aggrégation protoplasmique et contraction vacuolaire chez *Pinguicula vulgaris* L. Bull. Soc. Bot. de Genève II, 29:1–15, 1938.

MORREN, E., Observations sur les procédés insecticides des *Pinguicula*. Bull. Acad. roy. d. Sci. etc. Belg., 2 sér., 39:870, 1875.

NICOLOSI-RONCATI, F., Contributo alla conoscenza citofisiologica delle glandule vegetali. Bull. Soc. Bot. Ital. 1912: 186–193.

OLIVET, R. & A. MIRIMANOFF, *Pinguicula vulgaris* L. est-elle une plante carnivore? Bull. Soc. Bot. Genève II, 30:230–235, 1940.

OPPENHEIMER, C., Die Fermente und ihre Wirkungen. vol. 2, pp. 1106–1111. Leipzig, 1925.

REES, (*see* under *Nepenthes*).

TISCHUTKIN, N., Die Rolle der Bacterien bei der Veränderung der Eiweisstoffe auf den Blättern von *Pinguicula*. Ber. d. d. bot. Ges. 7:346–355, 1889.

WILL (*see* under *Nepenthes*).

VON WILLER, Vital-Microscopische Beobachtungen an Insektenfressenden Pflanzen. Trudy Inst. Fiz. Narkomprosa (Trav. Inst. Rech. Phys. Moscou) 2:517–519, 1936. Not seen. Describes a method of observing a single gland of *Pinguicula* exclusively, all others being left intact, to be stained vitally and otherwise experimented on.

Chapter X

DROSERA

Number of species. — Geographical distribution. — Habitat. — Form and habit of the plant. — Unfolding movements of the leaf. — The leaf (Form. Anatomy. Appendages. Tentacles. Sessile glands, origin and structure, function. Locus of absorption. Other glands). — Reproduction. — Carnivory, early observations. — Mucilage, origin. — Movements of the tentacles (Early observations. NITSCHKE and DARWIN). — Direction of bending. — Duration of response. — Leaf blade not receptive to stimulus. — Path of stimulus. — Intensity of stimulus. — Mechanism of movement. — BEHRE'S studies. — Aggregation. — Digestion. — Enzymes. — The significance of carnivory for the plant.

The genus *Drosera* contains more than 90 species found in almost all parts of the world. It reaches its greatest development in Australia and is well represented in S. Africa. The most widely known, at least historically, is the common sundew, ros solis, *D. rotundifolia*, the plant which chiefly formed the subject of DARWIN'S extensive studies. This and its allies, *D. anglica*, *D. intermedia* and *filiformis*, also well known in the North Temperate zone, are modest representatives of the genus as compared with such forms as *D. gigantea* of Australia or *D. regia* of S. Africa.

Habitat. — It is very generally understood that *Drosera* grows where the soil is poor in nutrient substances. Such a statement applies fully enough to the best known species of the northern hemisphere, *D. rotundifolia, intermedia, filiformis*, etc., but seems not to be true of some species such as *D. Whittakeri* of S. Australia, where I saw it growing on wooded slopes with a general vegetation. Even this, however, though probably a richer soil than that of a sphagnum swamp, is not a rich soil. One commonly finds *D. rotundifolia* in any swamp where *Sphagnum* grows, and it grows plentifully in the chinks of partially decayed floating or stranded logs, a favorite place. In the Sequoia National Park, California, it is found in the wet open meadows surrounded by *Sequoia gigantea*, growing on a dense floor of moss (not *Sphagnum*). A more accurate picture is afforded by WEBER (1902) in his monograph describing the great swamps of Augustumal, in the delta of the Memel River. There is in this swamp, as of course in swamps elsewhere, a zonation of the vegetation. As one proceeds from the margin to the middle, one finds that the ash content of the soil and soil water becomes more and more reduced. It is only in the more central parts that *D. anglica* and *D. rotundifolia* are to be found, and these are the parts which are most lacking in salts. The vegetation here consists of *Spagnum* with *Cladonia uncinalis, Scirpus caespitosus, Eriophorum vaginatum, Scheuchzeria palustris, Rhynchospora alba, Vaccinium oxycoccus*, and *Andromeda polifolia* — and therefore of few species. This habitat was found to have a soil with the following composition in absolute and relative terms. In quoting these data, SCHMID

	AUGUSTUMAL SWAMPS	DILUVIAL CLAY SOIL
Potassium	0.044 (1)	1.06 (24)
Phosphoric acid	0.075 (1)	0.18 (2.4)
Calcium	0.217 (1)	2.86 (13.1)
Magnesia	0.138 (1)	0.88 (5.9)

Francis E. Lloyd — 116 — Carnivorous Plants

points out the absence of data on the nitrogen content, and cites, in order to fill the gap, the fact, stated by WOLLNY (1897), that the soil (raw humus) of a pine forest as compared with that of the *Drosera* habitat, contains nitrogen in the proportion of 27:1. Even more striking than the fact that the habitat is of such poor quality in respect to salt content is the further observation that the first immigrants onto the newly cut turf surfaces after the removal of peats, is *Drosera*, and this remains for a long time the only inhabitant of these raw peat surfaces. We may recall in this connection that CORRENS (1896) showed that tap water at a high temperature (54.4° C.) does not cause movements of the tentacles, but that water devoid of $CaCO_3$ and CO_2 called forth reactions at that temperature. In this way he detected a toxic effect of Ca and inferred that this substance in the soil (at least too much of it) might be toxic.

Form and habit of the plant. — The commonest type of *Drosera* consists of a slender stem crowned by a rosette of leaves with flowering scapes growing in the leaf axils. It arises from a seedling (*D. rotundifolia*) which has a fugacious taproot, which, however, serves for the formation of the earliest rosette of leaves (NITSCHKE, 1860). According to HEINRICHER (1902) the taproot fails to elongate, but swells into a rounded mass covered with root hairs. The cotyledons are simple, spatulate, followed by leaves of the mature type, though small and with fewer appendages (tentacles) than the latter. As the plant grows the stem dies off behind. In winter the rosette is reduced to a tight compact winter bud which may have no extending stem or roots.

Growing as it (*D. rotundifolia* e.g.) does in mats of *Sphagnum*, the differential growth rates of these plants brings it about that *Sphagnum* by its more rapid growth during the cool months, overtops the *Drosera* and in the warmer months the latter in its turn overtops the *Sphagnum*. One sees, therefore, in a *Drosera* plant, which has grown in this way, successive dead rosettes clinging to the dead stem, ending above in a living rosette, as figured by NITSCHKE. Such are our familiar species of the northern hemisphere. The leaves of the rosette when fully expanded may be relatively small, as in *D. rotundifolia, intermedia*, etc., or very large and ligulate, as in a remarkable species, *D. regina*, described by Miss E. L. STEPHENS from S. Africa. In this species the leaves are 2 cm. broad by 35 cm. long. Or again the leaves may be large and fern-like in aspect, with strong terete petioles with a once to thrice parted leaf blade as in *D. binata, D. dichotoma* (S. Africa, Australia). These make showy greenhouse plants, and have often been cultivated and used for study, to be reported upon in some detail beyond.

Or again the main stem may be elongated upward, only slightly in *D. capensis*, an often cultivated form from S. Africa, with ligulate leaf blades supported on rather long petioles (*13 — 5, 7*). In the most stately species *D. gigantea* the stem may be a meter long and many plants together form a dense half shrubby tangle crowned with the numerous flowers in panicles. The stems climb or clamber, partly by twisting and partly by means of certain long-petioled leaves in which the leaf blade becomes a disc of attachment, its dense secretion forming an adhesive (GOEBEL 1923). The stems are wiry, the leaves peltate and deeply cupped. It is a pronounced sclerophyll, according to CZAJA.

Some species, after the seedling stage is passed, form tubers which perennate, and send up strong stems ending in a rosette or whatever type of above-ground parts it has. From the stems grow axillary, positively geotropic shoots (droppers), at the ends of which new tubers arise (*See beyond for details*). These species have no roots, while in general the roots are always meagre in numbers and extent, a fact which is well known (SCHMID). The root hairs are numerous in some species and their walls are suberized and persistent. In other species the root hairs are sparse. MARLOTH has reported both conditions in S. African species. In some species the roots are apparently replaced by rhizoids. DIELS has thus described for *D. erythrorhiza* the root-like productions one to three in number from the base of each scale leaf. These have no root cap, but are provided with "root" hairs (DIELS 1906). GOEBEL comments on the nature of these structures, called by the equivocal name of leaf-roots ("Blattwurzeln"), pointing out that in the apex, while no root cap is present, there is an apical meristem just behind the epidermis, the outer walls of which are thickened, and which are evidently a protective mail for a boring apex, which may be regarded perhaps as a reducing or reduced root end. Their origin according to DIELS, however, is exogenous, and he called them leaf rhizoids, but leaves details of their origin not fully understood. I have verified DIELS' observation.

I have examined the "leafroots" of *D. erythrorhiza* from West Australia and am able to confirm GOEBEL's observation of very thick outer cell walls of the apical cells (*15 — 19*). There is a meristem, but this does not lie immediately behind the epidermis, but just back of three cell layers within. The apex itself is composed of enlarged epidermal cells underlain by other cells of similar appearance derived from two subepidermal layers, and heavily loaded with large starch grains. The apical cells constitute a boring organ which does not slough off as does the root cap. If there is any renewal of substance, this would be in new secretion of cell wall. The plant grows, however, in very loose soil where friction against the growing tip is minimum in amount. At all events I have examined a large number of "leafroots" and have not found any evidence of renewal of epidermal cells.

In the axis of each rhizoid-bearing scale small tubers, having evidently the function of reproduction, can be produced (GOEBEL 1933).

Unfolding movements of the leaf. — In many of the species of *Drosera* (*D. rotundifolia, D. pygmaea*), the petiole is bent so that the upper face of the blade becomes applied to the petiole (*16 — 17*). This is brought about by the hyponasty of a more or less narrow zone of the petiole at the base of the blade. In other species, however, those in which the leaf blade is slender and filiform, there occurs true circination, as in *D. filiformis, D. regia* (with slender ligulate leaves with short petioles), *D. binata, D. dichotoma*, with the volute facing the stem, and due again to hyponasty. Just the opposite occurs in *Drosophyllum* and in *Byblis linifolia*. These two directly opposite behaviors appear, according to FENNER (1904), to be related to the need for protection of the tentacles since they are on the upper surface in *Drosera* and on the lower in *Drosophyllum*, but, it is to be noted, along the margins in both, with the result that in the volute a large number of the tentacles are exposed and cannot receive protection from the overlying turn of the volute. I have observed this and can confirm GOEBEL on the point. On the other hand, GOEBEL proposes a causal explanation as follows. The production of a great extension of surface by the growth of tentacles can act to inhibit the growth rate of that surface, and thus permit the more rapid growth of the other face of the leaf, the lower in *Drosera*, the upper in *Drosophyllum* (GOEBEL, 1924). In *Byblis gigantea* the leaf shows no such movements. The leaf grows in a basal zone, and the filiform blade extends always straight on. In this the glands are more numerous on the lower surface. Here the distribution of the very numerous glands either has no inhibiting effect, or has an equal effect on all sides of the leaf.

Of particular interest to us here are the leaves, which are the mechanism for catching and digesting prey. These present a variety of forms from a simple orbiculate bifacial leaf of small size (*D. rotundifolia* 1 cm. diam.) through linear (*D. filiformis*) to broad liguliform tapering at both ends (*D. regia*). Or the blade may be once to twice forked (*D. binata*, *D. dichotoma*) the petioles firm and cylindrical ("rush-like" as DARWIN put it). Further, the leaf may be peltate, either obliquely (*D. pygmaea*) or centrally (*D. gigantea*, *D. peltata*, *D. subhirtella*), sometimes with two basal lobes (*D. auriculata*) making the leaf base angular, a condition reaching its maximum expression in *D. lunata* (E. Asia). In the seedlings of the peltate leafed species the primary seedling leaves are usually non-peltate, those of *D. peltata* resembling the following leaves of *D. rotundifolia* (DIELS, GOEBEL).

The leaf is conspicuous because of its glands raised on elongated stalks, each bearing a drop of mucilage which is extremely viscid and serves to entrap small insects. ERASMUS DARWIN thought that "Drosera mucilage prevents small insects from infesting the leaves" (The Botanic Garden, vol. 2, Canto 1, p. 229).

Anatomy of the leaf blade. — The epidermis is composed of straight-walled cells in *D. rotundifolia* and *D. capensis*, but in *D. Whittakeri* the lower epidermis is wavy-walled, the upper straight-walled. In these species the cells have many chloroplasts, absent from the lower epidermis of *D. rotundifolia* (SOLEREDER).

The internal parenchyma has no palisade, as pointed out by NITSCHKE, the whole being made up of rounded cells in rather few courses, more in some species (*D. Whittakeri*) than in others (*D. rotundifolia*). In the latter species there are, in the case examined by me, 3 to 5 courses of cells. The smallest are in contact with the upper epidermis. Below there are much larger cells, the third course in contact with the lower epidermis unless a fourth course occurs, when the cells are somewhat smaller, but still larger than the upper course cells ($15 — 15$). All the cells, usually including the epidermis (SOLEREDER), contain chloroplasts. Stomata occur on both surfaces. The intercellular spaces are large. This general structure is, as SCHMID (1912) has said, rather primitive, a quality which is shared, in varying degree, with insectivorous plants in general, indicating that this quality stands in a probable relation to carnivory. In these plants the elaboration of starch and its metabolism and withdrawal are all slow processes.

It was observed by SCHMID that during the absorption of materials from the bodies of prey, the starch content of the tissues at the base of the tentacles is lost. According to SPOEHR (1923) the amino acids are concerned with the metabolism of starch. From this GIESSLER (1928) was prompted to investigate the influence of salts on the metabolism of starch in the leaf of *Drosera capensis*. He found that in this species, when the leaf is fed with insects or with various salts, there is a disappearance of starch from the leaf. The leaves of *D. capensis* are in summertime heavily loaded with starch. The starch content is not lowered even when the plant is kept in the dark. Even after 45 days in the dark in contact with distilled water, the leaf (at temp. 36-38° C.) showed no reduction in starch. The sugar content is minute. In winter the leaves are starch-free, but there is as little sugar as in summer. These facts, together with the high respiratory intensity, indicated to GIESSLER that the physiology of *Drosera* resembles rather that of the animal than of the plant, in that there is a protein respiration. He suggests that the starch is used in the secretion of mucilage and in supplying the energy for the bending of the tentacles and leaf blade in response to stimulation. In support of his thesis he points out the abundant occurrence of labile albumin (LOEW) in many carnivorous plants and mentions in support of this the work of ERNA JANSON on aggregation, to which reference is made elsewhere. It has often been asked if the carnivorous plants are not animal-like in view of their habits, and this is at present answered as above.

The absence of a palisade tissue in *Drosera*, already mentioned, is not confined to this genus, but is generally though not universally true of carnivorous plants. This lack stands, according to SCHMID, in relation to insectivory, the latter affording compensation. But KOS-TYTSCHEW questioned this, and did experiments which he regarded as proving that both *Drosera* and *Pinguicula* are quite as active as the control plants which he used. As his figures are the only ones available, I give them. The amount of CO_2 assimilated per 1 dm^2 of leaf surface: *Drosera rotundifolia*, 4 cc., *Tussilago farfara* (control) 3.8 cc., *Pinguicula vulgaris*, 38.4 cc., *Aegopodium podagraria* 18.1 cc.

"Thus KOSTYTSCHEW'S experiments answered the question whether a carnivorous plant can obtain its carbon nutrition through photosynthesis in the affirmative. The scant experimental data show, and the text implies, that *Drosera* and *Pinguicula* leaves, which have not had access to animal nutrition for some time, carry on photosynthesis at a normal rate. The observed rates are in good agreement with those established by WILLSTÄTTER and STOLL for a wide variety of green plants. KOSTYTSCHEW'S comparisons with *Auricularia* and *Lemna* also bear this out.

"From his data on photosynthesis of *Drosera* it appears, however, that the rate of carbon dioxide assimilation would have increased materially after feeding the plants with insects. The experimental details have not been recorded in sufficient detail to permit of a definitive decision. But the discovery of a measurable effect of the ingestion of animal material on the rate of photosynthesis would open up a new approach to a study of the problem of photosynthesis itself. The importance of such a possibility made it an easy matter to obtain the co-operation of Dr. W. ARNOLD in carrying out some preliminary experiments.

"*Drosera* and *Pinguicula* plants, previously not animal fed, were used for the experiments. Single leaves were placed in distilled water in the center-cups of Warburg vessels. A mixture of sodium carbonate and bicarbonate was introduced into the main chamber in order to insure a constant carbon dioxide pressure in the gas phase. Photosynthesis was measured manometrically at 27° C. The rate was constant over a period of six hours, at the end of which one leaf was fed with a fly and some egg albumen, while another was kept as a control. Repeated measurements over a period of some 20 hours following the feeding showed that the control leaf maintained a practically constant rate of both photosynthesis and respiration. The rate of oxygen production of the experimental leaf appeared somewhat depressed, but its respiratory rate was considerably higher than that of the control. By correcting the photosynthesis measurements for respiration in the usual way it was found that the corrected values do not differ significantly from the original ones. The increased respiration obviously resulted from the availability of substrates for oxidation on the outside of the leaf, and may be caused by the plant itself or by contaminating micro-organisms. These experiments lend no support whatever to the idea of an influence of feeding upon the rate of photosynthesis of carnivorous plants." (C. B. VAN NIEL, *in ep.*).

The appendages of the leaf. — There are several kinds of appendages but they are not all common to all species of *Drosera*. Some are important physiologically in relation to the carnivorous habit, others not. To the former belong the tentacles and sessile glands, common to all species; to the latter are the glandular and eglandular trichomes seen in *D. rotundifolia* and other N. hemisphere species and the glandular trichomes found in such species as *D. gigantea*, and distributed over the whole plant body (*15* — 16). We may add, at this point, that the fringes of trichome-like structures were regarded collectively as a ligule by NITSCHKE. It is a fringed membrane formed at the sides and across the leaf base in *D. rotundifolia* and some other species (*16* — 18), but is absent from many others (*D. Whittakeri, D. peltata, D. gigantea,* etc.) It has been regarded as stipular and is so called in the taxonomic literature (DIELS) though SMALL (1939) takes another view, that the apparent membrane is merely a linear cluster of trichomes. That similar trichomes are found abundantly on the rest of the petiole supports his contention. On the other hand it is difficult not to see in the huge ligulate "stipule" possessed by some species (*D. paleacea, D. pygmaea*) (*16* — 18) in Australia, in which they serve to protect the bud during periods of drought (DIELS), an integration of a fringe as it occurs *e.g.* in *D. rotundifolia.*

Tentacles. — Of these, the stalked glands or tentacles are the most conspicuous and have most frequently been described. They have often called forth exclamatory remarks of wonder at their complex structure. They have been described, but not always correctly, by GRÖNLAND, TRÉCUL, NITSCHKE, WARMING, DARWIN, HUIE, FENNER, HOMÈS and probably others. The tentacles occur on the margin and upper surface of the leaf blade and in some species on the tapering upper region of the petiole, excepting those species which are strictly peltate.

The "tentacle" consists of a tapering stalk topped by an oval gland. The stalk arises from the leaf surface, as a mass of tissue including all the elements of the leaf structure, epidermis, parenchyma and vascular tissue. The terms "trichome" and "hair" are therefore not suitable, though they have been used.

The term "tentacle" is not a strict one; it has been equated with "emergence" and serves if we think of the tentacle as an extension of the leaf adapted to certain functions which makes them so trichome-like that they are no longer distinguishable from trichomes (DIELS). NITSCHKE and others regarded the tentacles as extensions of the leaf, WARMING as trichomes and PENZIG as intergradients between phyllome and trichome.

In the upper reach the tentacle consists of the epidermis and one course of parenchyma cells surrounding a very slender vascular strand which extends from the leaf system up into the gland ($15 — 6$). This was seen by MEYEN in 1837, who supposed that it entered the gland. This structure led TRÉCUL (1855) to compare the tentacle with the dicotyledonous stem, and to regard the adventitious buds described first by NAUDIN as metamorphosed tentacles. GRÖNLAND called them lobes, and SCHACHT, projections of the leaf. On the surface as part of the epidermal system there are a few small sessile glands, these being found also on the general leaf surface. They formed convenient marks by which H. D. HOOKER was able to record changes in the length of the tentacles during movement. The widened base of the tentacle has, naturally, an increasing number of parenchyma cells as the general leaf surface is approached. Similarly the vascular system, consisting of spiral tracheids, may here consist of two or more vessels, but above there is usually found only a single strand except where two may overlap. FENNER did not see any phloem, and I can only support him in this ($15 — 7$). The single vessel sets into a dense mass of thick and short tracheids occupying the middle of the gland ($15 — 6$) which, oval in form save when on a strictly marginal tentacle, sits atop the narrow neck of the stalk. Those tentacles arising from the leaf margin are bilaterally symmetrical, the stalk being extended under the glandular structure proper in the form of a spoon holding the gland in its bowl ($15 — 9, 11; 16 — 1$-3). DARWIN records finding intermediate forms, which I have also seen. The tentacles springing from the surface are increasingly radially symmetrical as the margin of the leaf is left, are oval, and present the following structure.

The oval head of the tentacle consists of four layers of cells ($15 — 6, 8$). The innermost of these is a roughly oval mass of tracheids which is connected by means of the vascular strand of spiral vessels in the stalk with the system in the leaf. Surrounding this xylem mass, three outermore layers cover it as a thimble, the flaring mouth of it articulating with the somewhat expanded tip of the stalk. The layer of cells in contact with the xylem mass is distinctly bell-shaped, and was called by FENNER the parenchyma bell. The flaring wall of the bell is composed of a single layer of elongated, curved cells, the exposed ends of which come to the surface of the gland, and whose cuticle is continuous with that of the gland above and the stalk below. The inner ends articulate, at a point about half-way up the bell, with shorter cells, forming the top of the bell. Both the transverse and longitudinal walls of all cells are cuticularized so that when a gland has been treated with sulfuric acid, these walls remain as a network ($15 — 12$) or, as it were, a cage formed of a continuous band of cuticularized cell wall. In transverse section this band is T-shaped, the cross bar of the T being narrow and placed towards the outside with respect to the gland as a whole. HUIE believed that only the outer part of the wall (approximately one-half) is cuticularized, and abuts at the middle of the wall on a pit connecting adjacent bell cells, the inner moiety of the wall being lignified. FENNER did not see this, and I have been unable to verify HUIE's description. This parenchyma bell appears to function as an endodermis, though FENNER questions GOEBEL's view that water may pass only in one direction (outwardly). The outer ends of these cells form a continuous single row of rounded outlines like a string of beads, seen in an entire gland, which limits the gland proper from the uppermost transverse course of stalk cells. These cells were seen by WARMING, whose drawing DARWIN reproduces. But DARWIN (1875 2d. ed., p. 5) himself failed to see them, nor, said he, did NITSCHKE, though one of his drawings seems to indicate that he did. Neither did GRÖNLAND (1855) or TRÉCUL (1855) see them.

Fitting over the parenchyma bell are the two layers of glandular cells. The outer course is made up of columnar epidermal cells, polygonal *en face*, their outer ends covered by a cuticle and their radial, and sometimes outer walls strengthened by cellulose buttresses and beams (15 — 13), as shown by FENNER. They are most pronounced throughout the lateral reaches of the gland and diminish in stature toward its apex, from which they are quite absent (HUIE), though HOMÈS thinks they occur here, but are smaller, in much smaller numbers and far apart (1928). Careful examination persuades me to agree with HUIE. They are obvious in the apical cells of the glands of *D. pygmaea*. Naturally enough, the protoplasm of the cell fits into the bays between the buttresses, and by the use of weak H_2SO_4 for maceration, the protoplasts may be isolated and are then seen edged with crenellations, interpreted by HABERLANDT as sensitive papillae. If this is a correct view, we must think that the glands are more sensitive along their sides than on the apex, for which we have no evidence one way or another.

The cuticle covers over the whole of the gland and is continuous with that of the stalk. As HUIE has said, it is quite continuous and is not penetrated by pores (GARDINER) nor is it absent from the apical cells (GOEBEL). GOEBEL's statement to this effect appears to have been due to the observation of the earlier penetration of solutes through these cells, but I have satisfied myself that methylene blue enters equally rapidly over the entire surface of the gland. Prolonged treatment with sulphuric acid leaves a very delicate continuous membrane covering it. Yet as HUIE says, the cuticle is readily penetrated by silver nitrate, just as by methylene blue. Another observation of HUIE's I can confirm, namely, that in life the lateral walls of the apical cells are often separated from each other by fissures tapering inwardly between them, as if the walls had separated along the middle line. It is possible that this is what FRANÇA saw in *Drosophyllum*, interpreted by him as canals leading to the inner course of glandular cells. The nucleus of these cells lies near the base and the cytoplasm has a large vacuole in the outer moiety of the cell (in the resting condition — see beyond under aggregation).

The second layer of glandular cells lies between the epidermis and the parenchyma bell, and is composed of more depressed and irregular cells, overlooked by NITSCHKE, but seen by DARWIN, and correctly described by WARMING. The cells are irregular in shape fitting the irregular bases of the epidermal cells without intercellular spaces. The functions of these two glandular layers differ according to HOMÈS as we shall see.

The emplacement of the glandular tissues is different in the marginal tentacles. Here the end of the tentacle stalk is formed into a spoon, in the bowl of which lies the gland. There is, as it were, a torsion of the upper part of the tentacle so as to bring the gland on the upper ventral surface. The complete homology of the two types is seen on examination of a transverse section of the marginal gland ($15 — 9$, 11; $16 — 1$, 2).

To be included as a specialized portion of the gland, or better a portion of the tentacle acting in a specialized way in cooperation with the gland, is, according to FENNER (1904), the uppermost course of epidermal cells of the stalk, those, namely, which are in direct contact with the tissues of the gland at its base. These cells are short and being epidermal, they form a circle of 8–10 cells called by FENNER the "Halskranz", or as we may call them, the *neck cells*. Sometimes there are two rows of neck cells (KONOPKA), and this I note may be the case in *D. Whittakeri*. The neck cells surround the parenchyma cells of the same transverse course but these latter are not included in the "Halskranz", as defined by FENNER, who describes the anatomical relations as follows. The neck cells are in contact above with the lower ends of the emergent parenchyma bell cells, and with the outer zone of the xylem mass of the gland. Inwardly they lie in contact with the short parenchyma cells of the stalk, these in turn lying against the inner zone of xylem tracheids and with the end of the stalk vascular bundle. Below, the neck cells impinge on the stalk epidermis. They are, as one may say, in a strategic position to carry on a special function, if FENNER is right in his interpretation. That they have a function he believes is evidenced by the presence of numerous pits in their walls which lie against the parenchyma bell cells and those of the xylem, and furthermore, by the fact that their cuticle is porous. He gives the following interpretation. The neck cells receive water from the bell cells which bring water from the upper part of the xylem mass, and from the lower xylem cells, presumably also from the parenchyma transversely within the neck cells, and pass it outwardly through the pores of the cuticle supplying fluid to dilute the viscid mucilage secreted by the glandular cells above. The glistening drop of mucilage supported on the tentacle head is, says FENNER, pear-shaped, the broad part of the drop being around the neck cells because the fluid exudes chiefly from them. The reasoning here appears disingenuous. Nor is his statement that the cuticle is porous acceptable since dyes (methylene blue) never enter the outer surface of the neck cells, but pass into the stalk only by diffusion through the gland, as I have verified repeatedly. While crediting FENNER with imagination, it is still permitted to doubt the correctness of his interpretation and even the supposed facts on which it is based. KONOPKA indeed has taken issue with FENNER, and his view is stated beyond.

The development of the tentacle has been worked out by HOMÈS, and it becomes evident that the outermost layer of the gland is purely epidermic in origin, as would appear on the face of it. The second layer, which might be interpreted as of epidermic origin, is shown to be of parenchymatous origin. The third layer, the parenchyma bell, is partly epidermic and partly parenchymatous (FENNER). Those cells which come to the surface at the base of the gland are epidermic. They are narrower and longer than the others, which are of parenchymatous origin. The inclosed mass of reticulated, and annular and spiral vessels are obviously an extension of the leaf vascular tissue (*16* — 4-6). The developmental behavior of the gland in *Drosera* corresponds point for point with that of *Drosophyllum* (FENNER).

Functions of gland parts. — Such a complicated gland as above described can scarcely be a simple matter physiologically. The reception and transmission of stimuli, the secretion of mucilage, of one or more ferments, probably of an odoriferous principle, water, and in the opposed direction, the absorption of the products of digestion are carried on. Is it possible to assign any degree of specialization to the various elements of structure? HOMÈS (1929*b*), having studied with meticulous care the behavior of the cells in the matter of aggregation, assigned to the outer layer, the epidermis, the function of "responding directly to the necessities of secretion by the variation of its vacuome". Its cells elaborate the substance secreted. That of the second layer is the regulation of osmotic pressure. The third layer, the parenchyma bell, takes no part in secretion (HOMÈS, 1929*b*, p. 49). It may be assumed, of course, that the cells of the bell allow the rapid transfer of water from the inclosed xylem, but whether the movement is a one-way one only, as GOEBEL suggested, or not, is difficult to say.

Reference has been made above to HABERLANDT'S view that the protoplasmic processes lying between the buttresses of the epidermal cells are sensitive organs, analogous to those seen by him in tendrils and other plant parts. KONOPKA preferred another suggestion in 1930, that the increased surface due to crenellation may be important also in secretion and absorption, as a secondary advantage. GOEBEL has regarded them in this way.

With respect to other parts of the gland KONOPKA has made some further suggestions. The xylem bundle mass is, he says, composed of spiral vessels of narrower bore in the central part, with wider lumened tracheids surrounding them, and the more central vessels widen in contact with the apical portion of the gland. The central vessels are indeed often narrower than the outer, but other details it is difficult to accede. KONOPKA would attribute different functions to the two regions, but beyond this regards the whole as a water storage organ, which rather obviously it seems to be. He has, however, examined the behavior of the nuclei, and finds that during digestion and absorption there occur changes in them which he interprets as connected with taking up and transmitting nutrients from the outer tissues of the gland to the stalk cells. He asserts that the nuclei of the endodermis, of the xylem and of the stalk cells, show a gradient of such changes, the nuclei of the more superficial tissues showing greater changes in a quantitative sense than those of the deeper and more removed tissues. To the endodermis (parenchyma bell) he attributes the special function of a protective filter. It must be questioned whether KONOPKA has advanced sufficient evidence to support this hypothesis. Aside from the nuclear changes claimed to occur by KONOPKA, there is no other change such as characterizes the secretion cells, namely aggregation (HOMÈS), during periods of activity. This seems to indicate that whatever the function of the endodermis, it is a different one from that of the secretion layer, and this I believe is as far as we can go in interpretation beyond admitting that substances are transmitted, but not differentially.

KONOPKA also questions FENNER'S view about the neck cells. He does violence to FENNER'S definition of the neck cells by including the uppermost parenchyma cells which lie somewhat (but very little) above the level of the ring or circle ("Kranz") of neck cells. The neck cells, as he uses the term, have membranes which resist the action of concentrated sulfuric acid, and are similar in this respect to the endodermis cells. Discarding FENNER'S idea that they are especially concerned with the transmission of water to the surface, he thinks that, on the basis of his observation of the nuclear changes, which are similar to those seen in the endodermal, tracheid and stalk cells, they transmit absorbed materials downwardly to the stalk. This seems to be a simple and natural view of the matter. But I have been unable to see cuticularized walls in these cells, and FENNER says nothing of this ($15 — 12$). Nor have others (HUIE, HOMÈS, myself) seen nuclei in the xylem of the mature gland.

We may summarize what has been said in the few preceding paragraphs by emphasizing the very complex functioning of the tentacle gland, that it is, as a mechanism, relatively complex as compared with many other known plant glands, but that we are far from recognizing specific correlations between structure and function. It would seem that the complexity of function is much greater than recognizable structural differentiation.

Sessile glands. — In addition to the stalked glands or tentacles there are very numerous, small sessile glands, or, as DARWIN called them, "papillae". They were described for the European species by NITSCHKE and others, and in detail by FENNER, who traced their development. They are to be found on both leaf surfaces, on the stalks of the tentacles, and elsewhere (petioles, scapes). The glands project dome-shaped from the leaf surface, are little larger than the stomata in area, and consist of a capital of two cells, which may be rounded and compact, or more or less elongated into obliquely placed cylinders. These stand on a short stalk of compressed cells in two courses, each course of two cells. The basal cells have cuticularized inner walls. These in turn stand on two epidermal cells ($15 — 18$). FENNER describes also a variant of the fundamental form. It occcurs on the petioles, and consists of a more or less elongated stalk with a capital of about four cells.

The origin of the sessile glands is purely epidermal (FENNER). The mother cells are two short epidermal ones which by tangential division give rise to a pair of capital cells, the base of which is again cut off to make stalk cells. The remaining true capital cells are two in number and may remain rounded, or elongate more or less into two divergent short cylindrical cells, seen on the base of the tentacles and on the petiole (NITSCHKE). In *D. Whittakeri* these glands are much larger and more complicated in structure and consist of twelve cells, eight outer surrounding a core of four inner, the whole being supported on a very short biseriate stalk of longitudinally compressed cells.

Other glandular trichomes occur in *D. gigantea* (seen by DARWIN) and probably in other species. These are stalked, bear an oval gland, and look superficially like the tentacles, but do not have their elaborate differentiation. They are to be found scattered on the petioles and stems; on the latter they are quite numerous. I failed to observe any secretion. Though the gland is covered with cuticle, they absorb dye readily. Their structure is indicated in *15* — 16. In origin they are epidermal, but in the base there is a small involvement of parenchyma as it is rather broad, the stalk tapering upward into a uniseriate portion just beneath the gland. What function these can serve, if any, is not known. Small flies have been observed sticking to them.

Function of sessile glands. — DARWIN observed that aggregation takes place in the sessile glands during the digestion of prey, and thought therefore that they are concerned in the absorption of substances derived therefrom, "but this cannot be the case with the papillae on the backs of the leaves or on the petiole." It is not clear if he meant this merely because of unfavorable position. But FENNER held that the sessile glands of the concave leaf surface are alone capable of absorption, pointing out that those of the dorsal surface are small, and usually lose the capital cells. The active glands display cytoplasmic changes (DARWIN's aggregation evidently) during the absorption of nutriment. Because nuclear changes also intervene, ROSENBERG aligned himself with these authors. To all this KONOPKA opposes a contrary opinion. Nuclear changes such as ROSENBERG observed are also to be seen in other glands, certainly not concerned in the absorption of substances; and the "middle layer" (endodermis) also is to be found in nectaries, hydathodes, etc. He believes the sessile glands to be hydathodes. They never, he continues, show such far-reaching changes in nuclear behavior as do the tentacle cells, and there never occur the "Digestionsballen" which he found in tentacle gland cells. Nor have the glands any connection with the vascular tissues; they develop much earlier than the tentacles, and occur on both leaf faces. These points argue that the sessile glands are not absorptive. There is, KONOPKA believes, much greater probability that they serve the purpose of water secretion. In support of this view he cites as facts (*a*) the "not small" vascular system of the roots; (*b*) the rich supply of root hairs; (*c*) the wetness of the substrate; (*d*) the active passage of water through the plant and (*e*) the high relative humidity of the habitat, tending to reduce transpiration. And SCHMID, he says, had found that there is only a slow transfer of water to the tentacle glands following the experimental removal of the mucilage drop, while on the capture of prey there is an extraordinary increase of fluid supplied from the leaf during the digestion of prey (as DARWIN and others have observed), all speaking for a process of guttation. Admitting the above as facts (though SCHMID's results seem to question some of them) KONOPKA arrives at an interesting interpretation of the whole situation: the sessile glands draw off water from the leaf, supplying it for the process of digestion and thus at the same time exert suction on the tentacles, thus increasing absorption by them. These glands, he says, may be roughly compared with the animal kidney which withdraws water from the body thus making room for more to be absorbed.

In support of the idea he recalls the case of the trap of *Utricularia*, which is known to excrete water from the glands on its outer surface (glands not much dissimilar from the ones in question) and to absorb nutrition and water from the interior by means of the bifid and quadrifid trichome glands. Since these two sets of glands in *Utricularia* are the only non-cuticularized areas of the inner and outer surfaces of the trap and since the cuticle elsewhere is impermeable (*e.g.* to dyes) we are forced to recognize its peculiar glandular action as involving the two sets of glands, as CZAJA, MERL and NOLD have believed. This view would harmonize our ideas about the two apparently widely different structures, leaf and trap.

The free flow of watery secretion observed during the earlier stages of digestion or just previous thereto, even if KONOPKA's view is correct, does not preclude the possibility that the sessile glands may not contribute to the efficiency of the leaf by exercising the function of absorption as well. We may, therefore, direct our attention briefly to the specific question of locus or loci of absorption of the leaf.

The locus of absorption. — Previous to the studies of OUDMAN, there had always been a vagueness about the point of entrance of substances absorbed by the leaf. Three possibilities there are: (*1*) that they enter through the tentacles; or (*2*) through the papillae; and (*3*) through the epidermis, which according to NITSCHKE, has no cuticle. The last may be at once excluded as NITSCHKE's statement is not true. Aside from direct proof with sulfuric acid, the diffusion of *e.g.* caffeine (KOK) into the leaf takes place through the papillae, and not through nearby epidermal cells.

With regard to the tentacles the fact of aggregation in the stalk cells following on the application of various substances (insects, caffeine, etc.) would seem to indicate at once that absorption can and does take place through the glands. DARWIN indeed regarded aggregation as proof of absorption. PFEFFER, however, pointed out that this might be the result of the stimulating effect of minimal quantities of material with no quantitative relations indicating absorption. Some such substance has been thought to be necessary to procure aggregation, that is, a specific aggregation-stimulating substance formed in the gland (ÅKERMAN, 1917; COELINGH, 1929). ALI KOK determined the rate of transport of caffeine from the glands into the tentacle stalks. Changes in the structure of the cytoplasm and nucleus (studies by HUIE, ROSENBERG, KONOPKA and ZIEGENSPECK, and KRUCK on *Utricularia*), were referred by them to the activity of these structures (cytoplasm and nucleus) in response to the absorption of various foods. Taking up of food by the tentacles has been generally assumed, as *e.g.* by GOEBEL, FENNER, RUSCHMANN. OUDMAN points out, however, that there is little positive information and that even if the tentacles do absorb, their rôle may be small and of secondary significance.

That the papillae, small sessile glands of various sizes, smallest on the tentacle stalks, largest on the leaf blade, where they occur on both surfaces, are concerned in absorption has been expressed by DARWIN, and by ROSENBERG, both of whom saw the ready passage of substances through them into the tissues. ROSENBERG used methylene blue (as I have repeatedly done). FENNER and COELINGH, as also

DARWIN and ROSENBERG, saw that aggregation and granulation occur in response to the entrance of various substances, but this is true of the tentacles, also, and proves as much and as little in both cases. To be sure it was thought that the papillae produce no secretion externally escaping, and this has perhaps influenced the judgment. As OUDMAN remarks, here also as in the case of tentacles quantitative results had not been forthcoming. He therefore endeavored to supply these.

Having first assured himself that the N-content of the leaves (of *Drosera capensis*) under the circumstances under which he worked, is nearly constant, OUDMAN then arranged a simple experiment (*1*) so that the more marginal tentacles were surrounded by agar (2%), with asparagin (1.5%), and (*2*) so that the mixture was poured on the back of the leaf taking precautions against capillary flow. He obtained these results:

TREATMENT OF THE LEAF	N IN % OF FRESH WEIGHT	INCREASE IN 24 HOURS
Control	2.07	—
Asparagin on the marginal tentacles	3.54	1.47
Asparagin on the back of the leaf	3.31	1.24
A second experiment, greater precautions against capillary flow: —		
Control	2.01	—
Asparagin on the bordering tentacles	3.53	1.52
Asparagin on back of the leaf	3.38	1.37

From these figures it was evident that asparagin is taken up both by the tentacles and by the back of the leaf. By comparing the total area of the tentacle glands with that of the back of the leaf he found that the amount of asparagin absorbed by the tentacles was six times that absorbed by the back of the leaf. Two explanations presented themselves, namely, either that the tentacle heads (glands) are better adapted to this purpose than the leaf epidermis (which would be ruled out by the fact that the epidermis is cuticularized, as above said); or that the absorption by the leaf-back takes place only at certain points, that is, through the papillae, through which it has been observed that entrance can take place (DARWIN, ROSENBERG, KOK). OUDMAN adopted the latter view, and inferred that in nature both the tentacles and the papillae are made use of for the absorption of food, but rather the papillae of the upper side of the leaf than those of the lower. OUDMAN also examined into the question of the influence of various factors (temperature, concentration of the applied materials, the course of absorption in relation to time, the nature of the applied material, the influence of the glands and narcosis).

As would be expected, the higher the temperature within physiological limits, the more rapid the absorption. But whether this is due to the greater rapidity of transportation, or to the greater uptake by the glands, does not appear. The same with increasing concentrations of applied substance (asparagin). In the course of absorption, the rate was greater after the first period (3-6 hrs.), than at first, and falls off again after 9 hours. This, it may be suggested, may be due to the dilution of the applied material by the secretion of the glands during the beginning period, and to equilibrium during the later period.

All substances are not absorbed at equal rates. DARWIN noted that they did not procure aggregation at the same rate. OUDMAN found that caffeine is much more rapidly absorbed than asparagin, although the latter has the smaller molecule. This may be due to the path taken. Caffeine enters the vacuole and is there precipitated, and fresh caffeine must traverse the zone of precipitation. Asparagin probably passes along the path provided by the protoplasm. By following the localization of fluorescence it was shown that fluorescein does this. If the tentacles are removed, leaving the stalks open at the outer end (due to the operation), less material is absorbed, but the difference is not related to the exposed surface, it being much greater for tentacles with the glands removed. The glands therefore offer some hindrance, perhaps because they are quite complex organs, excreting at the same time as absorbing. The presence of an endodermis (the parenchyma bell, FENNER) may have some regulatory effect, but this is not known to be the case. It is worthy of note that narcosis (with ether) inhibits the penetration of asparagin more than caffeine, the former traversing the protoplasm, the latter the vacuole. Caffeine is known to penetrate into the vacuole with great rapidity (BOKORNY, ÅKERMAN, ERNA JANSON) and in any event it has to pass only a thin layer of cytoplasm while asparagin is forced to pass lengthwise the cells within the cytoplasm.

In a later paper by ARISZ and OUDMAN (1937), making use of an improved method of applying the reagents to the tentacles, OUDMAN'S figures describing the rate of absorption of caffeine and of asparagin were confirmed. Caffeine is absorbed in the fashion of a physical diffusion, while asparagin shows a maximum penetration in the second period, and low rates in the first and third periods. Nevertheless more asparagin penetrated into the leaf blade as shown by tests after the removal of the tentacles before analysis. It seems obvious that the conclusion that the paths followed by these substances are different is justified, namely that caffeine travels by way of the vacuoles and asparagin through the cytoplasm, yet in spite of the narrowness of the path through the cytoplasm, the latter moves more readily. This again seems to be due to the taking up of the caffeine by precipitation, a subsequent wave of diffusion having to overstep the zone of precipitation.

An attempt was made by ARISZ and OUDMAN to determine the influence of aggregation upon the transport of asparagin. Aggregation was first induced by suitable reagents (salicin 0.25% and KH_2PO_4 0.1% solutions) with a "remarkable result" that now more asparagin was taken up during the *first* period (contrary to the above mentioned rates). Since asparagin itself causes aggregation, during the first period aggregation takes place, and during the second period, aggregation now having taken place, penetration goes on more rapidly because of this earlier induced aggregation. This behavior, that is, aggregation, has on the other hand no effect on the rate of transport of caffeine.

Reproduction by seeds and by buds ("regeneration"). — While *Dros-*

era reproduces itself through seeds, it is, on the other hand, extraordinarily prolific by means of non-sexual multiplication making use of brood bodies (*D. pygmaea*, GOEBEL) and tubers, of strong axillary buds and especially and above all of budding from the leaves. So frequently and vigorously is the last method used that it would seem to rival that by seed (BEHRE).

The seedlings are very small, the cotyledons either escaping from the seed coat (NITSCHKE, LUBBOCK, GOEBEL) or remaining permanently embedded therein (*D. peltata* and *D. auriculata*, VICKERY 1933). The earlier leaves in all cases are rounded (spatulate), indicating this to be the primitive form for this genus (LEAVITT, 1903, 1909). The leaf blades are provided with a few glands, both marginal (NITSCHKE) and on the disc, 5 on each (*D. rotundifolia*, LEAVITT). The radicle is short, provided with root hairs and fugacious. As the shoot develops, adventitious roots put out from the stem, and, as this dies away with the extension of growth, new adventitious roots are produced above. The root system cannot be said to be abundant (SCHMID).

In some species, *e.g. D. rotundifolia* (NITSCHKE), the axillary buds below the rosette form at once secondary rosettes, similar to the chief rosette, and as the stem decays they are separated, to propagate the plant. In one group (*Ergaleium*) tubers are formed.. These have been described in their static condition by DIELS (1906) and MORRISON (1905), and very fully, from the point of view of development, by VICKERY, from whose paper (1933) the present account is taken. She worked with the two species *D. peltata* and *D. auriculata* which I saw growing about Sydney, N. S. W. When exhumed, the stem below the epigaeal rosette extends downward a matter of a few centimeters, is clothed with scale leaves, and emerges from a small hard rounded tuber clothed with loose membranous envelopes, which when peeled off leave a smooth white tuber. This at the upwardly directed apex bears an "eye", a depressed scaly bud which can develop into a new plant (*16* — 11, 12). The genesis of this structure is seen in the seedling as an axillary shoot bearing normally only scales and growing downwards (*16* — 13). This is a "dropper". Reaching a certain depth the end bends upward, and develops into a corm. While this structure normally elongates upward to form a rosette at the surface of the ground, if more or less exposed to light it may produce at once a partial or complete rosette of normal leaves. Such leaves may arise even from the extending dropper instead of scale leaves. An old tuber, as it becomes exhausted, is usually replaced by another produced laterally on the end of the dropper axis close to it. In Australia especially this form of reproduction is of common occurrence.

The underground tubers, as GOEBEL has pointed out, are doubtless important as storage reserves of food and water which can tide the plant over during a season when the rosette of leaves disappears. Some of the Australian species have strong coloring matter in their tissues, as is evident from the staining of herbarium sheets on drying. It contains two substances, a red one $C_{11}H_8O_5$, and a yellow $C_{11}H_8O_4$, the latter in only small amounts. RENNIE (1893) had shown "that the O_5-compound formed a triacetate and was probably a trihydroxymethylnaphthaquinone, whereas the O_4-compound gave a diacetate and appeared to be a dihydroxymethylnaphthaquinone." This was confirmed by MACBETH, PRICE and WINZOR, who called these substances hydroxydroserone and droserone respectively, determining the constitution of the hydroxydroserone.

Reproduction by means of gemmae. — The case of *D. pygmaea* described by GOEBEL (1908) is one of a small group of species in which a very highly specialized method of non-sexual reproduction takes place, *viz.*, by means of gemmae. *D. pygmaea* is a very small plant, about 1.5 cm. in diameter, and consists of a tight rosette of minute acentrically peltate leaves with fleshy petioles which appear to be the important chlorophyllous parts. On the approach of the resting season there are formed small brood bodies, resembling superficially those of *Marchantia*, clustered in the center of the rosette. The gemma itself is a small, ovate, hard mass of tissue, flattish on the dorsal surface, with a deep depression at the base of the ventral surface, in which develops a minute bud which gives rise to a plant (*16* — 14-17). At the base it is attached to a cylindrical hyaline stalk of some length. At the point of attachment to the brood body it is constricted, and is here fragile, so that the brood body is easily detached. The stalk is marcescent, drying up *in situ*. The brood bodies measure about 0.5 by 0.7 mm. and contain an abundance of food in the form of fat and starch.

I received material of *D. pygmaea* collected by Dr. PAT BROUGH near Sydney, N. S. W., in response to my request, on two occasions, *viz.*, in Nov., 1939 and in April, 1940. In the former no signs of gemmae were to be found; in the latter they were present in various stages of development. In none of the specimens could brood bodies be seen openly exposed, as represented in GOEBEL's drawing (1908). The plants were perhaps still too young. The structure of the gemmae was as GOEBEL described them. He suggested their homology with leaves, but it is to be noticed that there is no suggestion of stipules. They arise in a ring about a dished growing point, and stand in several ranks around it (*16* — 17). Around them young leaves have already begun development, the older of these expanding. The gemmae seem therefore to represent the culmination of a growth period, and they would be set free during the winter season in the natural habitat. Professor BULLER suggests to me that the rosette, with its gemmae at the center, may be regarded as a "splash cup", like those of the bird's nest fungi.

Of much more general occurrence is another method, namely, by budding from the leaf. This is by no means of recent observation. First seen by NAUDIN in 1840, it has been described by numerous others, at least thirteen in number. The historical aspect of this matter has been well summarized by BEHRE (1929).

NAUDIN in *D. intermedia* (1840) and KIRSCHLEGER (1855) in *D. longifolia* had observed the fact of budding from the leaf surfaces, and that the origin was "probably endogenous" (NAUDIN). NITSCHKE's account was sufficiently extended and exact so that BEHRE found little to correct, so far as general morphology was involved. The earliest anatomical study was made by BEIJERINCK (1886), establishing the exogenous origin of the leaf buds. LEAVITT (1899, 1903, 1909) pointed out that the earlier leaves of the leaf buds of even such extreme forms as *D. binata*, have rounded leaves characteristic of *D. rotundifolia*, regarding this a repetition of phylogeny. WINKLER (1903) observed the lack of polarity in the occurrence of leaf buds in *D. capensis*, as in *Torenia* and *Begonia*, and further for the first time showed clearly that the buds arise not from retained embryonal tissue, but by redifferentiation of the leaf tissues.

Exact studies of the mode of origin of the adventitious buds of the leaf surface have been made by BEHRE (1929) and by VICKERY (1933), the latter author independently confirming the former in all essentials. Such leaf buds arise on the blade always from the bases of tentacles, usually on the adaxial surface, but occasionally laterally or even adaxially (BEHRE). They are often visible in a few days if during that time the leaf has been separated from the plant and kept under moist conditions. The cells involved have in all cases arrived at maturity, and there is no sign of the persistence of embryonic tissue. The cells therefore undergo a true rejuvenation passing from an adult, vacuolated condition into one of high protoplasmic content with accompanying changes in the nucleus. They then undergo cell division previous to growth, the earliest divisions, in general, being anticlinal, followed by periclinal (*16 — 7, 8*). Increase in size now overtakes the newly active cells, and a simple outgrowth emerges exogenously, this gradually involving the whole of the base of the tentacle (VICKERY) (*16 — 9, 10*). The vegetation point having been defined at the scene of the earliest divisions, this is now raised by the growth activities of the parenchyma of the upper moiety of the mother leaf in the immediate vicinity, carrying up the tentacle so that this now appears to arise from the bud, rather than the bud from it. Whether the new vascular tissue, that of the bud, becomes articulated with the older, that of the leaf, is not clear. Doubtless this occurs if the leaf does not decay, as observed by VICKERY. If, however, the leaf does decay, this may be questioned. ROBINSON (1909) asserts that no connection occurs. The vegetation point having been established, leaves appear on the bud and a new plantlet becomes established, roots being formed secondarily. The earlier leaves frequently show abnormalities, as I have observed, such as the lateral fusion of contiguous leaf primordia, producing more or less laterally doubled leaves. Nepionic leaves occur. LEAVITT (1903) was able to produce such even from the terminal bud by cutting off the stem below it and removing the leaves as they expanded. *D. intermedia*, which bears only radially symmetrical tentacles normally, under such condition of "malnutrition" bears on nepionic leaves spoon-shaped lateral tentacles like those of *D. rotundifolia*. The frequency and ease with which all this occurs, as already mentioned, makes it probable that this method of reproduction rivals, in its results, reproduction by seed. I have at my hand now a small flower pot which a few months ago carried three small plants sent to me from Ontario by my friend Professor R. B. THOMSON. These at the present writing have died down to winter buds, and I count at least a dozen minute plantlets which I observed to have arisen from old and at length decaying leaves.

BEHRE has further described the origin of plantlets from the leaf stalk. As in the case of the blade, such always occur on the upper surface, with the exception of *D. capensis* and *D. binata*, in which they may occur on the under side. Due to the different anatomical structure, the origin is more various, for the epidermis may not in all cases take active part in the earlier cell divisions. These occur usually in the vicinity of stomata or near the bases of trichomes or of sessile glands, but can arise also on the stalk of the inflorescence or even from the latter itself, as axillary buds however (ROBINSON 1909). Since the flower stalk is radial in structure, the buds arise on all sides, and on account of the closed cylinder of sclerenchyma, they never articulate with the vascular system of the flower stalk. Adventitious buds may arise from roots also, in which case they are, as would be expected, endogenous in origin.

In the case of *D. spathulata* BEHRE found regeneration by bud formation to take place indirectly from callus, previously formed on the cut end of a leaf stalk.

Miss MOULAERT (1937) obtained adventitious buds from leaves, isolated petioles, hypocotyls, stems, scapes, receptacles and sepals. Following the formation of epiphyllous buds, she observed the development of cushions of tissue ("bourrelets") extending from the base of the plantlet toward the petiole. These are of three kinds, those which remain as mere thickenings in the parenchyma above the veins, and which she called "undifferentiated"; those which act as a liaison between the plantlet and a root which has already differentiated adventitiously nearby and in which a vascular connection between shoot and root becomes established; and third, a kind which is formed near the plantlet which does connect with it, an example of "affolement cellulaire."

Another observation made by MOULAERT is the occurrence of absorbing hairs, structures quite like root hairs, which arise from the upper surface of the leaf blade or from the basal part of the stem of the plantlet. They are very abundant and their walls are brown as in the case of root hairs.

Conditions determining the incidence of leaf buds. — It has generally been observed that the production of adventitious buds takes place only under conditions of high humidity, and apparently the higher the better. In order to obtain them the practice is to remove leaves and place them on moist moss, or float them on water, in covered vessels (GRAVES 1897; GROUT 1898; AMES 1899; ROBINSON 1909; LEAVITT 1903; SALISBURY 1915; VICKERY 1933, and others). But the matter seems not to be quite so straight-forward as this. DIXON (1901) found that such buds occur on plants in abundance when they have been allowed to dry out gradually on their bed of *Sphagnum* under a bell-jar, during a period of two months. Confirmatory of this is BEHRE's observation that leaves which had been removed and suspended in a moist chamber, but not so moist as to prevent some wilting, will produce many buds. A too great plenitude of moisture therefore appears to mask a delicate balance of affairs between the leaf and its environment.

As to temperatures, AMES (1899) thought that low temperatures were favorable. VICKERY found a wide favorable range. My own experience favors the idea that *D. rotundifolia* at any rate is active in this way at prevailing cool temperatures.

Wounding, necessary in such plants as *Begonia* (GOEBEL 1903), in itself is of no influence (BEHRE). It has been thought that the removal of the chief shoot (particularly the growing shoot) is a stimulus, that is to say, the disturbance of correlations (BEHRE), which is attained simply by the removal of the leaf. The weight of this point seems not to be great since budding occurs in abundance on leaves still attached, in the case of *D. peltata*, though rather more slowly than when the leaves have been removed (VICKERY). When some of the glands have been injured or removed, the leaf will still produce buds, but only from the bases of uninjured glands (VICKERY), indicating that the gland may contribute something in the form of a growth substance (see COE-LINGH 1929).

Nevertheless BEHRE did find certain correlations. The removal of the growing point always increased the leaf budding, though embedding it in gypsum plaster did not. If the removal of the growing point incited the development of an axillary bud, this itself would inhibit bud formation, though if at the same time the vascular tissue had been suitably cut, before the axillary bud was put into activation, buds were formed. BEHRE further did this experiment: after removal of the growing point the leaves were cut longitudinally in some cases and transversely, but not sufficient for amputation, in others. Only on the outer parts of transversely cut leaves did buds arise, while on plants similarly treated but with the growing point not removed, the result was negative. Yet BEHRE recorded the occurrence of an adventitious bud on a leaf on a plantlet, itself produced adventitiously from a scape, with the growing point active (1929, Fig. 1). These results with *D. rotundifolia* could not be obtained with *D. capensis*. But the facts as they stand support the view that there is a delicate interrelation between the growing point and the inclination to regeneration (GOEBEL) as observed in numerous other plants. Thus we are led to consider what the internal conditions in the plants may be which determine or control such phenomena. Here the food materials may play a rôle or hormones may act as regulators, but this question is too far away from our present purpose, though it may as well be pointed out that BEHRE did experiments in which he reduced leaves to a condition of pronounced hunger in darkness with the deprivation of CO_2 and yet obtained regeneration, from which he concluded that "there is no doubt that regeneration is put into activity by some other stimulus than a surplus of nutrient materials," thus indicating the presence of specific substances, hormones perhaps, which could procure the results.

Polarity. — The fact of polarity is one of so general observation that BEHRE naturally raised the question in regard to *Drosera*, finding but little evidence that it obtains, except to a slight extent in the case of *D. capensis* and *D. filiformis*. Adventitious buds are not related in position to the stronger vascular strands, but are found scattered indifferently, arising usually from the abaxial surfaces of tentacle bases, though they may be found on the side or on the adaxial aspect. If small pieces of the leaf blade are made, more buds arise than would otherwise, and even on the leaf margin where they do not occur except when a narrow band (1 mm. broad) is made by a cut parallel to the margin. They never arise on the lower leaf surface. That buds arise on other parts where there are no tentacles indicated that if it were possible to obtain leaf pieces large enough and free of tentacles, they would arise also from the upper leaf surface proper. The age of the leaf makes little or no difference. It is remarkable in this connection that even young leaves when removed from the plant will continue their development under suitable conditions of light and moisture. If the entire leaf, blade and stalk are removed, buds occur on the blade. If the blade is then removed, buds occur on the outer end of the petiole where there are tentacles, though not always on a tentacle base. If the tentacle bearing part is now removed, a bud may arise at any point, no polarity being shown. If now the conditions are so arranged that the petiole is kept moist and the blade relatively dry, the petiole will regenerate instead of the blade. In *D. capensis*, however, there is a distinct tendency for buds to appear near the leaf apex, this species having long leaves with narrow blade which unrolls during growth. This is true in both old and young leaves, and is regarded by BEHRE as evidence of polarity. This polarity may be easily masked, however, by placing a leaf with its petiole in moist sand and the blade in the air, when buds now appear toward the basal end. WINKLER (1913) had observed a similar behavior in *D. filiformis*, which has long cylindrical leaves. It is curious that the long slender leaves of such species as *D. binata* do not exhibit the same tendency. The readier production of buds near the leaf apex in *D. capensis*, but in the case of young, not older scapes, is conditioned by the young state of the tissues. The readiness of roots to produce buds is well known and made use of for propagating exotic species, but here also they may arise quite indifferently in position, and no polarity can be detected.

Carnivory. — The attention of botanists was first attracted to *Drosera* as an insectivorous plant by the observation that the tentacles are capable of movement. This was made in 1779 (HOOKER 1875), when a physician of Bremen, Dr. A. W. ROTH, noted as follows: "that many leaves were folded together from the apex toward the base, and that all the hairs were bent like a bow, but that there was no apparent change in the leaf stalk." When he opened the leaves he found captured insects, and was driven to compare *Drosera* with *Dionaea*, thinking that it had the same power of motion as the latter. He records an experiment which he did. "With a pair of tweezers I placed an ant upon the middle of the leaf of *Drosera rotundifolia* but so as not to disturb the plant. The ant endeavored to escape, but was held fast by the clammy juice at the points of the hairs, which was drawn out by its feet into fine threads. In some minutes the short hairs on the disc of the leaf began to bend, then the long hairs, and laid themselves on the insect. After a while the leaf began to bend, and in some hours the end of the leaf was so bent inwards as to touch the base. The ant died in fifteen minutes, which was before all the hairs had bent themselves" (*fide* HOOKER, 1875). At about this time (1780) similar observations were made independently by Dr. WHATELY, "an eminent London surgeon" (E. DARWIN: Botanic Garden, pt. 2, p. 24) as reported by his friend Mr. GARDOM, a Derbyshire botanist. "On inspecting some of the contracted leaves we observed a small insect or fly very closely imprisoned therein, which occasioned some astonishment as to how it happened to get into so confined a situation. Afterwards, on Mr. WHATELY's centrically pressing with a pin other leaves which were yet in their natural and expanded form, we observed a remarkable sudden and elastic spring of the leaves, so as to be inverted upwards and, as it were, encircling the pin, which evidently showed the method by which the fly came into its embarrassing position." (WITHERING 1796). It is unfortunate that Dr. WHATELY did not record his observations himself since the rate of movement seems, by a trick of memory, to have been exaggerated by the writer, Mr. GARDOM. As late as 1855 the facts were denied by TRÉCUL, but in 1860 NITSCHKE made a thoroughgoing study, substantiating the earlier observations, to be followed by DARWIN, who had been heralded both by HOOKER and by ASA GRAY, to whom DARWIN had previously communicated his results. Of 267 pages of DARWIN's book on Insectivorous Plants 230 are devoted to an extraordinarily minute examination of the activities of *Drosera*, attesting to his immense patience and determination to uncover every secret possible.

Following DARWIN various trends of investigation can be followed. His observation of the phenomenon of aggregation was the beginning of numerous studies of the cytological changes in glandular and other cells, summarized by HOMÈS. Other trends have been in the field of anatomy, already discusssed, of digestion and nutrition and of the nature of the movements, all to be duly considered.

Mucilage. — While the papillae have not been observed to throw off secretion, unless it be water (KONOPKA), the glands of the tentacles are very conspicuous because each bears a drop of mucilage of high viscidity, clear and glistening, secreted by and supported on it (*13* — 9). The glands are charged with red pigment, so that the shining drops of mucilage lend to the leaf a brilliant red hue. Since these persist as well during the sunshine as otherwhile, we have the name "sundew" common among Europeans. This mucilage, because of its brilliance and reflected color, may be interpreted as a visible lure; it is at all events an effective means of capturing prey of small dimensions, if it ventures to alight on the glands. A delicate fungus-like odor which has been detected by various observers (GEDDES) may be an additional factor of allure. The insect caught is soon (NITSCHKE: 15 min.) wet all over and smothered by the secretion, which upon stimulation is said to flow more freely. DARWIN investigated the secretion activity on the application of various kinds of substances and found that not only does the secretion increase in the gland directly stimulated, but in nearby glands as well, as the result of transmitted stimulus. When the stimulating material is nitrogenous the secretion becomes acid, supplying an important condition for digestion. The amount of secretion which becomes applied to the captured prey is increased not only by a more ample supply of secretion, but by the movement of the tentacles which bring more glands than originally stimulated into contact with the prey. The secretion, DARWIN showed, is possessed of antiseptic properties, and thus inhibits the action of bacteria. In his experiments he found that bits of meat and of albumen placed on the *Drosera* leaf underwent changes, shown to be due to digestion, and were found to be free of bacteria, while similar pieces of material placed on wet moss "swarmed with infusoria."

Chemically the mucilage appears to be a sort of hydrocellulose, but the seat of its secretion is not known. Like other cases of mucilage it may be a product of an alteration of the cell wall, or it may be an exudation from the protoplast. In any event it is permeated by other substances in which its power of digestion rests — enzyme, acid, some antiseptic substances, and latterly WEBER has suspected the presence of ascorbic acid.

SMALL (1939) has advanced the notion that the mucilage is secreted only by the lateral cells of the gland, and not by the apical cells. His evidence is seen in internal reflecting surfaces, stated to be present at the apex and absent from the lateral cells, between them and the mucilage. For my part I fail to find such reflecting surfaces. On the other hand, if a piece of leaf with glands which have been thoroughly wiped off with filter paper is placed in paraffin oil and carefully examined to find glands on which no trace of mucilage is visible, these in the course of one to several hours will show numerous droplets of mucilage oozing away from the surface as well at the apex as on the sides of the gland (*15* — 14). WEBER (1938) by means of sodium oleate has demonstrated to his own satisfaction rods or streams of mucilage radiating from the gland surface at every point. I have not been able to confirm this. If the glands are watched under a binocular dissecting microscope, in the course of a short time it will be noticed that the surface of an opalescent mucilage drop is wrinkled longitudinally, and by this time the surface of the drop has lost its glassy look. It is evident that there is a surface concentration of some substance or substances. As one watches steadily, one sees an occasional explosion on the surface as if some minute particle or droplet had on arriving there from inside immediately spread over it. As the wrinkling progresses the drop becomes pear-shaped, the broad end above the apex. With cessation of evaporation, the drop will assume its oval form. The mucilage is a jelly-like mass. If two glands with drops are approached so that they touch and then are moved apart, the drops will largely separate, adhering by only a slender thread. If a drop is touched with a corner of filter paper at its basal margin and, on adhering, the mucilage is pulled away upwards toward the gland apex, it will tear away and extend asymmetrically from the gland apex. When a drop is pulled out, it at first refuses to leave the gland. Only when there is sufficient adhesion and pull, the whole mass, after a certain amount of stretching, will pull away suddenly. These and similar evidences indicate that the mucilage has a sort of structure. When dry, it shows double refraction, but not when wet (WEBER). It is not so stiff a jelly as that of *Drosophyllum*, which pulls away readily in a mass, but is otherwise similar.

One other apparently trifling observation which I have made may be mentioned here. I have noticed that, over the apical half of a gland there are in the immediate vicinity of the gland surface minute plaques of clear colorless substance not soluble in sulfuric acid, rounded or sometimes angular in shape (*15* — 10). Sulfuric acid dissolves the mucilage, and the cuticle remains intact. They might be delicate flakes of cuticle exfoliated from the remaining cuticle, but of this there is no certainty.

Movements of tentacles and leaf blade. — We must go back to 1782 to find the first record of studies of the modes of behavior of the tentacles and leaf blade. These were carried on by the above mentioned Dr. ROTH, botanist as well as physician. He was stimulated to study *Drosera* by reading ELLIS' letter to LINNAEUS in 1770 announcing the discovery of *Dionaea muscipula;* and in his essay he makes cogent comparisons between these two, the only then known carnivorous plants.

According to ROTH, if an ant be placed on a leaf, the glands respond by bending, first the centrally placed, then, but much more slowly, the glands most distant. Finally the leaf blade bends either transversely, its apex approaching its base, or if the stimulus, say a small fly, has been placed laterally, the side may bend over. The rates of movement depend on external conditions, and are most rapid in warm sultry weather. He remarks that *D. longifolia* reacts more readily than *D. rotundifolia*, and that rain reduces sensitivity.

The next contribution of major importance, by NITSCHKE, did not appear till 1860, eighty years later. Meanwhile, however, several botanists had observed and discussed the matter. Somewhat previous to 1835 A. P. DE CANDOLLE had observed the response of the tentacles. TREVIRANUS (1838) quoted ROTH (1782) but said that he failed to get the results described by him. HAYNE (date about this time, see NITSCHKE 1860) saw the response of the tentacles and that, at length, the leaf blade bent and became spoon-shaped. In 1837 MEYEN reviewed previous observations and while he could confirm the fact that the tentacles as also the leaf blade were bent, he maintained the idea that it was due not to irritability, but to the activity of a struggling insect pulling over the tentacles toward itself. MILDE (1852), however, put this right by experiment. He placed small flies on the leaf, and observed in 5 min. the outer tentacles bending inwards. Next day the whole leaf was bent, and in 5 days again unrolled. A useful skeptic appeared in 1855 in the person of TRÉCUL, who thought that the insects were caught by young leaves which then retained their youth position. Came then NITSCHKE (1860), who was the first to attack the problem in a sustained way and with a critical attitude. His first argument was directed against TRÉCUL, and he established the general correctness of ROTH's observations. He believed that when a stimulus has been applied at some point by the application of an insect, the surrounding tentacles bend their heads *directly* toward this point, whether the position of the stimulating object is central or lateral. The marginal tentacles move, he says, always in the "most direct" path toward the point of stimulation. On this point the reader is referred to the work of BEHRE beyond. NITSCHKE regarded the behavior as an expression of true irritability, and that MEYEN's view that the action of the tentacles is purely passive is wrong for a number of reasons, especially cogent being the fact that young leaves do not secrete mucilage, and that neither they nor aged leaves are sensitive. First when the leaves are widely open and rich in secretion is this the case; even dead insects procure movements, if indeed somewhat less vigorous ones. He found, however, no response to simple mechanical stimulation, but this was found later to be wrong. Equally so his view that a stimulating body attached to the back of a leaf induced responses whereby the tentacles turned backward to embrace the body quite as well as forward. He found that the leaf may repeat the performance after recovery on renewal of secretion, and further that the effect of a given stimulus depends on the distance it has to travel. The movements can take place under water and in response to solid bodies and acids in weak solution. The rate of response is affected by temperature but not by light. It is then chiefly to NITSCHKE and to DARWIN that we owe many original observations which furnish a picture of the direction and rapidity of the movements of the leaf and tentacles. The general facts first and most readily observed are the following. If a suitable stimulus is received by any group of leaf tentacles, say near the middle of the leaf, or on or near the "disc" in the case of *D. rotundifolia*, in the course of a few minutes a bending of the nearby tentacles is to be observed until, the stimulus evidently travelling radially, it reaches even the extreme marginal tentacles which then bend over. If the stimulus is sufficient even the leaf blade responds in like manner. GOEBEL figures a leaf of *D. intermedia* which had completely folded over to embrace the body of a large fly which had been caught. *D. capensis* was found to be particularly good at this. I placed a single *Drosophila* flylet on a leaf and in the course of time the marginal tentacles, as well of course as those nearby, had responded. Finally the whole apex of the leaf bent over ($13 - 8$). With regard to the leaf blade not all the species of *Drosera* behave in this way. GOEBEL observed that *D. binata* does not, nor does *D. dichotoma*, and probably others. From such observations it is evident that the stimulus received by a tentacle travels to its base and radially from there to neighboring tentacles, which then respond. A casual glance at a leaf displaying these responses, one in which the tentacles are bent over towards the middle of the disc (speaking of *D. rotundifolia*) suggests that the normal movement of the tentacles is along radial lines. The dorsiventral flatness of the tentacles would seem to condition them to move thus. But NITSCHKE saw that the matter is not so simple. He said that the tentacles receiving the stimulus bend over in the direction of the point *at which the stimulus was received*, irrespective of its position, so that, if a fly is caught at some eccentric point, the tentacles affected bend over toward this point and not toward the center of the disc. Apparently the direction of movement of the stimulus determined the appropriate direction of movement of the tentacle. There is an apparent exception to be noted. DARWIN found that when a marginal tentacle is stimulated, it bends over, but no response is called forth in the neighboring marginal tentacles. Only when the marginal tentacle originally stimulated brings its glands with its stimulating material into contact with the glands of the disc, is a stimulus provided by the latter which now calls forth a response of the marginal tentacles hitherto not affected.

The duration of the response depends on the nature of the stimulus. Here I quote from DARWIN (p. 19) "The central glands of a leaf were irritated with a small camel's hair brush, and in 70 minutes several of the outer tentacles were inflected; in 5 hours all the sub-marginal tentacles were fully inflected; next morning after an interval of 22 hours they were fully expanded. . . . . . I then put a dead fly in the center of (a) leaf, and next morning it was closely clasped; five days after the leaf reëxpanded and the tentacles, with their glands surrounded by secretion, were ready to act again."

A given stimulus acting somewhere on one side of the leaf will affect the marginal tentacles on that side sooner than those of the other side further away; or indeed, only one side of the leaf may be called into action. In the case of a cup-shaped peltate leaf (*D. gigantea*) I have observed that the total result of such movements is to bring the prey into the depths of the cup, where, in the course of time, only the chitinous remains of the captured insects are to be found. This result is perhaps contributed to by the surface tension of the drop of secretion which more or less fills the cup.

It was thought by NITSCHKE that even the back of the leaf could accept stimuli and transmit them to the tentacles, but DARWIN was unable to cause any response by stimulating the leaf blade proper, on the front or the back. In order to locate the sensitive or sense perceptive points, DARWIN removed the gland from a tentacle, whereupon the latter made a brief response by slightly bending but soon regained its erstwhile posture. When stimulus was applied to the cut tentacle, no response followed. But if now the disc tentacles were stimulated, the amputated tentacle responded, as if the head were not missing. The stalk of a tentacle, no more than the leaf or petiole, can receive a stimulus. In any event, the marginal tentacles are not so sensitive as the rest, nor are they affected by rain drops. SMALL (1939) denies this. That the disc tentacles are more sensitive may appear to be the case because the stalks of these are very short, and the tentacles are closer together so that a given stimulus does not have to travel so far to elicit response. And although the stimulus travels radially from a point of stimulation, DARWIN found that it travels more readily longitudinally than transversely across the leaf blade. The stimulus may travel quite across the blade so that when it is applied to the tentacles on one margin, those of the opposite may respond; but in spite of repetition of the stimulus, the opposite tentacles will open again, from which DARWIN argued that the "motor discharge must be more powerful at first then afterward." It was asked by DARWIN whether the motor impulse travels through the vascular tissue, but this turned out not to be the case, certainly "not exclusively," for the tentacles of a group surrounding the point of stimulus will respond all at a uniform rate notwithstanding the fact that the vascular connections are very unequal in length; indeed the course of the vascular tissues in the leaf as a whole does not permit the view in question when the uniformity of response of the tentacles is considered.

The intensity of the stimulus necessary to procure response was a matter of much concern to DARWIN. He endeavored to get some measure of intensity by weighing small pieces of hair, etc., which would prove efficient. The following quotation embodies an expression of his reflections on this " . . . . . it is an extraordinary fact that a little bit of soft thread 1/50 of an inch in length and weighing 1/8197 of a grain, or of a human hair 8/1000 of an inch in length and weighing only 1/78740 of a grain (.000822 milligram) or particles of precipitated chalk, after resting for a short time on a gland, should induce some change in its cells, exciting them to transmit a motor impulse throughout the whole length of the pedicel, consisting of about 20 cells, to near its base, causing this part to bend, and the tentacle to sweep through an angle of above 80 degrees".

It was generally conceded by both NITSCHKE and DARWIN that dead bodies do not provoke so much response as living and therefore moving bodies. This was explained by PFEFFER by pointing out that mere constant contact does not produce response, but that there must be both direct contact with the gland and friction on its surface. The mucilaginous drop can prevent direct contact as in the case of rain or quicksilver (which PFEFFER tried) or even particles suspended in it unless by their weight they fall against the sensitive surface. That the minute particles of hair used by DARWIN should produce the results observed may be understood better when, as PFEFFER showed, vibration of the table or floor causes movements of such particles on the surface of the gland sufficient to stimulate it.

In addition to non-living substances, DARWIN tested the reactions of the tentacles to a large variety of organic materials with the purpose of determining what digestive juice or juices are secreted by the leaves of *Drosera*. His contribution to the problem of digestion will more suitably be considered under the appropriate caption beyond. Here it will be mentioned that he seemed to regard the movements of the tentacles and the length of time they remain inflected as evidence of the nutritional value to the plant of the material exposed to them. But he himself records a various behavior of the tentacles in this regard. He says in conclusion "The substances which are digested by *Drosera* act on the leaves very differently. Some cause much more energetic and rapid inflection of the tentacles and keep them inflected for a much longer time, than do others. We are thus led to believe that the former are more nutritious than the latter . . . . . " This generalization can hardly hold. ROBINSON found that pure creatin was digested but caused no bending of the tentacles. As SCHMID points out, DARWIN's work, rightly or wrongly, led emphasis to be too strongly placed on the *Drosera mechanism* being an adaptation for the obtaining of protein nutrition. While it is true that, to quote DARWIN again, " . . . . . inorganic substances, or such substances as are not attacked by the secretion, act much less quickly and efficiently than organic substances yielding soluble matter which is absorbed" it is also true that some nitrogenous bodies equally do not, and therefore it is impossible to formulate a rule. DARWIN himself records the failure of urea to procure movements. What explanation serves when HCl, boric acid, malic acid and camphor stimulate to movement when Ca, Mg and K salts generally do not? And ammonium phosphate was found more energetic than other ammonium salts though containing less nitrogen. But because potassium phosphate is taken up DARWIN argued a need for phosphorus. SCHMID, considering this phase of the insectivory problem, himself tested the action of pure salts and concluded that the movements of tentacles alone cannot lead to any real index of the value of insectivory from the nutritional-ecological point of view.

As little indeed may one thus argue as about the nutritional value of food taken by man from the action of the salivary glands, adds SCHMID. It seems proper to conclude that the reactions of the tentacles are general rather than specific. The length of time they remain inflected, however, seems, in the absence of injury (several times noted by DARWIN) to be generally correlated with their opportunity for absorption.

Mechanism of tentacle movement. — NITSCHKE pointed out that although the tentacles can bend, there are no special motile organs, such as occur *e.g.* in *Mimosa*. What then is the nature of the bending movements of the tentacle? Though DARWIN obtained no light on this question, it was answered by BATALIN (1877). He made spaced marks on the sides of the tentacle, and found that after a movement was completed, the distances had increased. When the recovery is complete, these distances are maintained, showing that the bending is a growth phenomenon. This was shown true also of the leaf blade. H. D. HOOKER (1916) investigated the matter more thoroughly. In making

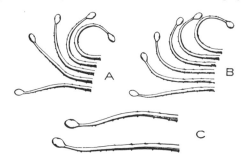

FIG. 3. — *Drosera rotundifolia.* — A, Side views of a tentacle in process of bending, beginning with the bottom figure; B, same in process of unbending, beginning with the top figure; C, Side views of the same tentacle before and at close of the reaction (after HOOKER).

his measurements of the tentacles during bending he made use of natural marks supplied by the minute sessile glands to be found on the surface of the tentacle stalk. By means of these measurements and of camera lucida drawings, he got a detailed record of changes in dimensions during bending and recovery. A set of his drawings are here reproduced (TEXT FIG. 3). HOOKER found, as did BATALIN, that the movement, whether bending or unbending, is a growth phenomenon. During bending acceleration of growth begins near the base along the back (the convex surface) of the tentacle, and moves upward during the bending phase, so that the tentacle end moves through an angle of 215 to 270 degrees, beginning the movement within 1.5 minutes, completing it in a few hours, or sometimes in as short a time as 17 min. 30 sec. (DARWIN). The unbending movement results from increased growth on the now concave side, and takes place at once if the stimulus was a brief one, or is delayed as when the tentacles have closed over prey. Here also growth begins near the base and moves upward toward the gland. During neither phase is the growth necessarily limited to one side, but the difference of rate is obvious and produces the same result. Since the movement of the tentacle is a matter of growth, and since there is a limit of total growth, the number of times bending may be repeated is limited. DARWIN found the number is three, and this was confirmed by HOOKER. Though the two movements constitute practically a continuous reaction, at least when a single brief stimulus is originally applied, the unbending reaction follows a stimulus inherent in the internal conditions (such as tissue tensions) set up during bending, and is tropic (autotropic, autonomous, BEHRE) in nature. Since the entire armament of tentacles may not be used in any one grasping of prey, the leaf as a whole may react more than three times, even though a single tentacle cannot. The short radially structured tentacles of the disc do not react by bending to stimuli applied directly to the glands, but only to stimuli received through the glands of other tentacles. HOOKER regards the response as tropic while the original response of the lateral tentacles is evidently nastic, though the unbending response is tropic. Both DARWIN and NITSCHKE recorded their belief that marginal tentacles when stimulated indirectly bend toward the point of stimulation. HOOKER takes exception to this, saying that he was unable to get evidence of it, and thinks that they normally bend toward the middle of the disc, that is, nastically.

Exceptions to this he thought "to be purely accidental." Nonetheless, HOOKER was sufficiently impressed with his observations to state that "most of the marginal tentacles which reacted to the conducted impulse" from the discal tentacles "in bending toward the center of the leaf bent likewise in the direction of the source of excitement." The bending of the discal tentacles is, however, always toward the point of original stimulation, and cannot be stimulated directly. The response is tropic, but "in all probability" the movements "are likewise the result of differential growth on opposite sides" of the tentacle base. The method used was not applicable to the determination of this fact.

BEHRE (1929) admitted that HOOKER'S conclusions were nearly right, but was evidently impressed by the discrepancies admitted by him. He, therefore, attacked the problem at this point, and analysed the movement of the tentacles more rigorously, controlling his observation by means of a horizontal measuring microscope with a scale in the field. He recorded accurately the movements of tentacles relative to each other and to the position of the source of stimulation, and made them available to the reader by means of maps showing the paths of movements.

In the case of *D. rotundifolia* he found that, according to their behavior the tentacles can be divided into three groups, namely, (a) marginal, the outermost standing exactly on, or very near to the leaf margin; (b) an outer zone of discal tentacles of one to three rows, called by him the "surface outer tentacles"; and (c) the discal tentacles within (b), or "central tentacles". With some slight differences due to the posture of the tentacles, the same holds for other species investigated (*D. binata, intermedia, capensis, spathulata*). His observations yielded the following results, and here it may be injected that he used in most cases small and uniformly sized objects for stimulation, *viz.*, the eggs of the wood-louse.

The responses of the strictly marginal ("outer marginal") tentacles are somewhat slower than those standing just within the margin ("inner marginal"). Their reaction to a direct stimulus (that is, one applied to the glands of these tentacles) is, however, always strictly nastic; their function is to bring the prey into contact with the discal glands. The sensitivity and quickness of reaction are surprising. The reaction may begin in 10 seconds, and was seen to make a complete excursion of 180 degrees in 20 seconds, the movement being visible to the naked eye. This was a maximum, however. It must be clear that the direction of movement was in a single plane normal to the leaf margin. Prompt and rapid as their response to direct stimulus is, they respond to indirect stimulus, derived from stimulated discal tentacles, only slowly and weakly. At best, a reaction may be detected in 10 minutes, but the total excursion is short. Only when the leaf is heavily fed, especially with living prey, do the marginal tentacles indirectly stimulated actually reach the prey. If the stimulus is derived from a small insect, the excursions of the marginal tentacles are incomplete, are soon reversed and can be of no use to the plant, though, since complete bendings can occur only three times at best, the meagreness of response may be regarded as an economy of effort. Full expenditure of effort is made only when the prey falls on the marginal tentacles, when by bending fully they bring it into contact with the inner tentacles thus exposing it to much greater digestive surface. The movements are at first nastic. Since in *D. rotundifolia* the orbicular form of the leaf results in nastic and tropistic reactions acting in the same direction, the observer is and has been naturally deceived. Only when the reactions are observed in such leaves as those of *D. intermedia* and *D. binata* is it seen clearly that, while the reaction of the marginal tentacles to direct stimulation is at first nastic, in the course of the excursion the direction of movement may be modified by tropistic reactions, especially clear in *D. binata*, and in this is the account of HOOKER amplified.

In the case of the central or discal tentacles, there is no response to direct stimulus, that is, stimulating material placed on a single tentacle produces no movement in that tentacle. But the stimulus is quickly transmitted to nearby tentacles and these then bend toward the point of stimulation, that is tropistically. The rate of reaction is here much more dependent on temperature — from an hour to 20 or so, according to circumstances.

Between the central disc tentacles and the marginal lies a narrow zone of outer surface tentacles, in size grading between them, being in such species as *D. binata* as long as the marginal tentacles, or longer. Their reactions are more complicated than those of the tentacles of the other two zones, since they combine properties of both. They react nastically to direct stimulus and as rapidly as the marginal tentacles, and this character distinguishes them at once from the central disc tentacles. Toward indirect stimulus their reactions are both nastic and tropistic, and the resulting excursions are rapid and more extended than those of the marginal tentacles to indirect stimulus, and result in bringing the glands into contact with the prey. The tropistic movement is slower. The case of *D. binata* well illustrates the behavior, because of the cylindrical form of the leaf. A small fragment of meat was placed on an outer surface tentacle. This responded at first quickly, and in the course of five hours brought the prey into contact with the discal tentacles. In two hours the nearby outer surface tentacles began their excursions which were at first (for four and a half hours) nastic. The next morning it was evident that tropistic movements had set in, since by then all the glands were in contact with the prey. When, however, in this species the stimulus is applied to the discal tentacles, the reactions of the outer surface tentacles are entirely, or very nearly entirely, tropistic. The case of *D. capensis* was of peculiar interest, since in this species stimulus of an outer tentacle procured tropistic reactions of its neighbors so that their glands would have travelled the shortest way to the place where the prey was deposited on the discal tentacles (the completion of the movement was not observed by BEHRE) and not as in *D. binata*, at first nastically (carrying the glands away from a direct path) and later tropistically, correcting the error.

BEHRE, having pointed out such minor differences in behavior as between different species, remarks that, since the nastic and tropic responses are influenced differently by different temperatures, as when the nastic responses are arrested by a high temperature while the tropistic are stimulated, such differences may account in part at least for various behaviors. By and large, however, the various species act in the same way.

Aggregation. — DARWIN observed that, following stimulation, the contents of the gland cells first and later of those of the pedicel, display changes in appearance due to a rearrangement of the protoplasm and vacuole which he termed "aggregation." The total effect is sufficient to be seen by the naked eye, if pigment is present, in the change of color of the gland. In this way it is possible to follow the direction, if not the extent of the movement of a stimulus. While DARWIN's description of these changes was incorrect, they stimulated a great amount of work directed toward their elucidation. Those who have seen at Down House the tools DARWIN worked with may well wonder at the extent and acuteness of observation which characterize his work in this particular. Taken with the general state of the knowledge of the cell in his day, the observations of DARWIN are the more surprising.

DARWIN gives his observations as follows: "If ..... tentacles that have never been excited or become inflected be examined, the cells forming the pedicels are seen to be filled with a homogeneous purple fluid. The walls are lined by a layer of protoplasm ..... ". "If a tentacle is examined some hours after a gland has been excited by repeated touches, or by an organic or inorganic particle placed on it, or by the absorption of certain fluids, it presents a wholly changed appearance. The cells, instead of being filled with a homogeneous purple fluid, now contain variously shaped masses of purple matter suspended in a colorless fluid ..... By whatever cause the process may have been excited, it commences with the glands, and then travels down the tentacles. ..... The little masses of aggregated matter are of the most diversified shapes, often spherical or oval, sometimes much elongated, or quite irregular with thread- or necklace-like or club-formed projections. .... they consist of thick, apparently viscid matter .... " " .... these little masses incessantly change their form ..... resembling the movements of Amoebæ, or white blood corpuscles." " We may therefore conclude that they consist of protoplasm."

FRANCIS DARWIN in 1876 concurred with his father, but later in 1888 reversed his position, pointing out that DARWIN was in error in thinking that the aggregated masses consisted merely of protoplasm, but that they are concentrations or precipitations of the cell sap, and that their amoeboid movements are the result of streaming protoplasm which moulds the passive masses into a variety of forms" (DARWIN, 2d. ed. 1875, note by FRANCIS DARWIN, p. 34) in agreement with PFEFFER's views as pointed out in his *Osmotische Untersuchungen.* FRANCIS DARWIN's *volte face* resulted from the publication of views by SCHIMPER, by GARDINER, and by DE VRIES. These we presently examine. SCHIMPER made his studies while in the U. S. A. where he was evidently impressed with his opportunities. He examined *Sarracenia purpurea, Drosera intermedia* and *Utricularia cornuta.*

Examining the epidermal and subepidermal cells of the tissues of the lower part of the pitcher of *Sarracenia,* when such cells had been exposed to nutrient substances, he observed that they showed, in contrast to those not fed, the following behavior. The single vacuole containing tannin was found to be now broken up into two or more, becoming, because of the concentration of their tannin solution, more highly refringent. These vacuoles were found not to be suspended in the cell sap, but themselves represented the whole of the sap, and were found now to be suspended in a swollen protoplasm. " That under the· influence of certain substances the protoplasm attains a greater capacity for swelling seems probably to be of direct significance for nutrition."

Recalling DARWIN's statement that the aggregations are suspended in the cell sap, SCHIMPER examined *Drosera intermedia* tentacles. Here he found, as in *Sarracenia,* that the protoplasm is swollen, the tannin bearing vacuoles contracted. " By plasmolysis (with NaCl) it is seen with the greatest clearness that here also that which appears to be the cell sap is really only the much swollen protoplasm. After extraction with alcohol, the protoplasm remains as a beautiful framework of meshes."

GARDINER in 1886, apparently without having seen SCHIMPER's paper, described his own observations thus. " The chief phenomena induced in the stalk cells" ..... " most marked when stimulated by food" ..... " are that the protoplasmic utricle swells up and encroaches on its own vacuole, that granules appear in the protoplasm and that the movement of rotation increases in vigor." The cell becomes less turgid. " The protoplasm in swelling abstracts water from its own vacuole and in so doing leaves the sap in a more concentrated condition." Going on to describe the protoplasmic activity of movement he says that the reduced vacuole becomes fragmented, the resulting small vacuoles become droplets, pear-shaped bodies and long string-like processes (*17 — 1*), just as described by DARWIN.

DE VRIES' studies were most illuminating. He examined cells of the tentacle stalk. He says that the whole process of aggregation falls into two periods. In the earlier period there is a pronounced increase in the rate of cyclosis of the protoplasm, accompanied by growing complexity of the currents ("differentiation"). Many accounts ignore this, though GARDINER mentioned it. During the second period there is a breaking up of the vacuole into a varying number of smaller ones, the more obvious phase usually seen. These periods are not sharply defined, the first passing over gradually into the second.

The rapidly circulating protoplasm, with its breaking up into new streams, furnishes a mechanism for subdividing the originally single vacuole which in the meantime loses some of its sap. This escapes through the wall of the vacuole (the "tonoplast") into the space between this and the protoplasm. This escaped sap retains its osmotic pressure, since tentacles in aggregation are as rigid as otherwise. Left behind, however, are the pigment, albuminoids and tannin which can be precipitated within the resulting vacuoles. The vacuoles, however, are now less rigid and more readily broken up by the cutting streams of protoplasm. There result eventually many lesser vacuoles as droplets of various shapes, especially slender tubular ones, constantly stirred up by the moving protoplasm, and thus constantly changing positions. DE VRIES attempts an interpretation of these changes by suggesting that the heightened circulation of protoplasm may serve to facilitate the movements of nutritive materials absorbed by the glands; that the contraction of the vacuoles is connected with the partition of substances (acids, enzymes).

Here it should be pointed out that the process of aggregation, thought to be observed in stimulated tentacles, is quite independent of the process of inflexion of the tentacles, as DARWIN pointed out. I myself have observed that the bending of the tentacles occurs in a region where no aggregation had taken place. As pointed out by JOST (BENECKE–JOST, 1924) aggregation takes place in a primarily stimulated tentacle downwards from cell to cell, but also later in those tentacles secondarily stimulated, but does not in these precede the bending movement, and moreover proceeds not from the base upwards but from the gland downward. Aggregation can, therefore, have no relation to the transmission of stimulus, likely enough as it first seemed.

I have mentioned above that, on the escape of sap from the vacuoles, there is left behind a variety of substances, pigment, tannin, albumin, which can be precipitated by various chemical agents (alkaloids, weak bases) and then appear as minute droplets or granulations which coalesce into larger ones, and which in the case of tannin and albumin can become brittle masses. Such precipitation was confused by DARWIN with true aggregation. GARDINER called this "passive aggregation," GOEBEL "granulation." GLAUER (1887) (fide F. DARWIN in DARWIN, 1875) and BOKORNY (1889) extended the distinction, the latter recognizing other kinds of aggregation to the number of four, viz.: the contraction of the entire protoplasmic utricle, contraction and division of the vacuoles ("true aggregation"), the precipitation of albumin in the vacuoles and fourth, in the protoplasm. The albumin in question has been called "active albumin" by O.

LOEW and BOKORNY, so designated by them because of its imputed peculiar properties which place it in a category of substances which may be regarded as bridging the gap between the non-living and the living parts of the cell. These peculiarities were recited by ERNA JANSON, who, working in LOEW's laboratory, examined aggregation from the point of view thus indicated. Her paper (1920) cannot be said to indicate a full apprehension of the observations of those workers (GARDINER, DE VRIES, ÅKERMAN, especially the last two named) who had described in much detail the curious and complicated happenings which take place during aggregation in the Darwinian sense. Before resuming JANSON's work, it would profit us to look first at that of ÅKERMAN, who while differing from DE VRIES in the interpretation of certain details, nevertheless agrees with him about the general trend of affairs. ÅKERMAN used pepsin as the stimulating substance which, when applied to the gland, quickly causes movement responses and aggregation. The course of events he described as follows:

At first the peripheral protoplasm is thin, and displays rotation (cyclosis). This movement, as threads and ultimately plates of protoplasm arise, becomes more complicated, and changes into a true circulation, becoming more and more active. Meanwhile the peripheral layer of protoplasm thickens, even to twice the original thickness. Folds of protoplasm, impinging on the vacuole, become strands which become thicker and more and more extensive till they cut into the vacuole and ultimately break it up into numerous small ones. The change in volume of the protoplasm is accompanied by a reduction in volume of the vacuoles, the substances in solution therein (the red pigment, tannin, etc.) becoming more concentrated till the specific gravity of the two are reversed, that of the sap increasing, as shown by centrifuging. At length the vacuoles display remarkable activity. They elongate, become vermiform and move, creeping about each other in a most dramatic fashion. In my own experience it has been found difficult to make drawings of them as the movements, apparently slow, are fast enough to defy adequate representation of the proceedings. ÅKERMAN affords a fair idea of the condition regarded for the moment as static in his Fig. 3, but even this does not do the matter justice. But the photographic reproduction of three exposures of a single cell two and fifteen minutes apart and two two minutes apart, are truly illuminating (17 — 1). We may here recall DE VRIES' own figures, not to be ignored. Such activity can be sustained for hours, even days. At last a reversal of changes sets in and proceeds till at length the primary condition is attained. During the forward progression SCHIMPER thought to have observed the formation of new vacuoles, new evidently as they did not contain red pigment; DE VRIES also. These ÅKERMAN did not see. He also supports GARDINER, SCHIMPER, GOEBEL in his view that there is no separation and independence of the vacuole walls ("tonoplast" of DE VRIES) from the peripheral protoplasm, and no accumulation of water between them. Indeed, he goes so far as to state it as his considered opinion that the important and characteristic feature of aggregation is the swelling of the protoplasm, the vacuolar phenomena being resultant and secondary. In support of this view ÅKERMAN again tested a long series of substances and found that some (albumin, pepsin, peptone, phosphoric acid, ethyl alcohol) cause swelling of the protoplasm and the accompanying appearances of aggregation, while others (basic substances such as ammonia, carbonates of ammonia, sodium or potassium, alkaloids), do not cause protoplasmic swelling, but only a precipitation in the vacuole with unchanged volume. Further, that these latter substances can inhibit the action of the former.

The difference between true aggregation and " granulation" in which merely precipitation occurs within the vacuole, is emphasized by the results of plasmolytic studies. ÅKERMAN found that during aggregation there is an increase in turgor pressure of about 5 atm. in the cells involved. DE VRIES, it is true, found no changes while GARDINER believed that they " lose their turgidity" (he made no experiments to show this). As COELINGH points out, the difference in the use of the terms turgidity and turgor pressure (dependent on the concentration of the sap) is to be noted. In the case of cells in which precipitation occurred, there is no change.

From experiments to determine if there is an influence of the gland on aggregation, ÅKERMAN found that in pieces of tentacle stalk from which (*a*) the gland with one-third and (*b*) with two-thirds of the stalk removed, no aggregation at all could be procured in the remaining portion of the tentacle. If only the gland and one-third of the stalk had been removed, a weak or no aggregation occurred, according to the test substance used. ÅKERMAN tried eight agents.

That injury is not involved is shown by the fact that aggregation intervenes in small pieces of the upper region of the tentacle when pepsin or meat extract are applied.

These results in ÅKERMAN's opinion pointed to the presence of a substance, resident or formed in the gland and in the more apical stalk cells, which can on suitable stimulation procure aggregation. It looks therefore, as if two substances are required to cause aggregation, one inherent and one which must be supplied from the outside as a stimulant. As DARWIN recorded, however, aggregation occurs when the tentacles are stimulated by mechanical means only. If a second substance is required, this must mean that the second substance is also formed in the gland when so stimulated (*see beyond*).

Miss COELINGH, working at Utrecht, where the study of growth substances was then being actively prosecuted, repeated some of ÅKERMAN's work, supporting his conclusion that during the progress of aggregation there is an increase in the osmotic value of the sap, but that this also takes place when the tentacles are successfully stimulated by mechanical means. Having also verified ÅKERMAN's observation on the effect of the gland on aggregation in the stalk (finding slight but not significant differences) COELINGH proceeded to test the value of his theory of an aggregation-promoting substance. To this end she made extracts of glands in distilled water. Such extracts may be preserved dry, and can then withstand heating to 100° C. In order to determine the virtue of gland-extract, COELINGH proceeded to obtain "empty" pieces of tentacle stalk, that is, such as would not show aggregation when a "stimulating" agent (beef extract) was applied. Such were obtained of four kinds: (*1*) small strips of leaf blade with mere stumps of tentacles, (2) such pieces, or short pieces of tentacle stalk placed for some time in a slightly hypotonic solution of cane sugar, remaining a few days to allow the putative substance to escape by diffusion; (3) young, still unfolded leaf tentacles, the glands being removed and (4) a young but fully unfolded leaf plunged into ethyl alcohol (96%) for 4–6 seconds. The alcohol because of the relative penetrability of the cuticles could not penetrate into the leaf beyond the glands so that living tentacles with dead glands were provided. Various difficulties involved need not be recited here.

On testing the responses of thus prepared material to a " stimulating" substance in the presence and absence of gland-extract, it was found that, with few exceptions, aggregation did not occur in the presence of either alone, but only when both were presented together. As control the author used extracts of *Drosera* leafstalks, with negative results.

COELINGH also suspected that the aggregation-promoting substance may occur also in the capital cells of other glandular structures of *Drosera* since by the use of a stimulant (such as pepsin) she found it possible to get aggregation in stalk cells of sessile and other glandular trichomes and in leaf blade cells, even on the lower surface opposite the bases of tentacles. On the other hand she could never obtain aggregation in other parts of the plant where tentacles do not occur: petals, sepals, ovary-wall, adventitious roots, young stipules.

It was found also that there are substances (saliva, diastase, trypsin) which act as the theoretical aggregation-promoting substance, and in a search for a possible clue as to its nature, some such substances were tested on " empty" tissues. Saliva added to pepsin acts positively, even after heating to exclude enzymes, but saliva also acts alone, as I have found. The composition of saliva being known, the various components were tried and only the phosphates were active. For example a 0.1% solution of Na_2HPO_4 was active and saliva diluted to this concentration of that salt was also. Aggregation follows on the use of pepsin plus growth-substance of Indian corn on "empty" pieces of tentacle, while pepsin or meat-extract alone have no effect. Among organic N-substances, aspartic acid, asparagin and leucine have the greatest action; creatin, alanine and urea are doubtful or negative; guanine and ethylurethane no effect whatever. Substances which lower surface tension (saponin, amylalcohol) have no effect. The presence of oxygen, as DARWIN had found, is necessary. Since the swelling of protoplasm is considered characteristic of aggregation, perhaps the chief one (SCHIMPER), it was thought that the pH of the aggregating agents would betray an influence, but on experimentation only negative results were obtained.

COELINGH in a discussion of all the facts observed fully agrees with ÅKERMAN, that two substances are needed to procure aggregation: 1) one with property A, which does not cause aggregation, but which conditions cells to aggregate; and 2) one with B, which provides a stimulus (pepsin, etc.) to aggregation. But it may not be assumed that all substances have only one of these properties A and B but not both, for some may have both in various degrees of efficiency. This is indicated in the behavior of various substances. It seems sure, however, that some substances have only the property B, such as meat extract, pepsin, peptone Witte, none of which can procure aggregation in empty cells, that is cells devoid of A. But substances having A only seem not to occur. On the other hand some substances can cause aggregation in both normal and "empty" cells, e.g., saliva, gland extract, etc., and these, therefore, seem to have both properties A and B. If this were true, we would be helped in understanding why aggregation can be procured by merely mechanical stimulation by assuming that a substance containing AB is secreted only on stimulation, then to diffuse into the stalk cells. To this it can be objected that the cells of tentacle stalks with the glands removed can respond to pepsin alone, indicating that B is already present in the stalk cells.

But more, for it appears that tentacles are to be found in a state of aggregation when they have never been stimulated in any way so far as this can be ruled out by conditions of culture, as HOMÈS subsequently showed. The hypothetical substance we are looking for must therefore inhere and have both properties A and B. Since, if this is to be assumed to be the case, aggregation may not be present till stimulation occurs, it must be argued that stimulation merely activates B.

Thus Miss COELINGH brings her argument into a purely theoretical atmosphere which she, herself, finds hard to breathe, and says that speculation without further experimentation affords no sure guidance. But it must be evident that the problem of aggregation is most intriguing.

To the previously cited results of SCHIMPER, GARDINER, DE VRIES, ÅKERMAN, in which they clearly distinguished between true aggregation and GOEBEL's granulation, ERNA JANSON took a diametrically opposite position, stating that all aggregation is due to the precipitation of materials in solution in the cell sap. Neither the tonoplast (DE VRIES) nor the swelling of the protoplasm have any part in the process. It does not appear in her paper, however, that she has taken sufficient cognisance of that condition called by DE VRIES "true" aggregation. Her figures, which are very crude, give no hint that she brought this into her field of consideration. She showed, what BOKORNY also had shown at length, that certain reagents (alkaloids, other weak bases) procure precipitations in the vacuoles. Beyond this she failed to show that "true aggregation" could thus be achieved. Nor did BOKORNY's figure of aggregation in *Drosera* show more. Considered as contributions to the nature of the vacuolar contents, these papers have value. As furnishing enlightenment on the nature of that kind of aggregation which follows on mechanical stimulation and on feeding with pepsin, peptone, etc. (though in these was suspected the presence of ammonia), the work of JANSON is very limited. For it is quite certain, and I speak now from my own observations, that during true aggregation there is no slightest evidence of precipitation from beginning to end.

Following the studies of DARWIN and GARDINER on aggregation a new phase of the subject was entered upon, in which the cytological changes taking place within the cells of the gland especially were examined. LILY HUIE examined the behavior of the nucleus during secretion, digestion and absorption (1897–9). Much later KRUCK (1931) did the same for the gland cells within the traps of *Utricularia* (to be mentioned elsewhere).

QUINTANILHA (1926) (on *Drosophyllum*), DUFRÉNOY and HOMÈS examined the cells as a whole with reference to the comportment of the vacuome. HOMÈS has carried on most meticulous studies. He set himself the task of determining first of all what happens during the development of the cell during the ontogeny of the leaf and gland. The next step was to determine if it is possible to describe definitely the conditions of the glandular cells during repose, so far as this condition might be realized. To this end he depended not on plants collected in the field, but on those raised under control, and which therefore, though secreting, were known not to have been stimulated by insects, etc., but only by light, humidity, temperature. He then studied glands during " digestion ", that is glands which were actively secreting enzymes and absorbing.

The development of the vacuome during the ontogeny of the various tissues, including the glands, follows a general course beginning with minute droplets of material in solution (primordia or metachromata). These enlarge, remaining spherical or more or less elongating, and then give rise to rods or fine filaments which are straight or curved, simple or branched, giving rise to thicker, short, large and massive rods, turning gradually into vacuoles of very irregular shape. From these by confluence arises a single massive vacuole with concentrated contents from which may arise a vacuome with a fine, becoming a coarser, even large and massive network from which in turn a definitive single vacuole with " diluted contents " arises. HOMÈS then remarks that these observed stages are not strictly common to all tissues, *e.g.*, parenchyma cells do not pass through a network stage, which stage in any event is very transitory, and marks tissues or cells which are very active, or are at a moment of particular cell activity. There are, he continues, the following two essential phases: growth by the augmentation of vacuolar substance, followed by growth by simple hydration. All tissues commence with a vacuome in the form of metachromata, and finish (certain tissues, including the glands, apart) with a single vacuole with dilute contents. The more, however, a region preserves the capability of specialization, the slower the evolution of the vacuole. The glands, therefore, remain in a relatively juvenile condition, and consequently more capable of immediate activity.

In his second paper HOMÈS followed the behavior of glandular cells in order to find out what happens in them during the secretion of mucilage only, so as to be able to distinguish later between this activity and that which takes place during digestion and absorption.

He found first of all that under natural conditions the gland cells presented no uniform structural condition. But since in nature, that is in plants studied *in situ*, it is impossible to know the precise history of a given leaf, since it may have been digesting and recovered, HOMÈS raised plants from winter buds under control, regulating within appreciable limits the amount of illumination and humidity. Much to his surprise, the glands of such plants were as little uniform in cytological features as those *in situ*. That is, instead of finding a uniform condition in the gland cells supposedly in a state of repose, he found all possible conditions. It should be here noted that various authors had previously described the resting condition in various ways. DARWIN, SCHIMPER, DE VRIES, BOKORNY, GOEBEL, ÅKERMAN thought that in this condition the gland cells have a single large vacuole. GARDINER described the gland cell as consisting of a fine meshwork of protoplasm holding red sap in the interstices. DUFRÉNOY held a similar view, believing that there are many small vacuoles. QUINTANILHA found a meshwork of threadlike vacuoles. Allowing for discrepancies of understanding it is obvious that HOMÈS' findings bring these various views into some harmony, since no one condition prevails in the resting gland cells.

Having compared living and fixed material it was established to HOMÈS' satisfaction that his fixative (osmic acid, 2%, 1 part; mercuric chloride 2.5%, 4 parts) preserved the cell structure accurately. Knowing also that the glands in the middle of the leaf are more active in secretion than those standing along the limb (since the inhibiting action of the environment on the former is less effective), he made a statistical study of the gland cells as to the form of the vacuome. But a statistical study called for standard conditions. These were supplied by growing plants under three sets of conditions, inciting minimum, medium and maximum secretory activity. From these plants HOMÈS obtained evidence of the behavior of the gland cells under these various conditions, and found that, though all states of activity occurred in all cases, there was a preponderance of one state over the others in any one experimental set of conditions. Relying on the relative abundance of the different structural states of activity, four " witness" glands were chosen to serve as criteria, called types A, B, C, and D. Briefly stated, and neglecting details, the outer glandular cells of these types have vacuomes of the following character:

Type A. the vacuome consists of a single large vacuole.
Type B. — — — — numerous small droplets.
Type C. — — — — fewer, larger droplets.
Type D. — — — — a thicker reticulum.

It was then found that glands at minimum, medium and maximum secretory activity displayed the above cytological characters in the following percentages:

GLANDS OF	A	B	C	D	VARIANTS
Minimum activity	97%	0	0	0	3%
Medium "	0	30%	65%	0	5%
Maximum "	0	15%	25%	60%	0

showing clearly that when glands are at minimum activity, the glandular cells are in the state in which they have a single large vacuole, while when in maximum activity, the vacuome is a thick reticulum. Intermediate conditions characterize glands of approximately medium activity. In the second layer there is a similar course of events, but these are not so pronounced, and do not follow the changes of the outer layer promptly, scarcely ever doing more than fragmenting the vacuole into two or three parts. The cells of the parenchyme bell (the third layer) never show these changes. There would, therefore, seem to be a difference of function of these layers, the innermost taking no part in secretion. Under severe conditions calling for active secretion, the outer layer may display a certain degree of plasmolysis, the cells recovering by drawing water from the second layer. Homès regards this plasmolysis as a normal event, and attributes it to the concentration of the mucilage by rapid evaporation so that it becomes hypertonic to the cell-sap. Though normal, it occurs infrequently in plants under usual conditions. Such plasmolysis can cause directly the fragmentation of the vacuole, as shown by plasmolysis studies in general.

Summarizing, it seems certain that the rate of secretion obeys changes in the external conditions, quite apart from any responses to irritability to chemical substances which are presented at and during digestion. The changes described as aggregation under which these can be subsumed are therefore not alone the result of stimulation in the usual sense (mechanical, chemical).

The purpose of Homès' final paper was to determine if during digestion there is a specific activity of the glandular cells different from that during secretion of mucilage. The same methods were used as previously and the various behaviors of gland cells fed with raw egg albumin compared with those from leaves without nourishment. We recall that during secretion, according to its intensity, any one of four types of condition above mentioned may be found, these types being a) cells with one large vacuole, b) cells with many small round droplets, c) cells with irregular droplets, and d) cells with a thick reticulum.

"If now the glands are fed, at whatever state they may be at the moment, a first *rapid* change will occur in the direction from A to D, or from B to D, but if they are already in the state D, no change will be apparent. Later, after the reticulum stage has been reached, a gradual concentration of the vacuole takes place till a single concentrated vacuole is present in each glandular cell. Then this single vacuole becomes more and more hydrated and finally a large diluted vacuole is present and persists till the end of the digestion. Practically any type of vacuole present during digestion can thus be found in a "resting" tentacle, and it is consequently impossible, by examining *a single tentacle*, to tell if it is, was or is going to be in the process of digestion.

"But the vacuolar changes revealed by the statistical study can also be related to the intensity of the secretory process or even more generally to the exchange of water between the gland and the external medium. The first change towards the reticulum expresses the increase of secretion which takes place immediately after feeding; the later hydration of the single vacuole indicates the decrease of secretion and the beginning of absorption.

"Aggregation is thus not the characteristic result of 'excitation' in a carnivorous plant, but simply the expression of any rapid change in the water content, as can happen during secretion or absorption of a liquid." (Homès *in ep.*).

Thus stands the problem at the present. We are impressed with what appears to be a relatively simple cytological behavior of the cytoplasm (not speaking for the moment of the nucleus) and by the physiological complexities indicated by the behavior of the glands and tentacles during the process of digestion during which there must be secretion and escape of enzyme (even though they may be already present in the mucilage), acid or acids, a substance inhibiting bacterial action (Goebel), perhaps an odorous principle, and a more active secretion of mucilage which ceases at the end of digestion and absorption. Meanwhile, absorption takes place. Simple as the cytological behavior may be, it is, I feel, not yet thoroughly understood.

From studies during the past three summers I can confirm Homès in his claim that resting glands, that is glands found on young vigorous resting leaves, can be found in a resting condition, meaning with cells having a single grand vacuole, or with its cells in a condition which is distinctly otherwise, that is, with an appearance which may be interpreted as a mass of smaller irregular vacuoles, or as a network, probably fairly represented by Homès' fig. 60–63, 1932. Guided by what we have seen in the tentacle cells, in which it seems reasonably certain that the vermiform condition can give rise by confluence to a network, temporary though it may be, we may agree that the same occurs in the gland cells, as Homès believes, and he may be quite right.

I have seen evidence, however, that, during the period after feeding (with raw and purified egg albumin, pepsin, peptone Witte, saliva) while aggregation follows in the tentacle cells, meaning specifically the breaking up of the grand vacuole into smaller ones, these becoming numerous, slender, actively agitated vermiform bodies of high refringence (as so well depicted by Åkerman), to suffer at length confluence and total reversion, this series of changes is not followed in the cells of both glandular courses, though some approach to it may be observed in the lateral epidermal cells seen *en face*, and in the apical cells of a gland which were distinctly not in the grand vacuolar state, having instead a number of smaller irregular vacuoles, in appearance at any rate.

Lateral cells viewed *en face* present a crenated outline in conformity with the buttresses which cut up the periphery of the cell into bays, seen by França in *Drosophyllum*. I observed that in these cells, in saliva, a droplet containing pigment would be formed in each bay, there being as many droplets as bays. Dufrénoy's drawings indicate that he saw the same condition, which he called aggregation, but apparently did not connect the early form of the vacuole with the crenated walls. These droplets formed in the bays might remain as such or might run together to form a single drop containing all the pigment of the cell, depending apparently on the size of the droplets and the vigor of the process. In the apical cells, also in saliva, the whole mass of vacuoles, whatever may have been their exact state, became confluent and there was formed a single large drop, corresponding to Homès' condensed vacuole. Here then we have a case which appears to conform with Homès' observations. On the other hand, when the gland cells are, to begin with, in the dilute vacuolar state, each having a single grand vacuole (Homès' "vacuole diluée") when treated with egg albumin, raw or purified, the first sign of response is to be seen in ten minutes in the cells of the internal course in the lateral region of the gland. The change advances toward its apex. In 90 minutes similar droplets appear in the epidermis lateral cells low down near the base of the gland, again advancing toward the apex. These droplets do not apparently appear in the grand vacuole but in the cytoplasm, but this is a point very difficult to make out. In the course of time the confluence of droplets yields a single large drop. This seems to be what Darwin saw: " In 15 min. I distinctly saw extremely minute spheres of protoplasm aggregating themselves in the purple fluid; these rapidly increased in size, both within the cells of glands and of the upper ends of the pedicels." In my preparations aggregation, in the generally understood sense, occurred in the upper end of the tentacle stalk. Similar appearances were seen in glands treated with pepsin, and peptone Witte (each 1% soln.), in that the first thing noted is the appearance of drops and there is no breaking up of the grand vacuole into parts, as is to be constantly observed in the tentacles. In KH$_2$–PO$_4$ (tried by COELINGH as a component of saliva) in 1% soln. the gland cells behaved so far differently that its action can be only doubtfully compared with that of saliva since vacuoles without pigment are formed which push aside the cell contents, producing a distinctly pathological effect. Aggregation occurred in the tentacles, but this also occurs in water. In order to check on my observation, I took a piece of leaf which had lain in oil for 48 hours, and which showed very clearly that there was no aggregation at all in any gland cells. After removing the oil, which does not adhere to the glands because of the mucilage, I treated it with saliva. In 15 min. droplets had appeared in the lateral cells of the inner course of gland cells (C–II), the epidermis (C–I) remaining quite clear. At the end of 50 min. all the cells of C–II had each a large drop, appearing in the apical cells last. All the lateral cells of C–I had drops in them, a few small droplets in some apical cells. In an hour's time, droplets had appeared in many of the apical cells of C–I and they were evidently enlarging.

These observations seem to indicate that during the ordinary course of events when the glands are secreting mucilage the condition of the gland cells may be found in various states such as HOMÈS had described. If the glands are fed they may follow one of two courses. If the gland cells are filled with smaller vacuoles (are aggregated), these become confluent to form a single large drop, the condensed vacuole of HOMÈS. If the gland cells are in the resting condition, that is, are in the grand vacuolar stage with no sign of aggregation, the course of events on feeding consists in the formation of small droplets in the cells of the inner glandular course in the lateral regions of the gland. This advances till the apical cells of this course have all formed droplets. These grow until by their size they form an optically dense layer. In the meantime, droplets have appeared in the epidermis, in the lateral region. This also progresses toward the apex, until all the epidermal cells are involved. The drops all contain pigment. In the course of change, the gland becomes denser and darker in color as DARWIN observed. During six hours aggregation had occurred in the tentacles and by next morning it had progressed quite to their bases and into the leaf tissue about their bases.

Whatever the final agreement as to the course of aggregation, which appears to be different in detail, if the same in results, in gland and tentacle, the whole activity is most extraordinary, and demands much further study before any final answer can be given as to the relation of aggregation to secretion and absorption.

Studies of cytoplasm and nucleus. — The studies of the living cell leading to our knowledge of aggregation led to a desire to know more of those details of behavior of the cytoplasm and especially of the nucleus which cannot be discovered by the methods used for observation of the living material. Accordingly the method of fixation followed by sectioning and staining came into use first by GARDINER, followed later by LILY HUIE, ROSENBERG and KONOPKA. HOMÈS' work we have already mentioned as especially bearing on aggregation. GARDINER believed that the mucilage of the glands is secreted as a " formed matter" within vacuoles which grow after stimulation, the protoplasm being reduced in amount to be later restored by new growth from the vicinity of the nucleus. He observed the presence of the crystalloid " rhabdoids". It is not unfair to say that his work was rather meagre in amount, and he did not use staining reactions. HUIE on the other hand did a sustained piece of work. She traced rhythmic changes in cytoplasm, nucleus and nucleolus, attempting to interpret these as chemical and morphological reactions connected with and following stimulation by food materials of various kinds, which, according to their nature, were followed by quantitatively various reactions, though qualitatively similar. We may leave out of account the reactions to non-organic substances which produced in any event only very fleeting cytological changes. Following feeding there is a reduction in the volume of the basophile cytoplasm until it becomes scanty in amount and eosinophile in character confirming GARDINER'S similar observation. Following this but preceding the restoration of the cytoplasm there is an increase in the volume of the basophile chromosomes accompanied by a reduced amount of nucleolar chromatin. The beginning of restoration of the cytoplasm is to be seen in an accumulation of neutrophile dense cytoplasm surrounding the nucleus corresponding chemically (as indicated by color reaction) and morphologically (size of granules) to the intranuclear plasm. At completion of cytoplasmic restoration the nuclear chromatin is reduced in amount, and the nucleolar chromatin increases. What is left of the chromosomal bodies (chromatin) is finally aggregated into definite V-shaped bodies of a constant number (eight) characteristic of the plant, which " proves" that this is a mark of nuclear activity and not merely a feature of mitosis. HUIE's second paper (1899) adds nothing to the above account in general, but she concludes that the nucleus is the seat of metabolic activity, and that the usefulness of a food can be judged by the condition of the " nuclear organs."

ROSENBERG (1899) supported and extended HUIE's studies. He saw similar changes, but in lesser degree, in the endodermis, tracheids and stalk cells. He diverged, however, from her interpretation of the masses of chromatin as chromosomal, for he found them in no constant number, nor did he find splitting as in prophase, but on the contrary much difference in form and size. He observed, however, certain bodies lying on or near the nuclear membrane, called generally "pseudonucleoli", which he termed prochromosomes. These occur in a constant number, and are the chromosomes.

KONOPKA and ZIEGENSPECK (1929) studied *D. rotundifolia, D. binata* and *D. anglica.* After the glands have been fed 24 hours with various proteins, including pollen, droplets appear in the cytoplasm near the nucleus (intermediate food products) at first always in the inner gland cells layer, later in the outer, and also in endodermis (parenchyme bell) tracheids, stalk cells and leaf blade cells. They increase in number and size, and at length are overtaken by a sort of disruption, show hollows and cracks, and appear to be in some vague but perhaps intimate connection with the nucleus, indicating that they are products taken up by it. At the " high point " of feeding the nucleus has enlarged and the membrane becomes less definite and finally disappears so that the chromosomes and nuclear materials appear to lie free in the cytoplasm, or at any rate in a nuclear lymph. KONOPKA observed in the resting stage the bodies which ROSENBERG called prochromosomes, but could not confirm his belief that they occur in a constant number, regarding them rather to be of nucleolar nature. After feeding the nucleoli become reduced in size, and lie in a large vacuole (" Hof ") from which, in many cases, he could observe canals leading to the cytoplasm, bringing the nucleus into more intimate contact with the cytoplasm. Here it is to be regretted that cost prevented the reproduction of his photographs, since the figures are unsatisfactory to a degree, and show no convincing evidence of this. The chromatin on the other hand exhibits increase and occurs in larger masses of various form. After 24 hours they become very evident by their clearness and size, and besides granules of various sizes there appear rod-shaped structures (" Rhabdoids"?) lying near the periphery (of the nucleus) sometimes paired and connected by fibers with the interior of the nucleus, but in no constant number. The nucleolus has now been dissolved, and appears as a pale, rather than, according to ROSENBERG, a distinct body. The chromatin rods now unite to form threads and rings. Among them the granules, which ROSENBERG thought to be prochromosomes, are secondary nucleoli, indicating enhanced nucleolar activity. They always lie in vacuoles (" Hof ") and have no connection with the nuclear structure, show disintegration and disappearance at the high point of the reaction. During long periods of digestion these events appear not to progress steadily, but rather to pulsate — there is a rhythm in behavior. These nucleolar structures are regarded by KONOPKA as supplying materials for forming mucilage and for digestion, and he is inclined to regard the central and peripheral nucleoli as having different functions. The whole aspect of the changes in the chromatin and nucleolus indicates that these changes are connected with ferment production. With the escape of the ferment the chromatin shrinks in ring forms, so that one might regard the nucleus now as being in a spireme stage, leading to mitosis, or merely as a reformation of chromosomes in a somatic condition. They are at all events true chromosomes.

It has been attempted to summarize the above work with not too great brevity, so that the reader may appreciate the difficulties of interpretation. It is not too much to say that, while it has been shown experimentally that changes in the cell do indeed occur during digestion, and while we have become aware to some extent what, in detail, these changes are, it must still be recognized that we are yet lacking general agreement as to the precise nature of many of these details, and much less are in a position to attribute precise functions to the various structures seen.

Digestion; enzymes. — DARWIN (1875) proclaimed the digestive power of the secretion of *Drosera* tentacles. He fed the leaves proteins, connective tissue, cartilage, gelatin, to find that these were attacked.

The presence of acid being a condition for peptic digestion, he observed that the inner tentacles of the disc of the leaf were more acid than the outer. This may have been because of the greater number of tentacles per unit of area. DARWIN thought that the acidity of the secretion of the leaf is increased on the absorption of nitrogenous substances derived from the captured insect.

Opposed to the general trend of opinion was that of MORREN (1875), BATALIN (1877), TISCHUTKIN (1889), and of DUBOIS (1899), all of whom were persuaded that the digestion of insects by *Drosera* is always the result of bacterial action, so that the results of others, to be detailed below, were not without opposition.

REES and WILL (1875) made a glycerin extract of the leaves and found it weakly acid and to contain an enzyme which in the presence of weak HCl exercised a peptonizing action. LAWSON TATE (1875) collected the secretion from the tentacles, sweeping the leaves with a feather (he used *Drosera dichotoma*), mixed it with water and precipitated it with cholesterin. The precipitate was found to coagulate milk, and this he referred to the action of a ferment which he named droserin. In 1911 Miss J. WHITE reinvestigated the matter; leaves were removed, washed with previously boiled water with added chloroform and chopped with a sterile knife. The bits were then placed in lukewarm boiled water with chloroform as antiseptic, shaken vigorously for 2 hours. To the filtrate was added an equal part of saturated ammonium sulfate, from which a filtrate was obtained which contained a principle which could attack fibrin but only in an acid medium. The product gave the biuret reactions. ABDERHALDEN (1906) had found that in its presence peptides are not split.

DERNBY in 1917 obtained a glycerin extract of the leaves from which by means of dialysis he obtained an enzyme which he regarded as a pepsin. This worked at an acidity of pH 5 as optimum. No tryptase or ereptase was found.

Miss ROBINSON (1909) tested the digestive effect of *Drosera* on " purer proteins" then available. She found that acid-albumin, alkali albuminate and edestin were digested, but " somewhat less readily" than dry egg-white, fibrin, tendo-mucoid and nucleoproteins. Collagen and elastin proved entirely indigestible. Though creatin did not cause a bending of the tentacles, it was readily dissolved, meanwhile remaining in contact with the leaf for three days. It is important, in view of DARWIN'S opposed idea, that the lack of movement of the tentacles is not an indication of the non-nutritional value of the substances applied; nor did DARWIN find that the positive response indicates the contrary.

Beginning in 1930 OKAHARA published a series of papers dealing with the matter. He first dealt with the question of the actual occurrence of a digestive ferment in *Drosera*. The leaves were extracted with glycerine and water for several days (with toluene) and the press juice then filtered off. The mother solution thus obtained showed strong acidity. The enzyme was separated by means of acetone and redissolved for experimentation.

He concluded that there exists in the leaves of *Drosera* a powerful proteolytic enzyme which, acting on proteins, hydrolyses them to proteoses and peptones, with an optimum activity at pH 1.5, an acidity high for plant enzymes and suggesting a resemblance to animal pepsin. In order to determine to what extent the *Drosera* pepsin is identical in action with animal pepsin, OKAHARA observed the influence of poisons (quinine hydrochloride and atoxyl) on them. He failed to find a strict parallel, since the enzyme activity under certain conditions was repressed in the one and accelerated in the other.

OKAHARA'S second paper (1930*b*) is of a more general nature, dealing with the effect of toxic substances on pepsin with a view to illuminating his earlier observations cited just above. Though the subject may be regarded as controversial, it remains true that there is a substance capable of digestion of proteins in *Drosera* leaves.

In a third paper (1931) OKAHARA gave the results of inquiry into the optimum acidities of various acids for the enzyme activity. He had observed the occurrence of formic acid in *Drosera*, and was prompted to investigate the comparative effect of various acids on the action of a proteolytic enzyme on edestin and found that the optimum acidities for various acids differ, and that the decrease from the optimum acidity parallels the decrease of the electrical dissociation constant.

While OKAHARA'S second and third papers do not immediately concern *Drosera*, they have been mentioned in this connection since their bearing will doubtless be made clear by further studies. His fourth paper, however, bears directly on the controversial question, do bacteria play a rôle in the digestion of carnivorous plants and in particular of *Drosera*? *Nepenthes* was examined also in this connection. The paper was published in 1933. The author isolated from the plants studied a series of bacteria and moulds. Experiments with these in media held at two acidities, pH 5–6 and pH 3.3, afforded the following results. Three of the moulds acted on Witte's peptone and glycocoll at pH 3.3. The other organisms attacked various nitrogenous compounds supplied (Witte's peptone, glycylglycine, glycocoll and alanine) falling into two groups which cooperate to reduce these substances to ammonia. OKAHARA concludes, that, while the plant enzymes may themselves take a leading part in the breaking down of proteins, such organisms as were isolated from the plants mentioned "may also cooperate in the completion of the process." OKAHARA to this extent supports the views of LABBE (1904) and of STUTZER (1926), the former for *Drosera* and the latter for *Utricularia*.

Following OKAHARA, LINDERSTRØM–LANG and HOLTER (1934) again raised the question whether digestion in *Drosera rotundifolia* is essentially different from that in other plants and similar to that in animals, or do they depend on resorption of the products of bacterial action?

Accordingly, the secretions from the glands and from the leaf tissues (from the blade, that is) were examined separately, in order to answer specific questions, to wit: (1) whether proteinase is secreted by the glands; (2) what position among the proteolytic enzymes it takes; (3) in what quantities it occurs and how these quantities behave in relation to the endoproteinase to be expected in the leaf tissues.

Their method of obtaining the enzymes was as follows. The secretion of the glands was taken up by filter paper and because of its viscosity was diluted. That of the leaf tissues was extracted with glycerin. Both were tested on edestin.

It was found that the gland secretion, with its optimum at pH 3.3, was far more active than that of the leaf blade, with its optimum at 4.6, or even of the secretion, extracted from removed glands with maximum activity at pH 3.8. It is admitted that the last may be due to the overlapping of the action of the two enzymes in question. The authors concluded, "We have to do with a quite different distribution of two enzymes, of which the one occurring in the secretion is a proteinase for the purpose of digestion." Further it was pointed out that the distinct function of a proteinase, optimum activity at pH 3.2, does not harmonize with DERNBY's results who found the maximum activity on acid albumin at pH 5, nor with OKAHARA's with carmine fibrin, maximum activity at pH 1.4. DERNBY's results may have come about because he used masses of total leaf, but those of OKAHARA's are regarded as distinctly antagonistic. This may be due to the possibility that the Japanese plant may differ physiologically from the European. MERCK's pepsin acted on edestin at pH 1.8; therefore, the proteinase of *Drosera* and pepsin are not identical.

Recent and still unpublished work done by Å. ÅKERMAN and L. G. M. BAAS BECKING using *D. capensis* yielded definite evidence that peptic fermentation takes place. The method used was the following: A single tentacle on the leaf edge was plunged into distilled water held in a small paraffin cup. Under these conditions the water retained its initial pH of 5.8 for at least 24 hours. When, however, a solution of NH_4Cl (conc. 25 mgr/L) was used the pH fell from 5.8 to 2.0, from which it is evident that this salt served to stimulate the production of acid. Equivalent solutions of $CaCl_2$, NaCl and $MgCl_2$ gave no action, while KCl produced only a very slight change in pH. When egg albumin (pH 7.0) was placed on a tentacle, the pH changed to 3.0. Carmine-fibrin when treated with a leaf extract was digested indicating the presence of a peptic enzyme, effective at an optimum pH of 2–3.0 while it has been shown by J. DE ZEEUW that digestion in *Nepenthes* takes place at about pH 4.0. Since the leaf extract was not bacteria free, Prof. BAAS BECKING (Sept. 1935) pointed out that the proof for *Drosera* is not absolute, and final proof will require experiments with bacteria-free plants. It is further noted that *Drosera* proteinase takes a middle position between pepsin and papain (*in ep.*).

DARWIN observed that milk when placed on *Drosera* leaves was soon coagulated. GREEN mentions this under the heading "Vegetable Rennet," presumably because of the more obvious inference that milk coagulation is brought about by a rennet, as perhaps is the case when *Galium verum* is used for the preparation of curds for cheese making, also mentioned by GREEN. As has been seen, a similar action of *Pinguicula* in coagulating milk is not attributed to the presence of a rennet (DERNBY 1917), and if so, this may be equally true of *Drosera*. DARWIN does not speak of a rennet, but does remark on the digestive effect of the secretion on casein, which harmonizes with DERNBY'S view that a trypsin is present (in *Pinguicula*).

The general conclusion may be drawn from the foregoing summaries of work done on digestion in *Drosera* that this plant does indeed secrete a ferment which can act upon proteins and reduce them to substances which can be and are absorbed for nutriment. If food materials in the form of an abundance of insects, pollen, etc. (DARWIN) are present so that the antiseptic effect is incomplete, bacteria may (particularly according to OKAHARA) assist in rendering such foods available to the plant.

The abundance of fats in the bodies of insects would suggest the presence of a lipase in *Drosera*, but such has not been found. Whether lecithin and fatty acids might be absorbed by infiltration (as lecithin is taken in by the human intestine according to SHOCOTYOFF, *fide* SCHMID, 1912) is a matter of speculation, though GOEBEL thought that he found fats to be absorbed by the glands of *Pinguicula* and *Utricularia*.

Significance of carnivory for the plant. — Although DARWIN left no room for doubt that *Drosera* is able to catch, digest and absorb the products of digestion, it remained a question if this ability is of advantage to the plant in furthering its growth and development. It was natural that FRANCIS DARWIN (1878) should take up the cudgels in his father's behalf. He grew plants, obtained from the field, in shallow dishes duly protected so as to prevent insects from reaching them. These he divided into two lots, one of which he fed, the other remaining unfed. The result showed the indubitable conclusion that the plants which were fed were more vigorous, produced more and stronger inflorescences and seed than the unfed. Similar results were obtained by KELLERMANN and v. RAUMER (1878). BÜSGEN (1883) then pointed out that plants grown from winter buds show a wide range of development to begin with, so that an experiment with these is really a handicap race. To avoid this he used plants grown from seed, so that his plants started out from scratch. The results were even more striking than those of the previous workers. In the table herewith the results of the three authors are compared in terms of percentage, the quantities for the unfed plants being 100: —

	FR. DARWIN 1878		KELLERMANN & v. RAUMER, 1878	BÜSGEN 1883
Number of inflorescences	164.9:	100	152: 100	300: 100
Number of capsules	194.4:	100	174: 100	533: 100
Total weight of seed	379.7:	100	capsules 205: 100	
AND IN TERMS OF DRY WEIGHT:			SOLUTION NUTRIENT	SPRING WATER
Winter buds, 1 Feb............................			173: 100	
Winter buds, 3 Apr..............	213:	100		
Entire plant, end of 2nd. year.........................296: 100				174: 100
Inflorescences...................	141.1:	100		
Plants minus Inflorescences.......	121.5:	100		
(*fide* BÜSGEN)				

While these figures speak for themselves, I venture to quote briefly from these authors. KELLERMANN and VON RAUMER: "The general result is not to be doubted, that in all essential points the fed plants forge ahead of the unfed"; Büsgen: "We must therefore take it as proven that animal stuffs are transferred to the plant and that they are of great significance to it for its development, namely, for the development of its fruit, etc."; and finally Francis Darwin said: "These results show clearly that insectivorous plants derive great advantage from animal food."

Just previously to the publications of Kellermann and v. Raumer's work Pfeffer (1877) had grown *Drosera rotundifolia* plants from winter buds under cover to prevent the access of insects, and observed that they grew vigorously, evidently leading to the conclusion that the carnivory is not always a necessity. Regel (1879) went further than this, claiming that the carnivorous habit is a distinct disadvantage because he observed that the leaves (*Drosera filiformis*) were often injured by feeding, and that fed leaves die sooner than unfed ones. It is, however, well known, as Goebel pointed out, that overfeeding often causes decay of the leaf; and to deplore the earlier passing of fed, not overfed, leaves is to ignore the possible good which may have accrued to the plant in the meantime. And Haberlandt was of the opinion, based on field observations in Java, that *Nepenthes* pitchers appeared to have but a meagre booty, that insectivory is a sort of semi-superfluous, luxus adaptation. In this Massart (*through* Haberlandt), having had similar field experiences, agreed. Nor did Goebel regard the rôle of insectivory in the struggle for existence very seriously — it is useful, he said, but not obligatory, and the plant does not meet much competition in its natural habitat. Such more or less contrary views have in the long run been brought to a focus in the idea now generally accepted that carnivory is a very striking and useful adaptation, which, though not always obligatory, can under circumstances better the condition of the plant. Additional questions, no less important, however, arose. It will be noted that the above researches were overshadowed by the sole idea of animal food, as supplying chiefly proteids, and this has crept into the textbooks as the dominant thought. Stahl, in 1900, published a long dissertation on the significance of mycorrhizal arrangements in plants, in which he instituted comparisons between those plants with the carnivorous plants, all of which grew in sterile soils. *Sarracenia* had been shown by MacDougal (1899) to be free of mycorrhiza, nor had it been found otherwise in *Pinguicula* (Schlicht, 1889, *through* Stahl), *Drosera*, or *Nepenthes* (Janse, 1896, *through* Stahl) and this is now known to be the case for all carnivores. As compared with true parasites, mycorrhizal plants and autotrophic plants with very extensive roots, those plants which avail themselves of capillary water and in which many forms of animal life perish and are entangled in the foliage (*e.g.* mosses), and carnivores have poor roots and therefore little means for obtaining the materials of the soil notably lacking in salts, especially those of phosphorus and potassium, in which they grow. And while it may be true that it may be shown by experiment that carnivores may obtain all their requirements through their roots, if plentifully supplied to the substrate, this does not show that in a state of nature their arrangements for obtaining these materials are superfluous or useless, since they live in nature and not under experimental conditions. STAHL indicated the low ash content of the leaves of carnivores, and advanced this additional fact as an argument for the significance of carnivory. There is generally also a depression of transpiration due to situation in the habitat, and where transpiration is low, some other means of obtaining salts is called for. The leaves of *Nepenthes*, when exposed to situations where transpiration can act freely, do not make pitchers, and have a higher ash content than those low down and exposed to higher humidity, where also, as in the case of seedlings (GOEBEL), pitchers are immediately produced following the cotyledons. STAHL thus argues: the carnivory has been dominated by the idea that it is an adaptation to obtain proteins; but the soils in which carnivorous plants grow are notoriously poor ones, and therefore the question of how the carnivorous plants obtain substances aside from nitrogen is in need of investigation. This in 1900. PFEFFER had indicated this problem (1877), thinking particularly of phosphorus compounds, and his and STAHL's suggestions were fruitful ones.*

In 1912, WEYLAND and SCHMID both entertained this idea, WEY-LAND showing that there was little of K and P to be found in the meagre roots of *Drosera*, and SCHMID finding these elements present in the leaves of this plant after insect feeding, whereas before this they were not to be found or only in meagre amounts (RUSCHMANN, 1914). OOSTERHUIS (1927) pushed investigation further along in this direction. He asked the question whether the lack of any particular mineral in the soil could be compensated for by insect feeding. He summed up his experiments by saying that (1) mineral nutrients can be taken up by the roots; (2) even if an abundant supply of nutrient salts is present, the plants can not grow as well as if insect-fed; (3) in view of the fact that in his experiments plants grown on a substrate poor in salts but insect-fed prospered beyond plants grown on salt-rich medium but not insect-fed, he argued that the significance of insectivory lies in the uptake of the cleavage-products of proteins out of insects by the plant. The absorption of salts from the insect is not excluded, but is not the important factor. Summarily stated, in the lack of nitrogen in the soil, the plants can be supplied this by insect prey, and then flourish better than when grown in a substrate with Knop's solution supplying all elements. That plants fed with insects have a higher nitrogen content than those grown as seedlings on turf carrying Knop's solution strengthened him in this view.

BEHRE (1929), stimulated by an expression of doubt by DIELS (1906) as to the value of insectivory, asserted that such value had not been proved, and instituted experiments of his own to test the matter. He found that plants grown in distilled water but plentifully fed with flies or meat throve very much better than those grown in distilled water, or even in a weak Knop solution ($\frac{1}{4}$ conc.), in both cases not fed. The differences noted became much more evident toward the end of the second summer. He concluded that insectivory is indeed of great moment to the plant. An important value, it seemed to BEHRE, lies in the taking up of inorganic salts, and that

---

* PEYRONEL (1932) argues that if mycorrhizal fungi are parasitic, they should be found in carnivorous plants, but he found none in *Drosera* or *Pinguicula*. Mycorrhiza occurs chiefly when soils are poor in nitrates and ammoniacal salts, but rich in organic matter.

the lack of such salts in the natural environment is compensated for in this way.

Came OUDMAN in 1936 with further proofs. The virtue of his experiments lies in the fact that his experimental plants (*Drosera capensis*) were grown from seed, and the seedlings carefully chosen for their uniformity, and in the further fact that the plants were grown on a very uniform substrate of powdered peat which had previously been very thoroughly washed. Several sets of plants with (*a*) distilled water, (*b*) nutrient solution without N, and (*c*) Knop's solution, were set up and either not fed at all, or fed with asparagin 1.5%, peptone 1.5%, gelatin 2% (against dist. water alone), gelatin plus Knop (against dist. water only in the substrate), Knop solution alone, and finally with insects. He found that plants grown on salt-poor substrate, but fed insects, were quite normal. Plants grown on N-free substrate could make use of asparagin and peptone as well as the N-compounds occurring in insects. Plants well supplied with nutrient salts, incl. nitrogen compounds, can grow well in the absence of leaf-feeding with insects. *Drosera* can obtain nitrogen if this is not present in the substrate, through its leaves, and this in organic form. It can also take up through its leaves not only N, but other salts as well. OUDMAN'S conclusions correspond quite fully with those of OOSTERHUIS. There can, therefore, be no sort of doubt that the ability to absorb substances (mineral salts as well as N) is of significance to the plant. It should be added that gelatin and glutin, a derivative of gelatin, cause degeneration of the tentacles, so that in time they entirely disappear.

The presence of ascorbic acid in *D. intermedia*, suspected by WEBER (1938), was soon after demonstrated in the leaves of this plant by NEUBAUER (1939) who claims to have found a content nearly as high as that of a "well known paprika preparation", which itself contains 20-fold that of lemon juice. On this WEBER (1940) again examined the leaves of the same species after having been fed peptone powder, and obtained evidence of a heightening of cell activity, accompanied by an increase in vitamin-C content. This being a non-nitrogenous compound, the significance of these results is quite problematical.

Literature Cited:

ÅKERMAN, Å., Untersuchungen über die Aggregation in den Tentakeln von *Drosera rotundifolia*. Bot. Notiser 1917:145–192.

AMES, O., An easy method of propagating *Drosera filiformis*. Rhodora 1:172, 1899.

ARISZ, W. H. & J. OUDMAN, On the influence of aggregation on the transport of asparagine and caffeine in the tentacles of *Drosera capensis*. Proc. K. Akad. Amst. 40:3–11, 1937.

BATALIN, A., Mechanik der Bewegungen der insektenfressenden Pflanzen. Flora 60:33–39; 54–58; 65–73; 105–111; 129–144; 145–154, 1877 (*Drosera*, 33–73; *Dionaea*, 105–150; *Pinguicula*, 150–154).

BECK, A. B., A. K. MACBETH and F. L. WINZOR, The absorption spectra of hydroxynaphthoquinones and of the coloring matter of *Drosera Whittakeri*. Austral. Jour. Exp. Biol. Med. Sci. 12:203–212, 1934.

BEHRE, KARL, Physiologische und zytologische Untersuchungen über *Drosera*. Diss. Hamburg, 1929. Planta 7:208–306, 1929.

BEIJERINCK, M. W., Beobachtungen und Betrachtungen über Wurzelknospen und Nebenwurzeln. Verzamelde Geschriften van BEIJERINCK 2:7–121 (1886).

BENECKE, W. & L. JOST, Pflanzenphysiologie. 4. Aufl., Jena 1924.

BENNETT, A. W., The absorptive glands of carnivorous plants. Mo. Microscopical Journ. 15:1–5, 1876 (*n.v.*).

BOKORNY, TH., Über Aggregation. Jahrb. wiss. Bot. 20:427, 1889.

BÜSGEN, M., Die Bedeutung des Insektenfanges für *Drosera rotundifolia*. Bot. Zeitung 41:569–577; 585–594, 1883.
DE CANDOLLE, A. P., Physiologie Végétale. Paris, 1832. (Translated by J. ROEPER. Stuttgart and Tübingen, 1835) (vol. 2, p. 652 of this refers to *Drosera*).
COELINGH, W. M., Over stoffen, die invloed uitoefenen op de aggregatie bij *Drosera*. Proefschrift Amsterdam, N. V. Hollandiadrukkerij, Baarn, 1929, 74 pp., *cf.* also her English résumé in K. Ak. Wet. Amst. 32:973, 1929.
CORRENS, C., Zur Physiologie von *Drosera rotundifolia*. Bot. Ztg. 54:21–26, 1896.
CZAJA, A. TH., Insectivoren. Handwörterbuch der Naturwissenschaften 5:655–666, 1934.
DARWIN, CHARLES, Insectivorous Plants. 2nd. Ed. of 1875.
DARWIN, ERASMUS, The Botanic Garden. London 1791; New York 1798.
DARWIN, F., The process of aggregation in the tentacles of *Drosera rotundifolia*. Q. Jour. Mic. Sci. 16:309–319, 1876.
DARWIN, F., Experiments on the nutrition of *Drosera rotundifolia*. J. Linn. Soc. Bot. 17: 17–32, 1878.
DERNBY, K. G., Notiz betreffend die proteolytischen Enzyme der *Drosera rotundifolia*. Bioch. Zeitschr. 78:197, 1917.
DIELS, L., *Droseraceae*. Das Pflanzenreich, IV, 112, 1906.
DIELS, L., Blattrhizoiden in *Drosera*. Ber. D. Bot. Gesellsch. 24:189–191, 1906.
DIXON, H. H., Adventitious buds on *Drosera rotundifolia*. Notes Bot. Sch. Trinity Coll. Dublin 144–145, 1901 (*n.v.*).
DRUDE, O., Die insectenfressenden Pflanzen. SCHENK's Handbuch der Botanik 1:113–146, 1881 (Literature complete up to 1881).
DUBOIS, R., Absence de zymase digestive des albuminoïdes chez le *Drosera longifolia*. Ann. Soc. Linn. de Lyon II, 45:79–80, 1898, 1899 (*n.v.*).
DUFRÉNOY, J., Modifications cytologiques des cellules des poils de *Drosera rotundifolia*. C. R. Soc. de Biol. 97:86–89, 1927.
FENNER, C. A., Beiträge zur Kenntnis der Anatomie, Entwickelungsgeschichte und Biologie der Laubblätter und Drüsen einiger Insectivoren. Flora 93:335–434, 1904.
FRANÇA, (*see under Drosophyllum*).
FRANKLAND, Acids of the secretion of *Drosera* tentacles, *in* DARWIN's Insectivorous Plants, 2d. ed., pp. 73–76, 1875.
GARDINER, W., On the phenomena accompanying stimulation of the gland cells in *Drosera dichotoma*. Proc. R. Soc. London, 39:229–234, 1886.
GEDDES, (*see under Pinguicula*).
GIESSLER, A., Einfluss von Salzlösungen auf die Stärkeverarbeitung bei *Drosera*. Flora 23:133–190, 1928.
GLAUER, Jahresber. (1887) d. Schles. Gesellsch. f. vaterl. Cultur 3:167, 1886.
GOEBEL, K., Pflanzenbiologische Schilderungen, II. Marburg 1891.
GOEBEL, K., Bull. Torrey Bot. Club 30:179–205, 1903.
GOEBEL, K., Brutknospen bei *Drosera pygmaea* und einigen Monokotylen. Flora 98:324–335, 1908.
GOEBEL, K., Organographie der Pflanzen 3:1497, 1617, 1923, Ergänzungsbd. 171, 212, 1924.
GRAVES, J. A., Notes on *Drosera*. Plant World 1:28, 1897.
GREEN, J. R., (*see under Nepenthes*).
GRÖNLAND, J., Note sur les organes glanduleux du genre *Drosera*. Ann. d. Sci. nat., IV sér. Bot. 3:297–303, 1855.
GROUT, A. J., Adventitious buds on *Drosera rotundifolia*. Am. Nat. 32:114, 1898.
HABERLANDT, G., Eine botanische Tropenreise. 1893, S. 228.
HABERLANDT, G., Physiologische Pflanzenanatomie. 6. Aufl., Leipzig 1924.
HAYNE, F. G., Getreue Darstellung der Arzneigewächse. (*through* NITSCHKE, 1860).
HEINRICHER, E., Zur Kenntnis von *Drosera*. Zeitschr. des Ferdinandeums f. Tirol 3, 46, 1902.
HOMÈS, M., Évolution du vacuome au cours de la différenciation des tissus chez *Drosera intermedia* Hayne. Bull. Cl. Sci. Acad. R. Belg., 5 sér., 13:731–746, 1927.
HOMÈS, M., Développement des feuilles et des tentacules chez *Drosera intermedia* Hayne. Comportement du vacuome. Bull. Cl. Sci. Acad. R. Belg., 5 sér., 14:70–88, 1928.
HOMÈS, M., La question des plantes carnivores, principalement au point de vue cytologique. Bull. Soc. R. Bot. Belg. 61:147–159, 1929a.
HOMÈS, M., Modifications cytologiques au cours du fonctionnement des organes sécréteurs chez *Drosera*, I. Modifications dans les feuilles non nourries. Mém. Acad. R. Belg. Cl. Sci., sér. 2, 10:1–54, 1929b; II. Modifications dans les feuilles nourries. *Ibid.* 1241–44, 1932.
HOOKER, H. D., Jr., Physiological observations on *Drosera rotundifolia*. Bull. Torr. Bot. Club 43:1–27, 1916.
HOOKER, H. D., Jr., Mechanics of movement in *Drosera rotundifolia*. Bull. Torr. Bot. Club 44:389–403, 1917.
HOOKER, J. D., Address to the Dept. of Botany and Zoology, B. A. A. S. Belfast Meeting, 1874. Report, pp. 102–116, 1875.
HUIE, L. M., (*a*) Changes in the cell organs of *Drosera rotundifolia* produced by feeding with egg-albumin. Q. Journ. Mic. Sci. 39:387–425, 1897.

(*b*) Further studies of cytological changes produced in *Drosera*. Q. Journ. Mic. Sci. 42:203–222, 1899.

(*c*) Changes in the gland cells of *Drosera* produced by various food materials. Ann. Bot. 12:560–561, 1898.

JANSE, 1896 (*through* STAHL 1900).

JANSON, E., Studien über die Aggregationserscheinungen in den Tentakeln von *Drosera*. (Diss. München, extracted and repaged from Beih. bot. Centralbl. 37, 1920, 33 pp.).

JOST, L., *see* BENECKE–JOST.

KELLERMANN, CH. & E. v. RAUMER, Vegetationsversuche an *Drosera rotundifolia*, mit und ohne Fleischfütterung. Bot. Ztg. 36:209–218; 225–229, 1878.

KIRSCHLEGER, M., Note sur quelques anomalies végétales. Bull. Soc. Bot. France 2:722–724, 1855.

KOK, ALIDA C. A., Über den Transport körperfremder Stoffe durch parenchymatisches Gewebe. Proefschrift, Groningen. Rec. des Trav. bot. néerl. 30:23–139, 1932/3.

KONOPKA, K., Die Rolle des Kerns bei Verdauung, Sekretion und Reizbewegung der *Drosera rotundifolia*. Schriften Königsberger Gelehrt. Gesellsch. Naturwiss. Kl. 7(2):13–112, 1930.

KONOPKA, K. & ZIEGENSPECK, H., Der Kern des *Drosera*tentakels und die Fermentbildung. Protoplasma 7:62–71, 1929.

KOSTYTSCHEW, S., Die Photosynthese der Insektivoren. Ber. D. Bot. Gesellsch. 41:277–280, 1923.

KRUCK, M., (*see* under *Utricularia*).

LABBE, E., Du rôle des microorganismes dans ... digestions observés chez *Drosera rotundifolia*. Thèse École Pharm. Paris, 1904. (Bot. Centralb. 102:333, 1906) (*n.v.*).

LEAVITT, R. G., Adventitious plants of *Drosera*. Rhodora 1:206–208, 1899. Reversionary stages experimentally induced in *Drosera intermedia*. Rhodora 5:265–272, 1903. Seedlings and adventitious plants of *Drosera*. Torreya 9:200–203, 1909.

LEAVITT, R. G., Translocation of characters in plants. Rhodora 7:13–20, 1905.

LINDERSTRØM–LANG & H. HOLTER, Ergebnisse der Enzymforschung 3:309–334, 1934.

LUBBOCK, J., A Contribution to our Knowledge of Seedlings. London 1892.

MACBETH, A. KILLEN, JR., J. R. PRICE, F. L. WINZOR & A. B. BECK, The coloring matters of *Drosera Whittakeri*, I. The absorption spectra and colour reactions of hydroxynaphthaquinones. Journ. Chem. Soc. I:325–333, 1935.

MACBETH, A. K. & WINZOR, F. L., The coloring matters of *Drosera Whittakeri*, II. Journ. Chem. Soc. 1935:334–336.

MacDOUGAL, D. T., Symbiotic saprophytism. Ann. Bot. 13:1–47, 1899.

MARLOTH, R., Flora of South Africa, II (1):26, 1925.

MASSART, J., Un botaniste en Malaisie. Gand 1895, p. 253.

MEYEN, F. J. F., Über die Secretionsorgane der Pflanzen. A memoir published in 1837.

MILDE, J., Über die Reizbarkeit der Blätter von *Drosera rotundifolia* L. (*through* NITSCHKE, 1860). Bot. Zeit. 10:540, 1852.

MIRIMANOFF, A., Remarques sur la sécrétion des tentacules de *Drosera*. Protoplasma 33, 1939.

MORREN, É., La théorie des plantes carnivores et irritables. Bull. de l'Acad. Roy. Belg., II, 40:1040 seq., 1875 (1876) (seconde édition revue et améliorée dans Bull. Féd. Soc. Hort. 1875).

MORREN, É., Note sur les procédés insecticides du *Drosera rotundifolia*. Bull. Acad. Roy. Belg. II, 40:7, 1875 (seconde édition dans la Belg. Hort. 25, 1875).

MORREN, É., Note sur le *Drosera binata*, sa structure et ses procédés insecticides. Bull. Acad. Roy. Belg., II, 40, No. 11, 1875.

MORRISON, A., Note on the formation of the bulb in Western Australian species of *Drosera*. Trans. Proc. R. Bot. Soc. Edin. 22:419–424, 1905 (*n.v.*).

MOULAERT, B., La régénération asexuelle chez *Drosera*. Bull. Soc. R. Belg. Bot. 19:154, 1937.

NAUDIN, M., Note sur les bourgeons nés sur une feuille de *Drosera intermedia*. Ann. d. Sci. Nat., II sér. bot., 14:14–16, 1840.

NEUBAUER, MARIA, Vitamin C in der Pflanze. Protoplasma 33:345–370, 1939.

NITSCHKE, TH., Wachstumsverhältnisse des rundblätterigen Sonnentaues. Bot. Ztg. 18:57–61; 65–69, 1860.

NITSCHKE, TH., Über die Reizbarkeit der Blätter von *Drosera rotundifolia*. Bot. Zeitg. 18:229–234; 237–243; 245–250, 1860.

NITSCHKE, TH., Morphologie des Blattes von *Drosera rotundifolia*. Bot. Zeitg. 19:145–151; 233–235; 241–246; 252–255, 1861.

OELS, W., Vergl. Anat. der Droseraceen. Diss. Breslau, 1879.

OKAHARA, K., Physiological studies on *Drosera*, I. On the proteolytic enzyme of *Drosera rotundifolia*. Sci. Rep. Tohoku Imp. Univ., 4 ser. Biol., 5:573–590, 1930*a*.

OKAHARA, K., Studies, II. On the effect of quinine and atoxyl on pepsin. *Ibid.* 5:739–755, 1930*b*.

OKAHARA, K., Studies, III. The effect of various acids on the digestion of protein by pepsin. *Ibid.* 6:573–595, 1931.

OKAHARA, K., On the role of microorganisms in the digestion of insect bodies in insectivorous plants. Bot. Mag. Tok. 46:353–357, 1932 (In Japanese with résumé in English).

OKAHARA, K., Physiological Studies on Drosera, IV. On the function of microorganisms in the digestion of insect bodies by insectivorous plants. Sci. Rep. Tohoku Imp. Univ., 4 ser. Biol., 8:151–168, 1933.

OOSTERHUIS, J., Over de invloed van insectenvoeding op Drosera. Diss. Groningen, 1927.

OUDMAN, J., Nährstoff-aufnahme und Transport durch die Blätter von Drosera capensis. K. Akad. v. Wetensch. Amsterdam, Proc. 38:3–15, 1935.

OUDMAN, J., Über Aufnahme und Transport N-haltiger Verbindungen durch die Blätter von Drosera capensis. Proefschrift, Groningen. Amsterdam, Mulder & Zn. 1936. Ext. Rec. Trav. bot. Néerl. 33:351–433, 1936.

PEYRONEL, B., Bol. Sez. Ital. Soc. Int. Microb. 4:483, 1932.

PFEFFER, W., Osmotische Untersuchungen. Leipzig 1877.

PFEFFER, W., Über fleischfressende Pflanzen und über die Ernährung durch Aufnahme organischer Stoffe überhaupt. Landwirtsch. Jahrb. 6:969–998, 1877.

PFEFFER, W., Zur Kenntnis der Kontaktreize. Unters. Bot. Inst. Tübingen 1:483, 1884.

QUINTANILHA (see under Drosophyllum).

REES, M. & H. WILL, Einige Bemerkungen über fleischfressende Pflanzen. Bot. Zeitung 33:713, 1875 (see also under Nepenthes).

REGEL, E., Futterungsversuche mit Drosera longifolia Sm. und Drosera rotundifolia L. Bot. Zeitung 37:645, 1879 (n.v.).

RENNIE, E. D., The coloring matters of Drosera Whittakeri. Journ. Chem. Soc. 63:1083–1089, 1893.

ROBINSON, W. J., Experiments on Drosera rotundifolia as to its protein digesting power. Torreya 9:109–114, 1909.

ROBINSON, W. J., Reproduction by budding in Drosera. Torreya 9:89–96, 1909.

ROSENBERG, O., Physiologische und zytologische Untersuchungen über Drosera rotundifolia. Upsala 1899.

ROTH, A. W., Von der Reizbarkeit des sogenannten Sonnentaues. Beitr. z. Bot. 1, 1782.

RUSCHMANN, G., Zur Oekologie von Pinguicula und Drosera. Diss. Jena, 1914.

SALISBURY, E., On the occurrence of vegetative propagation in Drosera. Ann. Bot. 29:308–310, 1915.

SCHIMPER, A. F. W., Notizen über insectenfressende Pflanzen. Bot. Zeitung 40:225–234; 241–248, 1882.

SCHLICHT, 1889 (through E. STAHL).

SCHMID, G., Beiträge zur Oekologie der insektivoren Pflanzen. Flora 104:335–383, 1912.

SMALL, J., Intimate camera studies of flowers and plants. Gard. Chron. 105:178, 1939.

SOLEREDER, H., Systematische Anatomie der Dicotyledonen. Stuttgart 1899 und 1908.

SPOEHR, H. A. and J. M. McGEE, Studies in Plant Respiration and Photosynthesis. Carnegie Institution Publ. 325, 1923.

STAHL, E., Der Sinn der Mycorhizenbildung. Jahrb. wiss. Bot. 34:539–668, 1900 (re carnivorous plants, pp. 656–661).

STEPHENS, E. L., A new sundew, Drosera regia Stephens, from Cape Province. Trans. R. Soc. S. Afr. 13:309–312, 1926.

STUTZER (see under Utricularia).

TATE, LAWSON, Insectivorous Plants. Nature 12:251, 1875.

TISCHUTKIN, N., Die Rolle der Bacterien bei den Veränderungen der Eiweisstoffe auf den Blättern von Pinguicula. Ber. d. D. Bot. Gesellsch. 7:346, 1889.

TREAT, MARY, Observations on the Sundew. Am. Nat. 7:705–708, 1873.

TRÉCUL, A., Organisation des glandes pédicellées des feuilles du Drosera rotundifolia. Ann. Sci. nat., IV sér. Bot., 3:303–311, 1855.

TREVIRANUS, C. L., Physiologie der Gewächse. 2(2):759, Bonn 1838 (n.v.).

TROLL, 1939 (see under Nepenthes).

VICKERY, JOYCE W., Vegetative reproduction in Drosera peltata and D. auriculata. Proc. Linn. Soc. N. S. W. 58:245–269, 1933.

VRIES, H. DE, Über die Aggregation im Protoplasma von Drosera rotundifolia. Bot. Zeitung 44:1, 17, 23, 57, 1886.

WARMING, E., Sur la différence entre les trichomes .... Verhandl. der Natur. Gesellsch. in Kopenhagen 1873 (n.v.).

WEBER, FR., Notizen über den Drosera-Tentakel-Schleim. Protoplasma 31:289–292, 1938.

WEBER, FR., Vitamin-C-Gehalt gefütterter Drosera-Blätter. Ber. d. d. b. Gesellsch. 18:370–373, 1940.

WEYLAND, H., Zur Ernährungsphysiologie mykotropher Pflanzen. Jahrb. f. wiss. Bot. 51:1–80, 1912.

WHATELY, in E. DARWIN, Botanic Garden, London 1791.

WHITE, J., The proteolytic enzyme of Drosera. Proc. R. Soc. London B. 83:134–139, 1911.

WINKLER, H., Über regenerative Sprossbildung auf den Blättern von Torenia asiatica L. Ber. D. Bot. Gesellsch. 21:96–107, 1903.

WINZOR, F. L., The coloring matters of Drosera Whittakeri, III. The synthesis of hydroxydroserone. Journ. Chem. Soc. 1935, I:336–338.

WITHERING, W., Arrangement of British Plants, ed. 3, London, 1796.

WOLLNY, EW., Die Zersetzung der organischen Stoffe und die Humusbildung. Heidelberg, 1897.

Chapter XI

CARNIVOROUS FUNGI

Occurrence. — Habit. — Glands. — Secretion. — Digestion.

Among the multifarious activities of fungi, that of zoöphagy has been well known for a very long time. Of this one of the best known examples is the behavior of *Cordyceps*, which invades the bodies of caterpillars of various species and sizes. After displacing the substance of the body of the larva attacked, preserving its form, however, in the sclerotium thus formed, the fungus then sends up a linear stalk bearing the fruiting bodies, the sclerotium being buried in the soil (since it was there that the larva was destroyed), and the fruiting stalk rising above in free air. The study of this kind of pathology in relation to lower forms (algae, small water animals) was being pursued by the botanist, W. ZOPF, in Austria, when there came to his attention just previous to 1888 a fungus which attacked eelworms (*Anguillulidae*).

In the various cultures which he was observing, there were numerous living eelworms and many dead ones tangled with and variously penetrated by the hyphae of the fungus. The question then arose in his mind as to whether the fungus is purely saprophytic, penetrating only already dead worms, or does the fungus attack and kill the living animal? In answering this question experimentally, ZOPF made the first discovery of a fungus which traps a living animal.

The fungus was *Arthrobotrys oligospora*, first described by FRESENIUS (1850–63). It is found in all kinds of more or less decayed matter — mats of old algae for example — and makes a thin veil of mycelium of septate hyphae over the surface. From it there extend slender septate conidiophores bearing pear-shaped two-celled spores. The peculiar feature is the occurrence on the hyphae of many slings or loops of various sizes, formed by the sharp curving of a growing branch which turns upon itself and fuses by its end with its base. From one loop a second and from this a third may arise, and thus is formed a tangle of loops lying in all positions, as WORONIN had already observed. It was ZOPF, however, who first saw that living eel-worms were actually caught by these loops, either by the tail or by the head. The fact that when once the worm has by chance inserted one end or the other into a loop, it cannot free itself again, was definitely observed. The eelworm he used was *Telenchus scandens*, which infests wheat. One observed, on being caught, struggled violently for a half-hour, then became quieter and finally died in 2.5 hours. Why the eelworm cannot free itself when once trapped he attempted to explain by analogy, using as a model a rubber loop just big enough to allow a finger to enter. When one attempts to withdraw the finger, the rubber band clamps on the surface and holds the finger. The clamping effect is due to springiness of the loops, he thought. After the animal succumbs, branches from the loop penetrate its body, and withdraw nutriment (TEXT FIG. 4).

What happens in the case of another similar organism, *Dactylella bembicoides* Drechsler, was explained by Couch (1937). In this plant the loops are composed of a short branch of three cells turned upon themselves. Fusion occurs between the end and basal cells, and a neat ring is thus formed. By growing the fungus on agar to allow of clear microscopic observation, he saw an astonishing thing, that when an eelworm pokes his head or tail into a ring, the ring immediately clamps on it by the sudden swelling of the three cells (TEXT FIG. 4, D, E, I). COUCH records his opinion that the rings are formed most abundantly in media poor in "available food supply,"

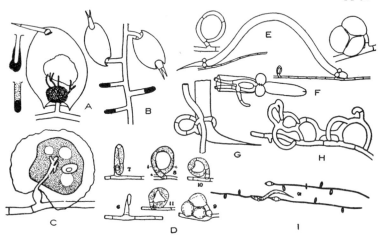

FIG. 4. — A, B, *Zoophagus insidians* (after GICKLHORN 1922); C, *Dactylella tylopaga* attacking Amoeba (after DRECHSLER 1935d); D, E, F, *Dactylella bembicoides* which attacks nematodes (after COUCH 1937); G, H, *Arthrobotrys oligospora*, which attacks nematodes (after ZOPF 1888); I, *Dactylella bembicoides* (after COUCH).

judging from experiments which he did. He attempted to get rings to close on fine glass rods, with limited success, so that it seemed unlikely that mechanical stimulation suffices. He did find, however, that heat (water, at 33 to 75° C.) will cause the rings to close, but that the temperature of the animal's body enters in as a factor in nature is quite unlikely. COUCH therefore fell back on the perhaps correct explanation that the fungus responds to a chemical stimulus from the worm's body. A 1% solution of lactic acid caused a slight swelling. While this was uncertain, COUCH observed that in every case "when a nematode thrusts its head or tail into one of the rings it closes practically instantaneously by the simultaneous swelling of the three cells of the ring." Later, new hyphal branches penetrate the body of the prey. Among these predacious species are included *Trichothecium, Arthrobotrys, Dactylaria, Monacrosporium* and *Dactylella,* all figured by DRECHSLER (1934a). Still others may be expected to turn up.

But not all the ring forming fungi act in the same way. We owe much knowledge about these to DRECHSLER, who points out (1933c) that some species have loops the component cells of which do not swell to constrict the loop, and that these catch their prey by means of a strong adhesive found on the inner surface of the loop. It is not unlikely that this is the case in the plant studied by ZOPF who did not observe constriction of the loops. One species has the loop borne on a very slender stalk which may be broken off during the struggles of the worm, but this does not obviate death and destruction, as the cells of the loop can still form their penetrating hyphae (DRECHSLER, 1933d).

Some of these species, e.g. Dactylaria candida (Nees) Sacc., have in addition to the loops a second organ for the catching of the prey, called "globular" bodies. These are round knobs on short hyphae. On the knob is secreted a patch of strong adhesive, by which the eelworm is caught. In the course of a short time, a penetrating haustorium grows through the adhesive pad and enters the animal's body. In these and the other cases above mentioned, after the prey is permeated with haustorial hyphae, and after these have withdrawn all the available nutriment, the fungal protoplasm withdraws, leaving an empty shell (DRECHSLER, 1933b, c; 1935c).

A similar method of capture is used by a species in which the catching organs consist merely of the ends of hyphal branches, provided, as on the globose organ, with an adhesive. The penetrating haustorial tube swells up after entrance, and from the swelling the haustorial complex of hyphae grows.

A similar, very striking case of a fungus which catches armoured Rotatoria, the first of its kind known, was described in 1911, following ZOPF's original discovery of a carnivorous fungus in Arthrobotrys, by SOMMERSTORFF under the name Zoophagus insidians n. gen., n. sp. This plant grows epiphytically on Cladophora, and consists of a network of septate hyphae which bear "short" branches scattered at irregular intervals along them. These short branches have dense glistening contents, and are the organs of capture. Rotatoria (of the genera Salpina, Metopidia, Colurus, Monostyla), feeding among the threads of the algae and associated fungus, take hold of the ends of the short branches, and remain attached, unable to break loose. By pulling off a newly captured animal he (SOMMERSTORFF) was able to determine that the end of the hypha had enlarged, apparently by the swelling of the membrane, which now took up methylene blue with avidity. Previous to having captured an animal, there appears to be no adhesive, since no detritus could be observed sticking to the ends of the short branches, nor did they take up the stain. SOMMERSTORFF concluded that the swelling takes place on the stimulation occurring when the animal takes the short branch into its mouth. Generally the prey cannot escape, despite his size. But as it has no other organs of locomotion save the cilia, the 'tail' only is available for struggling. If he can get leverage with this on a neighboring algal filament, he may and sometimes does escape. After struggling ceases and death is intervening, the capturing branch grows into a penetrating tube which then sends numerous thin-walled haustorial hyphae to withdraw nutriment.

This organism was studied later also by MIRANDE and by GICKL-HORN. The former generally verified SOMMERSTORFF's observations. He observed, also, the capture of *Stylonychia* and of other organisms than armoured *Rotatoria*, which have the same manner of feeding. By staining he thought to have identified a substance in the short hyphae capable of quick swelling.

GICKLHORN however paid closer attention to the contents of the short hyphae, the organs of capture. By means of staining and solubility tests he came to the conclusion that an oval glistening body, observable in the short hyphae, is a discrete body of callose capable of great swelling. It is always present in organs ready for capture as a definite plug. In unstimulated branchlets it is always on the inside; on stimulated ones it occurs as a mucilaginous cap. Dead organs are always free of the mucilage and are cut off from the bearing hypha by a partition. After a short time following capture (10–30 minutes) the callus plug is emptied into the maw of the prey and spreads out entangling the whole of its ciliary mouth apparatus. There is no further discharge of mucilage after the expulsion of the one shot. These results were indeed foreshadowed by SOMMERSTORFF, but not proven. His suggestion that the mucilage was provided by the swelling of the outer membrane GICKLHORN could not verify. GICKLHORN on the other hand failed to show how the callus plug makes its escape, since no pore or other point of exudation could be observed (TEXT FIG. 4A, B).

GICKLHORN studied the mode of capture and its sequelae, confirming and amplifying such observations as had been made by SOMMER-STORFF. He observed in freshly caught animals which had succeeded in escaping that the ciliary apparatus was in a swollen condition. He asserts that only certain sorts of *Rotatoria* are caught (*Colurus*, *Distyla*, *Metopidia*, *Monostyla*, *Salpina* and *Squalella* species) and never those which are supplied with a strong ciliary apparatus, such as *Brachionus*, *Noteus*, *Anuria*, *Rotifer* and *Philodina*, all of which were subjected to experimental observation. He was unable to observe that infusoria such as *Stylonychia*, *Stentor*, *Paramaecium* and the flagellates *Euglena* and *Paranema* were ever caught. This fact, which he held to be such, indicates at once that not only is the plant a capturing one but that the animal must be capturable. He admits observing some infusoria "caught", but they were stuck to the catching organs, and this does not prove that they were properly caught in the manner of *Rotatoria*. He concludes that instead of speaking of the animal as being caught one should say that it gets itself caught, since only those armoured *Rotatoria* which are able to swallow the bait can be caught. In a culture with many animals the process was followed and this account is given. If an animal hits against the main hypha or against a short hypha sideways, these bend a little under the impact and then recover. The animal, on hitting, infolds its ciliary apparatus; if, however, it approaches a short hypha, the trapping organ, end on, so that it enters the ciliary apparatus, the latter immediately clamps down on it and draws it in. This is done repeatedly for 5–10 minutes during which interval repeated attempts are made by the ciliary apparatus to open, only to clamp down again in response to the mechanical stimulus provided by the short hypha. At the end of this interval it can now be shown by staining methods that the callus plug has been emptied and that it has swollen and spread out to involve the entire ciliary apparatus, which is now rendered useless. In this condition the animal finds its weak foot useless in effecting escape, and in the course of another period of twenty minutes it ceases to struggle. From these observations GICKLHORN draws the following conclusions. In the first stage of capture, there is no adhesive effect on stimulation of the short hypha, as SOMMER-STORFF thought, but repeated mechanical grasping of it by the retractile ciliary apparatus of the animal. Secondarily there follows the excretion of the mucilage. This is an active process on the part of the living short hypha on stimulus, and is not a simple swelling of the membrane. He tried, with success, to stimulate short hyphae to throw off their mucilage by stroking them with a fine hair. The short hypha now begins to send out haustoria which penetrate throughout the body of the animal. Even at the end of digestion, the mucilage plug, which can still be seen, is found to have hardened and become yellow in color, holding the shell of the animal in position. The growth of the haustoria proceeds till the interior of the body is a mass of hyphae which send out conidiophores projecting from the animal and in swarm-spores produced in a sac which escape through the mouth end.

A plant with a similar method of capturing its prey as that employed by *Zoophagus insidians* is *Sommerstorffia spinosa*, described by ARNAUDOW (1923). Both of these species have been collected in Massachusetts and observed by SPARROW (1929).

An extraordinary group of fungi which prey upon species of *Amoeba* and shelled rhizopods has been uncovered and studied by DRECHSLER. His accounts include the minutiae of taxonomic interest as well as the mode of capture. We need not take consideration of the former here. They are nearly all plants with septate hyphae producing conidia of various forms, and in some cases the sexual method of reproduction is known. The method of capture is quite similar in all cases. The species of Amoeba appear to be large, *Amoeba terricola* or related species being often the victim. There is evidence that certain fungi can attack only one kind of Amoeba and not another. In some fungi an adhesive has been observed, in others not, leaving it for conjecture that a non-visible adhesive occurs. There is seldom any preformed structure with the function of capture, but this occurs in *Dactylella tylopaga* Drechsler. In this "prolate ellipsoidal protuberances" are provided with an adhesive. An animal sticks to one of these, which then sends out a tube of penetration. This grows inside the animal into a branching mass of short hyphae which absorb the body of the animal.

Pedilospora dactylopaga captures shelled Rhizopods (DRECHSLER 1934). Eight species of *Acaulopage* have been described by DRECHSLER, all of which capture Amoebae in much the same way as *Dactylella tylopaga* except that there is no special organ involved in capture. "An *Amoeba* after capture is always to be seen attached whether to a mycelial element or as is often the case in some species, to a fallen conidium by means of a minute mass of golden yellow adhesive material." "From the mycelial element or the conidium is thrust forth a narrow process which passes through the deposit of adhesive material and perforates the animal's pellicle to give rise inside to a more or less characteristically branched haustorium or haustorial system. When the protoplasmic contents of the Amoeba are nearly exhausted, the protoplasm of the haustorium begins to withdraw back into the parent mycelial filament. Eventually the haustorium is completely evacuated and thereupon, like the collapsed pellicle surrounding it, becomes altogether invisible; so that an instance of capture is afterwards found recorded, and then usually only rather dubiously, in an inconspicuous scar-like or slightly protuberant modification of the contour of the hypha or conidium" (TEXT FIG. 4C), (DRECHSLER 1935b, p. 183). In the case of another fungus, *Endocochlus asteroides* Drechsler, the animal is attacked by conidia picked up in its wanderings. Sticking to the surface of the pellicle, they form a small bulbous body, serving apparently as an appressorium, through which a slender tube punctures the pellicle and enters the animal, passing in to some distance. There the end swells up, taking in the protoplasm of the conidium, which becomes detached and is usually thrown off by the animal. Sometimes the conidium is ingested, however. Owing to the fact that the animal may be infected a number of times, because of the numbers of fallen spores, it may have a corresponding number of bulbous bodies, each derived from a conidium. After the conidium with its germ tube is loosened and cast off, the remaining globular thallus becomes considerably enlarged and turgid. As it lengthens it curves and with elongation becomes a helicoidal mass. In the meantime, the animal remains alive and active, so that we are contemplating here a case of parasitism. The briskness of action persists for some time, until the bulk of the animal becomes reduced, and it finally succumbs. The inclosed fungus then sends out slender hyphae which penetrate the pellicle to the exterior, where spores and sexual apparatus are produced, to produce new hyphae which begin the cycle again. The same story is presented by *Cochlonema verrucosum* Drechsler, and in *C. dolichosporum*, but in these it is started by conidia which are first ingested by the animal, one having the same dimensions as *Amoeba sphaeronucleus*. In *Bdellospora helicoides* Drechsler the infection takes place as in *Endocochlus asteroides*. In *Zoopage phanera* Drechsler the manner of capture is a matter of inference rather than direct observation. The animal captured is an Amoeba from 35–110 micra in diameter. An adhesive is indicated, though DRECHSLER suggests that the small botryoidal organs seen in a captured animal could be taken for grappling organs. At all events they are very distinctive in form as his figure shows.

In the forms above described it is evident that we are dealing with organisms that stand between plants which have elaborated organs designed — if we may use the word — for first trapping an animal before disposing of it, and those which infect an animal by a process which must be repeated in a very many cases, as for instance that of *Cordyceps* and related plants already mentioned. Carnivorous the latter are, but they can hardly be regarded as "trapping" plants.

The significance of carnivory for *Zoophagus* (and hence by implication for fungi in general) has been indicated experimentally by GICKLHORN (1922). By culturing it for two months in properly prepared water, free of animals, he found that it could persist saprophytically, as many other fungi do. Under these conditions, however, it became a "hunger form", with the "long hyphae", though normal as to branching, weakly developed, and with depreciated cellular contents. In two days after the addition of *Rotatoria*, the hyphae became appreciably stronger and were well filled with contents, "After such evidence one can hardly avoid the thought that the capture of animals by *Zoophagus* supplied an important source of nutrition and that we have before us a highly specialized adaptation" (*l.c.* p. 217).

Literature Cited:

ARNAUDOW, N., Zur Morphologie und Biologie von *Zoophagus insidians* Sommerstorff. Jahrb. d. Univ. Sofia 15–16:1–32, 1918–(1921) (Bulgarian with German summary).

ARNAUDOW, N., Ein neuer Rädertiere (Rotatoria) fangender Pilz (*Sommerstorffia spinosa* nov. gen., nov. sp.). Flora 116:109–113, 1923.

ARNAUDOW, N., Untersuchungen über *Sommerstorffia spinosa* nov. gen., nov. spec. Jahrb. d. Univ. Sofia Bd. 19, H. 2, Abt. 1a, 1923.

ARNAUDOW, N., Untersuchung über den Tiere fangenden Pilz *Zoophagus insidians* Som. Flora 118–119:1–16, 1925.

BUDDE, E., Über die in Rädertieren lebenden Parasiten. Arch. f. Hydrob. 18:442–459.

COUCH, J. N., The formation and operation of the traps in the nematode-catching fungus, *Dactylella bembicoides* Drechsler. Jour. Elisha Mitchell Sci. Soc. 53:301–309, 1937.

DRECHSLER, C., Morphological features of some fungi capturing and killing Amoebae. J. Wash. Acad. Sci. 23:200–202, 1933a.

DRECHSLER, C., Morphological diversity among fungi capturing and destroying nematodes. J. Wash. Acad. Sci. 23(3):138–141, 1933b.

DRECHSLER, C., Morphological features of some more fungi that capture and kill nematodes. J. Wash. Acad. Sci. 23(5):267–270, 1933c.

DRECHSLER, C., Several more fungi that prey on nematodes. J. Wash. Acad. Sci. 23(7): 355–357, 1933d.

DRECHSLER, C., Organs of capture in some fungi preying on nematodes. Mycol. 26:135–144, 1934a.

DRECHSLER, C., *Pedilospora dactylopaga* n. sp., a fungus capturing and consuming testaceous rhizopods. J. Wash. Acad. Sci. 24:395–402, 1934b.

DRECHSLER, C., Some conidial Phycomycetes destructive to terricolous Amoebae. Mycol. 27:6–40, 1935a.

DRECHSLER, C., Some non-catenulate conidial Phycomycetes preying on terricolous Amoebae. Mycol. 27:176–205, 1935b.

DRECHSLER, C., A new species of conidial Phycomycete preying on nematodes. Mycol. 27:206–215, 1935c.

DRECHSLER, C., A new Mucedinaceous fungus capturing and consuming *Amoeba verrucosa*. Mycol. 27:216–223, 1935d.

DRECHSLER, C., A new species of *Stylopage* preying on nematodes. Mycol. 28:241–246, 1936a.

DRECHSLER, C., New conidial Phycomycetes destructive to terricolous Amoebae. Mycol. 28:363–389, 1936b.

DRECHSLER, C., A Fusarium-like species of *Dactylella* capturing and consuming testaceous rhizopods. J. Wash. Acad. Sci. 26:397–404, 1936c.

DRECHSLER, C., New *Zoopagaceae* destructive to soil rhizopods. Mycol. 29:229–249, 1937a.

DRECHSLER, C., Some Hyphomycetes that prey on free-living terricolous nematodes. Mycol. 29:447–552, 1937b.

DRECHSLER, C., New *Zoopagaceae* capturing and consuming soil Amoebae. Mycologia 30:2:137–157, 1938.

DRECHSLER, C., A few new *Zoopagaceae* destructive to large soil rhizopods. Mycologia 31:2:128–153, 1939.

DRECHSLER, C., Five new *Zoopagaceae* destructive to Rhizopods and Nematodes. Mycologia 31:4:388–415, 1939.

FRESENIUS, Beiträge zur Mycologie. Frankfurt, 1850–63, p. 18, pl. 3, figs. 1–7 (*fide* ZOPF).

GEITLER, L., Über einen Pilzparasiten auf *Amoeba proteus* und über die polare Organisation des Amoebenkörpers. Biol. Zentralbl. 57:166–175, 1939.

GICKLHORN, J., Studien an *Zoophagus insidians* Som., einem Tiere fangenden Pilz. "Glasnik" Kroat. Nat. Ges. 34(2):199–288, 1922.

GICKLHORN, J., *Aphanomyces ovidestruens* nov. spec., ein Parasit in den Eiern von *Diaptomus.* Lotos 71:143–156, 1923.

KONSULOFF, ST., Untersuchungen über Rotatorienparasiten. Arch. f. Protistenk. 36:353–361, 1916.

MIRANDE, R., *Zoophagus insidians* Sommerstorff, capteur de Rotifères vivants. Bull. Soc. Myc. Fr. 36:47–53, 1920.

RENNERFELT, E., Untersuchungen über die Entwicklung und Biologie des Krebspestpilzes, *Aphanomyces astaci* Schikora. Mitt. Anst. f. Binnenfischerei bei Drottningholm, Stockholm, No. 10, 21 pp., 1936.

SCHERFFEL, A., Endophytische Phycomyceten-Parasiten der Bacillariaceen und einige neue Monadinen. Archiv Protistenk. 52:1–141, 1925.

SCHIKORA, F., Über die Krebspest und ihren Erreger, *Aphanomyces Magnusi* Schikora. Verhandl. Bot. Verein Prov. Brandenburg 63:87–88, 1922.

SOMMERSTORFF, H., Ein Tiere fangender Pilz (*Zoophagus insidians* nov. gen., nov. sp.). Oest. Bot. Zeitschr. 61:361–373, 1911.

SPARROW, F. K., Jr., A note on the occurrence of two rotifer-capturing Phycomycetes. Mycol. 21(2):90–96, 1929.

VALKANOV, A., Über Morphologie und Systematik der rotatorienbefallenden Pilze. Archiv Protist. 74(1):5–17, 1931.

VALKANOV, A., Über die Morphologie und Systematik der Rotatorien befallenden Oomyceten (bulgarisch). Jahrb. Univ. Sofia, 27, 1931.

VALKANOV, A., Nachtrag zu meiner Arbeit über rotatorienbefallende Pilze. Archiv Protist. 78(2):485–496, 1932.

ZOPF, W., Zur Kenntniss der Infectionskrankheiten niederer Thieren und Pflanzen. Nova Acta d. Leop.-Carol. Akad. d. Naturf. 52:315–375, 1888.

Chapter XII

DIONAEA MUSCIPULA AND ALDROVANDA VESICULOSA

Dionaea: general description. — Early discovery. — Original description by Ellis. — Work of Curtis (1834), Oudemans (1859), Canby (1868), Darwin, Goebel. — Morphology (Seed and seedling. Structure of mature leaf: trap. Lobes, glands, sensitive hairs. Internal structure). — Physiology. — *Aldrovanda:* general description. — Discovery, distribution. — Morphology (Seed. Germination. Mature leaf. Posture of the trap). — Physiology.

These two monotypic genera are members of the family *Droseraceae*, and while the former, *Dionaea*, is well known, it being widely grown in greenhouses, *Aldrovanda* is well known chiefly to such botanists as have a special interest in these curious plants. *Dionaea* has a very restricted geographical range, *Aldrovanda* a very wide one. Though the method of trapping animals is identical, the one is a land plant, and *Aldrovanda* a submersed water plant. We consider these separately.

Dionaea muscipula Ellis, **Venus' fly trap:** — This is a small plant (*17* — 2), consisting of a rosette of leaves three to six inches across arising from a rootstock growing more or less horizontally. The rootstock is apparent even in the young seedling (Smith 1931). Long scapes are sent up bearing several flowers in a short cyme with two to fourteen flowers. These are of pentamerous structure, five small elliptical sepals alternate with five white cuneate and somewhat oblique petals, usually fifteen stamens. The leaf consists of two regions, a basal "footstalk" as Darwin called it, articulated by means of a short cylindrical portion (midrib) with the blade which is a trap. The footstalk is a more or less expanded leaf-like structure, either broadly obcordate to narrowly obcordate in form, depending on exposure to light and the presence of surrounding vegetation. The upper part of the leaf, a "striking and noteworthy" trap, to quote Goebel, consists of two dished lobes of trapezoidal form. The outer margins are "ciliated," that is, are provided with a row of coarse projections, prongs or teeth. Ellis (1770) spoke of the arrangement as "a miniature form of a rat-trap," and Curtis (1834) compared it to "two upper eyelids joined at their bases." Springing from the upper surface of the two lobes there are six slender, sensitive hairs, three on each side placed in triangular position (in exceptional cases a smaller or larger number has been noted (*18* — 1). The rest of the surface is covered rather densely with two kinds of sessile glands, most of which under usual circumstances are colored with brilliant red pigment, giving a bright red tinge to the surface. When with suitable temperatures the sensitive hairs are moved, the two lobes swing swiftly on their common axis, and the finger-like cilia intercross to form a barred cage. Darwin interpreted this initial posture as an arrangement to allow small insects, relatively valueless on account of their size, to escape before final closure, a view for which F. M. JONES has adduced constructive evidence. Subsequent movement progressing during $\frac{1}{2}$–12 ± hours approximates the lobes more closely and even causes them to become flatter, bringing the inner surfaces into closer apposition.

If by this reaction an insect, the normal agent of stimulation, has been caught, the body may be more or less compressed between the lobes ($17 — 3$). The glands then secrete a digestive fluid and in a few days the insect body disintegrates and the products are absorbed. In the course of ten days the lobes open again, and are ready to catch other prey. This may be repeated two or three times before the leaf reaches its complete maturity, when it dies. Of this arrangement CURTIS (1834) remarked, "if it were a problem to construct a plant with reference to entrapping insects, I cannot conceive of a form and organization better adapted to secure that end than are found in *Dionaea muscipula*."

"This plant, which LINNAEUS called *miraculum naturae*, appears to have first been discovered by ARTHUR DOBBS, Governor of North Carolina, and he sent the following account of it to Mr. COLLINSON in a letter dated at Brunswick, Jan. 24, 1760. After describing the *Schrankia*, he proceeds: — 'But the great wonder of the vegetable kingdom is a very curious unknown species of sensitive; it is a dwarf plant; the leaves are like a narrow segment of a sphere, consisting of two parts, like the cap of a spring purse, the concave part outward, each of which falls back with indented edges (like an iron spring fox trap); upon anything touching the leaves, or falling between them, they instantly close like a spring trap, and confine any insect or anything that falls between them; it bears a white flower; to this surprising plant I have given the name of Fly Trap Sensitive.' Mr. COLLINSON, in a memorandum, has recorded the death of Governor DOBBS in 1765" (DILLWYN 1843).

It may be inferred from the note by Governor DOBBS, written in 1760, but which did not gain publicity till the appearance of the *Hortus Collinsonianus* in 1843, that the *Dionaea* was well known in North Carolina when, in 1763, a Mr. YOUNG, "the Queen's botanist," had his attention drawn by some friends to a "peculiar plant" which he subsequently found in great abundance in North Carolina and in some parts of South Carolina. Still later YOUNG brought living plants to England, he also introduced them in Kew (SIMS 1804) and from these ELLIS, a London merchant, drew his description and figure sent by him to LINNAEUS in 1770 (YOUNG 1783). These were published in a small volume entitled, *Directions for Bringing over Seeds and Plants from the East Indies and other Distant Countries in a State of Vegetation*, in 1770. ELLIS' description was published in Latin at a subsequent date in *Nova Acta Soc. Scient. Upsaliensis* 1:98, 1773. Though ELLIS' description was based on living material, he had just previously received from JOHN BARTRAM of Philadelphia, through Mr. PETER COLLINSON, an herbarium specimen which furnished material which enabled Dr. SOLANDER and himself to determine that they had before them a new genus allied to *Drosera* (ELLIS 1770). But ELLIS, who from the dried material got no hint of the motility of the leaves, did so when he examined the material brought to England by YOUNG, and he was the first to publish a definite statement of the carnivorous habits of the plant. It is this, expressed in the letter to LINNAEUS, which interests us here. Having recalled that *Mimosa* is irritable, but shortly recovers from its position of response, ELLIS continues:

"But the plant, of which I now inclose you an exact figure, with a specimen of its leaves and blossoms, shews, that nature may have some view towards *nourishment*, in forming the upper joint of the leaf like a *machine* to catch food: upon the middle of this lies the bait for the unhappy insect that becomes its prey. Many minute red glands, that cover its inner surface, and which perhaps discharge sweet liquor, tempt the poor animal to taste them; and the instant these tender parts are irritated by its feet, the two lobes rise up, grasp it fast, lock the rows of spines together, and squeeze it to death. And, further, lest the strong efforts for life, in the creature thus taken, should serve to disengage it, three small erect spines are fixed near the middle of each lobe, among the glands, that effectually put an end to all its struggles. Nor do the lobes ever open again, while the dead animal continues there. But it is nevertheless certain that the plant cannot distinguish an animal, from a vegetable or mineral, substance; for if we introduce a straw or a pin between the lobes, it will grasp it full as fast as if it were an insect."

The above paragraph, quoted also by HOOKER in 1875, was taken from the original, a copy of which is to be found in the Library of Congress, Washington. It shows us clearly what ELLIS thought about the plant. LINNAEUS, to whom was sent the letter containing the above quotation, did not, however, fully respond to ELLIS' evident enthusiasm, and merely regarded the movement as a special case of irritability like that in *Mimosa*, and believed that on reopening the captured insect was released (*Mantissa plantarum altera*, Holmiae 1771); nor did he see eye to eye with ELLIS about the function of the "three small erect spines" whether from sagacity, as HOOKER suggests (1875), or as part of his general non-responsiveness to ELLIS' interpretations, it is hard to say. It happens, of course, that ELLIS was wrong; the idea was even fantastic. No less was that of ERASMUS DARWIN who wrote: "In the *Dionaea muscipula* there is a still more wonderful contrivance to prevent the depredations of insects: the leaves are armed with long teeth, like the antennae of insects, and lie spread upon the ground around the stem, and are so irritable, that when an insect creeps upon them they fold up and crush or pierce it to death." (*The Botanic Garden* 2: canto I, p. 39).

É. MORREN (1875) in a footnote calls attention to a description by the French encyclopaedist DENIS DIDEROT (1713–1784) of "Plante de la Caroline appellée Muscipula Dionaea", of which he says, at the close of his description "Voilà une plante presque carnivore". The essay from which this is quoted is said to be dated 1774–1780, not 1762 as M. CATALAN told Dr. MORREN. It is of interest to record DIDEROT's speculation "Je ne me doute point que la Muscipula ne donnât à l'analyse de l'alcali volatil, produit caractéristique du règne animal."

In 1834 M. A. CURTIS (quoted on p. 177), a minister resident in Wilmington, N. C., published his observations, which led him to think that the sensitiveness resides only in the hair-like processes, and that other parts of the leaf may be touched or pressed without any response. This is not quite true, as has later been found. Further, that insects captured are not always crushed on being caught, for if the trap were opened again they might escape; but that in time they were surrounded by a mucilaginous fluid by which the insects were more or less consumed. The fact that a special sensitivity resides in the six slender hairs of the upper surface of the trap had been noted by a botanical draughtsman, SYDENHAM EDWARDS, employed by Dr. JOHN SIMS in illustrating CURTIS's *Botanical Magazine.* This observation was recorded by SIMS (1804) in the description of plate 785 of vol. 20 which reads: "These small spines are mentioned and figured by ELLIS and supposed by him to assist in destroying the entrapped animal; but that they are only irritable points, and that any other part of the leaf may be touched with impunity, was discovered by our draughtsman, Mr. EDWARDS, several years ago, when taking a sketch of a plant flowering at Mr. LIPMAN's, Mile End, and has since been repeatedly confirmed. The same observation was made, without knowing it had previously been noticed, by our friend Mr. CHARLES KONIG" (HOOKER 1875).

In 1859 OUDEMANS, a Dutch botanist, rediscovered the sensitivity of the trigger hairs, and did a number of experiments which afforded results which anticipated some of DARWIN's. He found that there is no periodic closure of the trap, as MEYEN has claimed, and that traps, after closure, opened again during the night. MEYEN had said that the closure was too slow to catch insects, to which OUDEMANS answered that at sufficiently high temperatures it is rapid, which we now know to be true. He recorded that the trap does not open after catching prey until several days after its death. When the trap does, the prey is found lying in a slimy liquid; and further that the trap does not remain closed over inanimate objects such as paper, reopening in 36 hours or less. Though he thought that the stimulus was transmitted to the mid-vein, he attributed closure to alterations of strain in the parenchyma.

In 1868 CANBY thought it might be that the fluids collecting in the closed trap might escape and, flowing down the petioles of the leaves, might enrich the soil at the base of the plant. Experiments showed him, however, that this is not the case, but that, on feeding the leaf, the insect is entirely destroyed and absorbed, thus confirming CURTIS, thirty-four years his predecessor. He concluded by saying, "so that, in fine, the fluid (secreted by the leaves) may well be said to be analogous to the gastric juice of animals, dissolving the prey and rendering it fit for absorption by the leaf."

That, however, the sensitive hairs are the only sensitive spots in the leaf was shown by DARWIN and by GOEBEL (1891) not to be true. "It is sufficient to rub the upper or lower surface, and not too strongly, with a solid object to procure immediate closure of the two halves of the trap" (GOEBEL). This, as will be seen, has later been confirmed.

We now direct our attention to certain of the more intimate details of the life history and structure of the plant.

The seed and seedling (SMITH 1931). — The seed is a small pear-shaped mass with a lid at the micropylar end. The embryo, also pear-shaped, lies with its two broad cotyledons in contact with an abundant endosperm. The cotyledon-ends remain in contact with the endosperm for an extended period, while their bodies enlarge, become green, and eventually spread apart, becoming elongate in form. Meanwhile the primary root has developed, bears a mass of root hairs, but does not persist. From the plumule there arises at once a rhizome bearing small leaves which are similar to the mature leaves in all points, except that they are small (GOEBEL 1891, HOLM 1891), the shape of the trap is more rectangular, and the glands are fewer in number. This story, as we shall see, is similar to that of *Aldrovanda*.

Although, as Miss SMITH says, the juvenile leaves (those of seedlings) are similar to those of mature plants, there are differences worthy of note, among which are the following: Traps 2 mm. long have poorly developed marginal spines of rather irregular form and little rigidity, and may arise symmetrically, so that those of the opposing lobes face each other (*18* — 8); or there may be a conspicuous lack of symmetry and a disparity of number (18 on one side and 13 on the other), some teeth displaying branching to some extent (*18* — 9). Traps of larger size (4 mm. along the midrib and 7 mm. along the free margins) have well developed spines with posture and rigidity comparable to traps on mature leaves. The number of glands in juvenile leaves is much smaller, while the size of the glands approaches that of maturity. They are rather widely scattered. I counted about 70 in the 2 mm. trap (*18* — 9). There is a wide zone between the outer limit of this glandular region and the lobe margin; and in the outer zone of allure, a narrow zone just within the margin, the nectar (?) glands are only 2 to 12 in number, confined to the outer angles of the lobes in the 2 mm. traps examined; while as many as 50 were found in the 4 mm. trap. As would be expected, the structure of the lobes is of much greater delicacy as compared with that of mature leaves. In the 2 mm. trap the lobe was found 0.5 mm. thick at the level of an inner sensitive hair (*18* — 17, 18). The inner (upper) epidermis cells were somewhat larger than those of the outer in the ratio of 1.4 to 1, and had somewhat thicker outer walls. The number of parenchyma cells between ranged from two to four courses with large interspaces, in this feature again resembling the mature leaves of *Aldrovanda* much more than do the thicker mature leaves of *Dionaea*. It is easier, thus, to see the parallelism of action in these two plants, to which reference is made beyond. The sensitive hairs are much smaller and simpler in construction (*18* — 3). They are about 0.6 mm. long, the outer stiff "lever" being somewhat more than half that. The basal portion is deeply constricted, and the bending cells are relatively large and impinge on each other in the middle of the hair, there being no medullary cells. These latter seem, therefore, of no importance beyond that of a filler in the large, sensitive hairs of the mature leaf.

In young plants derived from leaf cuttings (seen growing in Munich) the lobes of the traps were usually quite oblique in form, and the cilia were very irregular and often very small. Both kinds of glands were present in small numbers. I counted six alluring glands clustered near each of the outer angles of the lobe in one, and three in another trap. The digestive glands were more numerous, but still few and scattered. The sensitive hairs were absent in one case, and from one to two occurred in several others. While small, they showed all the normal histological details.

During development the blade and trap both display circination. In the latter the two lobes are rolled inwardly and gradually unfold, the cilia being the last to unroll. The blade lobes are inrolled longitudinally at first, but as it develops the axis of the roll gradually comes to lie more transversely, the last portion of the blade to unroll being the apex. At first also the trap is bent sharply back on the blade, but lying asymmetrically on its right lobe, which presses against the blade surface. With further growth the trap swings forward on its stalk, and now comes to lie more or less on its left lobe, or otherwise expressed, the trap is twisted more or less to the left (as seen from above) (*18* — 7). This posture is more evident in small plants, with small traps, than in plants large enough to produce normal sized traps. It is, however, often quite evident in the latter, as I have myself observed in plants growing under my eye. In the account beyond of *Aldrovanda*, it will be seen that in this plant the trap always lies on its left side, a position which offers distinct advantages in the trapping of prey. Much less marked, however, is the posture just mentioned for *Dionaea*, and it cannot be said to be of any significance. I have never seen the trap bending to the right (as seen from above).

Structure of the mature leaf. — The structure of the leaf has often been the subject of examination (OUDEMANS, 1859; DARWIN, 1875; KURTZ, 1876; DE CANDOLLE, 1876; FRAUSTADT, 1877; GOEBEL, 1891; HABERLANDT, 1901; GUTTENBERG, 1925). The winged form of the petiolar region traversed by a single vascular bundle, which presents nothing further of special interest, is regarded by GOEBEL as a physiological compensation in the interest of photosynthesis, such compensations being generally found among the carnivorous plants. In seedlings the petiole is relatively much larger.

The outer part of the leaf, the blade, is the trap. This consists of two lobes, trapezoidal in form, united along the middle line by a thick midrib, which has often been considered a hinge, but which has no hinge function (*18* — 1). At their bases the lobes have their greatest thickness, thinning off gradually as the margins are approached (*18* — 4b). Here, however, they are thickened locally by the enlarged bases of the marginal cilia. These are prominent, tapering, finger-like processes, evidently emergencies (SOLEREDER), which are so placed that when the lobes are approximated they interweave like the fingers of closed hands. The cilia have been thought to be homologous with the tentacles of *Drosera*, but, as GOEBEL pointed out, the comparison fails in that the cilia show no trace of glandular tissue, and have evidently a widely different function. The whole trap acts, to quote

LINDLEY (1848), like the jaws of a steel trap. The simile may not be applied too rigorously since it is not the edges of the lobes which catch the prey.

The two lobes, when the leaf is widely open, stand at an angle of 40–50 (DARWIN: "80") degrees to each other, published drawings being often in error on this point ($18 — 4a$). They are clothed with a distinctly firm epidermis of straight walled cells, elongated parallel with the veins, becoming somewhat wavy on approaching the margins, which lends a surprising stiffness to the trap. When once a lobe is cut, as in making sections, it becomes evident that the epidermis is the only mechanical tissue present. The outer surfaces bear scattered stellate trichomes ($18 — 11$) which are found also in the bays between the cilia of seedling traps, and even slightly invading their inner surfaces. The inner surfaces are supplied with very numerous glands, all having the same structure. They consist of two basal epidermal cells, placed parallel with the midrib, and whose walls are thickened by cellulose ridges, producing an appearance which led MACFARLANE (1892) to take them to be "intercellular protoplasmic connections." What he saw, it seems, are only layers of cytoplasm lying between the cellulose ridges, but this is not to deny that such protoplasmic connections may not also be present. Surmounting the two basal cells is a second course of two small cells, with cutinized diametrical wall, constituting the stalk. This supports a large capital of about 32 cells in two courses, the lower capped by the upper to form a bun-shaped mass ($18 — 12, 13$). There are two physiological kinds of these glands, as evidence adduced by FRANK MORTON JONES indicates (1923), namely digestive (and absorptive) and alluring. The former, thought by ELLIS "perhaps" to discharge a sweet liquor, occupy the major area of the surface and are so numerous that they often crowd on each other ($18 — 1$). The alluring glands occupy a narrow zone just within the ciliated margin. Between the two groups of glands there is a narrow zone quite free of glands (JONES). Though identical in structure, the digestive and alluring glands display some differences. The digestive glands ($18 — 12, 13$) are rendered conspicuous by their deep red color, due to anthocyanin present in the sap of their cells, and are responsible for the deep red note of color of the inner surface of the trap. The alluring glands (in the traps I examined) contain no pigment. These are imbedded somewhat in the epidermis ($18 — 14$), while the digestive glands stand out prominently. These also are larger (0.096–0.1 mm. in diam.) than the alluring glands, which measure 0.06–0.073 mm. in diameter. That the alluring glands secrete a sugar (or something attractive to insects) is supported strongly by JONES' observations already alluded to: ". . . these little ants were observed to occupy a uniform position on the upper surface, their heads close to the bases of the marginal spikes. As they moved slowly across this belt of the leaf they made frequent and prolonged pauses, during which their mouth parts were observed under the lens to be in motion against the surface of the leaf. A larger and winged hymenopteron was observed to be engaged in the same performance. Obviously they were feeding upon some attractive exudation of the leaf. The behavior of visiting insects is entirely convincing to the observer that a baited area extends across the leaf surface just within the bases of the marginal spines. This baited marginal band is so situated upon the leaf surface that a visiting insect *in length too small to reach from the bait to the trigger hairs*, usually does not spring the trap. Whether or not these conditions are to be interpreted as adjustments to that end, the effect of the arrangement, in conjunction with the peculiarities of the closing movement by which small insects are given an opportunity to escape, is to limit the captures of the leaves to insects approximating one quarter of an inch or more in length." JONES examined the captures of fifty closed traps and found that, of all the prey "only one was less than 5 mm. in length and only seven less than 6 mm.; they were 10 mm. or more in length, with a maximum of 30 mm." (JONES 1923). In this way was corroborated DARWIN's suspicion that the posture first assumed by the trap on closure in which the marginal spines form a cage is one which permits small insects to escape. I have observed larger ones, small centipedes, doing their best to force their way between the spines, but without success. A wood louse was seen to free itself because its position was such that its carapace held the lobe margins open just enough to allow escape, which was evidently facilitated by the fact that the lateral projections of the carapace allowed leg movement. Many a wood louse is not so lucky.

The closure of the trap, a seismonastic movement, normally follows when sensitive or trigger hairs are disturbed as CURTIS recorded in 1834. "Each side of the leaf is a little concave on the inner side where are placed three delicate, hair-like organs, in such an order, that an insect can hardly traverse it, without interfering with one of them, when the two sides suddenly collapse and enclose the prey with a force which surpasses the insect's efforts to escape." Though usually three in number on each lobe, there may on occasion be more or fewer. When three, they stand at the angles of a triangle placed in the middle of the lobe with its base nearer and parallel to the outer ciliated margin. If we examine one of these hairs we find that it is multicellular and displays two distinct regions. The outer of these is a slender cone (*18* — 2) in form, about 1.5 mm. in length and 0.15 mm. thick at the base. It is composed of elongated, thick walled cells and constitutes a lever; any slight movement causes a bending in the basal region, to which OUDEMANS (1859) attributed a special sensitivity. This is only 0.15 mm. in height and is conspicuous on account of a deep constriction slightly below the base of the lever, first described by GOEBEL (1891). This constriction, the hinge or bending place (GOEBEL), is made up of a single transverse ring of cells of which their outer walls are deeply indented (*18* — 15, 16). Their lateral walls are thick and collenchymatous in character, their end walls thin. Because of the indentation, the outer wall is thinner at this point. Within the ring of indented cells there is a medullary group of elongated cells, tracheidal in character (GOEBEL), absent from the small trigger hairs of seedling leaves, which measure only 0.15 to 0.2 mm. in length, of which the lever occupies well over a half, the greatest width being 0.03 mm. (*18* — 3). The indented cells are surmounted by three layers of flattish cells under-

lying the base of the lever, and stand upon a base of about four or
five courses of cells, meeting the general leaf surface. All the cells
have rather thick walls, and there are no intercellular spaces. This
whole basal region is the podium. Its histological character just
mentioned is such as to permit bending. It is, however, the whole
podium which bends, and not merely the cells under the constriction
($37 — 5$). I noted while cutting hand sections that the podium readily
stretches and compresses, bending being a combination of these. But
although the whole podium bends notably when the lever is much
displaced, it is quite clear on watching with the microscope that
slight bending is evident first and at once in the constricted zone,
as GOEBEL recorded.

The hinge cells were thought by MACFARLANE (1892) to be devoid of a cuticle, or to have a very thin one. HABERLANDT, however,
denied this. The cuticle is fairly thick and displays a certain amount
of wrinkling, which would allow freer movement of the collenchymatous cell walls beneath. It further appears finely punctate, interpreted by MACFARLANE as due to the presence of pores. HABERLANDT
regarded this to be due rather to denticulations of the inner surface
of the cuticle which prevent loosening of the cuticle under repeated
bendings by anchoring it to the cellulose wall. It is easier to agree
with HABERLANDT that the points seen (of which there is no doubt)
are not pores, than that they are extensions of the cuticle into the
cellulose underneath. Nevertheless, it is possible to see minute irregularities on the inner face of the cuticle, so that the interface
between the cuticle and cellulose is greater than it would be otherwise.

The medullary cells show some peculiarities. In addition to a
fine porosity (GOEBEL), HABERLANDT records the presence of minute granular inclusions of high refringency in the middle layer
between the walls and between these and the hinge cells. He describes these as cutinized granules. Some cutinization certainly occurs.

There is no vascular connection between the medullary cells of
GOEBEL and the leaf, since there is no vein in the hair.

The internal structure of the leaf blade or trap was described by
MUNK in 1876, concerned as he was with the direction of movement
of electrical currents, in much detail as to form and position of the
component cells. We recall that the trap has a massive midrib traversed longitudinally by a double vascular bundle which gives off
branches, running parallel to each other, towards the margins, approaching which they form a coarse zig-zag network. All the remaining space between the two epiderms is occupied by a thin-walled
parenchyma, of large-sized cells inside and smaller against the epiderm, those against the inner epidermis being larger than those against
the outer, where they are much smaller and more numerous. There
are more smaller cells opposite the vascular bundles and more cells
of very large size between the vascular bundles ($18 — 10$). The
walls beneath the inner epidermis and the cells of the first parenchyma
course are thickened into a collenchyma ($18 — 5$) and to some extent also, those between this and the next course. This mechanical

element is absent from the outer epidermis region. There is a total absence of palisade tissue, a feature common to many carnivorous plants, as SCHMID showed. The parenchyma cells are elongated in different degrees according to position. Below the chief vascular strands in the midrib their long axes run lengthwise, above at right angles to it and here are shorter. Those of the lateral regions run up into the two lobes, and here they attain their greater longitudinal dimensions, the largest, in the middle, being the longest. Approaching the margins, they become shorter and, as MUNK points out, are shortest, though not round, at the base of the cilia, lengthening again in the cilia themselves. The intercellular spaces are large and extensive, and while the protoplasm is very tenuous, chloroplasts are present and much starch may occur, as BROWN pointed out.

Physiology. — If the question is asked how the structure just described is related to the movement of the lobes, the answer is indicated by comparing it with that of the lobes of very small traps found in seedlings, and with those of *Aldrovanda*. They all show the same capacity for movement, whether the parenchyma consists of one course of cells only (*Aldrovanda*) or of a few, as in seedlings traps. The evidence indicates that the seat of movement resides in the epidermis first of all. Further complication of structure is connected with the mechanical strength of the lobes naturally greater in the massive leaves of adult *Dionaea* plants. That is, the machine as such is stronger (involving parenchyma cells) and can exert more energy in the last, without any difference in the seat or directions of movement. All movement occurs in the lobes and, as BROWN showed, none in the midrib, which is therefore not a hinge in any sense. This is indicated in the diagram, borrowed from ASHIDA, shown in *18 — 4a*, though this does not indicate the extreme possibilities of closure, better shown in *18 — 4b*.

The stimulus leading to action. — In nature the walking of an insect across a lobe of the trap almost inevitably results in the disturbance of the sensitive hairs, ensuring the prompt closure of the trap. This CURTIS (1834) clearly observed. ELLIS (1770) had thought the movement as following irritation of the glands by the feet of the prey, and BROUSSONET (1784) believed that it was due to the loss of turgidity caused by the pricking of the surface by insects. But from the time of CURTIS it was supposed that it was necessary only to touch a hair to bring about closure, until the work of BURDON–SANDERSON demonstrated the fact of summation of stimuli. MACFARLANE found independently that under usual circumstances (temperature is important) in order to effect closure of the trap, it requires two stimuli, either by touching the same trigger hair twice, or any two different ones with an interval of time neither too short (about 0.75 sec.) nor too long (over 20 sec.). This was in 1892. Previous observers, with the exception above noted, had failed to notice this behavior, very obvious when once seen. For example, DARWIN says: "It is sufficient to touch any one of the six filaments to cause both lobes to close ...," but observed that an extremely delicate stimulus might be inadequate. DARWIN does remark, however, that " on another occasion two or three touches of the same kind were necessary before any movement ensued," but failed to indicate a general rule.

Following in the trail left by BURDON–SANDERSON and MUNK, the method of electrical stimulation has been used by BROWN and SHARP (1910) to study time and intensity relations. They found first of all that at 15 deg. C. two stimuli were always required, and must be applied within an interval of from 1.5 to 20 seconds. But at the higher temperature of 35 deg. C. frequently only one stimulus was required, while at 40 deg. C. only one stimulus was required in 50% of the instances. In order to elucidate this behavior, BROWN and SHARP tried the effect of electrical shock in various intensities and found that the number of shocks required varied inversely with their intensity. The authors then proceeded to determine the number of stimuli (by bending the sensitive hairs) required when applied at various intervals, viz., 20 seconds, 1, 2, and 3 minutes, and found that for these intervals, 2.0, 3.8, 6.2 and 8.7 stimuli (averages of several tests) were required. It thus appears that "the number of stimuli necessary for complete response varies almost directly with the length of the intervals. It would seem, therefore, that the response follows on a definite amount of accumulated effect, "possibly the accumulation of some chemical substance as the result of excitation." It should be added that the physiological condition of individual leaves has a modifying effect — at a given time and place all leaves are not equally sensitive.

In 1873, stimulated by DARWIN's studies, J. BURDON–SANDERSON published the first observations on the electric current in leaves as indicating physiological disturbance, using those of *Dionaea*. Having demonstrated that there is a normal current from base to apex of the trap while there is one in the reverse sense in the petiole, related quantitatively so that if the petiole were cut off at different lengths, the current in the trap was increased, he then studied the effect of stimulating the sensitive hairs on the current. Whenever a fly was allowed to walk into the trap it disturbed the hairs and at once there was observed a deflection of a galvanometer. If the stimulus were repeated, the galvanometer indicator came to rest in a different position (more to the left) each time. Disturbance of the hairs with a camel's hair brush had the same effect. Thus the fact that movements of the sensitive hairs constitute a stimulus was demonstrated by noting consequent electrical disturbance.

Localization of perception. — It had been generally accepted since OUDEMANS' time, in spite of MEYEN's evidence to the contrary, that stimuli leading to closure could be received only by the sensitive hairs. OUDEMANS could not repeat MEYEN's (1839) result, namely, causing closure by scraping the midnerve. DARWIN, however, found both the area within the triangle formed by the sensitive hairs and the surface along the midrib to be sensitive, so that when scratched or pricked with a needle, closure followed. MACFARLANE found that this occurred on pinching the blade of the trap with steel forceps, but that two stimuli were required. BROWN and SHARP confirmed MACFARLANE's observation, only qualifying the numerical expression since they found that one only, or two or more pinches might be required to procure reactions. They also found that the trap may be stimulated to close by the application of strong electrical stimuli to the petiole. That various kinds of stimulating agents (cutting, hot water at 65 deg. C., various chemicals, electrical stimuli) can effect response has been abundantly shown by DARWIN, BURDON-SANDERSON, MUNK, MACFARLANE, BROWN and SHARP. But it is easier to stimulate by cutting, etc. the upper face of the leaf than the lower. If the lower face is cut, it must be cut deeply so as to reach the upper face tissues (MUNK). Stimulation is not procurable by cutting the outer marginal zone of the cilia (MUNK). It appears therefore that the more ventral tissues (MUNK: the parenchyma) are sensitive, not the more dorsal. But it remains the central fact that normally the closure of the trap results from the stimulation of the sensitive hairs, even though very slow closure may take place in response to applied protein (chemonasty), after the power to react seismically has been lost. It was natural for earlier observers, from CURTIS on, to suppose the whole of the hair to be sensitive, as did DARWIN. "These filaments, from their tips to their bases, are exquisitely sensitive to a momentary touch" (1875). Sixteen years previously, however, OUDEMANS had succeeded in showing experimentally that the sensitivity resides in the basal region of the hair, to which MUNK (1876) and BATALIN (1877) agreed. DARWIN appears to have attached importance to the flexible base in allowing the hair to bend rather than be broken by the closing lobes. He saw that there is a constriction about the base, merely mentioning it. GOEBEL (1891), in view of the configuration of the cells of the constriction (as well as of the organ in general), believed that these receive, on movement of the "lever," a "much stronger stimulus than any other leaf cell." The stimulus is hindered from moving upward by suberized cells in the two courses above (in which I find very little if any suberization).

The cells of the constricted zone were regarded by HABERLANDT (1901) as special sense organs. The cells respond to compression, but not to release from a constrained bent position (BROWN and SHARP), and if the hair is amputated, pressure on the remaining base will procure closure (BROWN and SHARP 1910).

The mechanism of closure. — The first effort to explain the mechanism of closure in the trap of *Dionaea* was made by MEYEN, in 1839. To him the spiral vessels of the nerves, because of their spiral-spring-like structure, seem to afford a suitable mechanism. If the idea is naïve, it still indicates the early desire and effort to answer the question.

ZIEGENSPECK much later (1925) (*through* VON GUTTENBERG) attributed importance to a hinge mechanism, saying that closure is due to the loss of turgor by the cells of the tissues above the midvein. VON GUTTENBERG (1925) showed this to be incorrect.

DARWIN described the closure of the trap as passing through two phases. There is first a sudden response, bringing the edges of the lobes into some approximation, enough at least to bring the cilia in position so as to make a sort of cage preventing the escape of sufficiently large prey, and allowing small ones (ants especially) to escape (JONES) (*17 — 6*). This is followed by a slow movement during which the lobes are closely apposed, pressing together, their marginal regions being curved outwards. ASHIDA in his studies of *Aldrovanda* has called these the "shutting" and the "narrowing" phases of closure. We are now to consider the first of these, to which more attention has been paid than to the latter. DARWIN investigated the mechanism of closure by making marks on the upper surface of a lobe in the transverse sense before stimulation, viewing the same through a window cut in the opposite lobe. When closure had been effected, the marks were found to be closer together and he concluded from this that closure is accompanied by a transverse contraction of the more superficial cells of the whole upper surface and sub-surface. He thought also that the tissues above the midvein took part with a hinge-like action.

This contraction was attributed by MUNK (1876) to the loss of turgor by more sensitive superficial tissues ("parenchyma") lying beneath the upper epidermis, accompanied by the active expansion of the tissues of the lower layers of parenchyma near the under epidermis. DE CANDOLLE, from anatomical study, seems to have held essentially the same view.

BURDON–SANDERSON, seeking for a "resistance" which has to be removed in responding to stimulation, could find it only in the turgor of the leaf. "In the case of cells which are excitable the immediate effect of excitation is suddenly to diminish the power (of turgescence) and thereby produce a diminution of the volume of the cells which is equal to that of the water (probably holding diffusible bodies in solution) which is discharged into the intercellular spaces." It was already known from the work of BRUECKE, cited by MUNK, that the only mechanism of the actual movements of the sensitive plant (*Mimosa*) was such a diminution of turgor in the sensitive region of the pulvinus.

BATALIN (1877) re-examined the matter and, confirming DARWIN'S observations, extended the account to include subsequent opening. Using the same method as DARWIN, namely, measurements of changes between ink marks during closure, BATALIN came to agree with him that there is a real contraction of the upper side of the lobes and a concomitant expansion of the lower, both longitudinal and transverse. He takes issue with DARWIN (and ZIEGENSPECK, 1925), however, holding that the midvein takes no part, or at least a very small and unobservable part. When the trap remains closed, as it does for a week or ten days (or even longer) if it has been fed a living insect, it enters at once into a second phase of movement. The lobes begin to compress together mutually, so that in a half-hour (as I have observed) much of their inner surfaces are in actual contact, leaving however a space above the midvein. The compression is such that the margins of the lobes are turned outwards and the cilia come to lie more nearly parallel to the general plane of the lobes (*18 — 4b*). As BATALIN observes, the pressure exerted is enough to crush a soft-bodied insect. DARWIN thought that this compression is owing to the absorption of animal matter. BATALIN said that it is caused by the reduction of the expansion of the lower surface, for he determined that during the slow compression of the lobes together after the initial closure, there is actual and measurable shrinkage of that surface, except where the body of the insect propped it out. ASHIDA (1934), we remember, compares this movement with the slow movement which supervenes on "closure" in *Aldrovanda*, calling it the "narrowing" movement.

But the main contention of BATALIN, in which he was in agreement with DARWIN, was that during closure there is an actual shrinkage of the upper or inner surface, accompanied by expansion of the lower. This amounts to saying that the tissues including the epidermis, contract in the upper region, and expand in the lower. This was made an issue by BROWN (1916). Using again the same method, he found extension in the lower surface and decreases in the upper. But the latter amounts were very small, amounting to only 1.5% of the original distances, while for the lower surface the differences of dimension range between 3.3 to 10, or an average of 6.7%. Furthermore, and this is of prime importance, BROWN found that there is an error of observation due to changed surface curvatures, so that the actual surface retains dimensions which it only seems to lose, since what one measures is not the curved surface, but the chord of its arc. BROWN's opinion, based on the measurement of a model, was that "if there is any change in the area of the upper surface during closure it is probably in the direction of an increase rather than in that of a decrease," in this squarely contravening previous opinions. During subsequent opening, however, the reverse obtains. The upper surface now expands (to the amount of 9.4% of the original measurements) while the under surface maintains its enlargement merely. True there is a small apparent expansion which is attributed by BROWN to the same sort of error as that detected in the measurements of shrinkage of the inner surface. It was shown also that as the result of stimulation the growth of the lobes of the trap was greater by a good deal than their growth during a long period when there was no stimulation, from which it appears that stimulation is a liberator of growth and that, accordingly, the responses to stimulation become less vigorous if the stimulus is repeated often. This recalls BATALIN's experiments which showed that when a trap was stimulated seven times on ten successive days, the ability to respond was not lost, but was progressively very materially weakened.

What then takes place during the response movement? MACFARLANE allowed that the contraction observed by DARWIN would be due to the escape of water through pores in the protoplasm, and sought for some visible evidence of such. He ventured to suggest that appearances in the parenchyma cells of the motile tissue, consisting of "rows of extremely minute globules or pores in the protoplasm," suggested a parallel with animal voluntary muscle, and that on ultimate analysis the activity might be explained, as in the case of plant cells, by water movements. This is not the same as saying that "MACFARLANE believed that there are structures in the leaves ... which resemble animal muscles."

BATALIN, not being able to detect any change in translucence of the tissues, which would be expected if there were any effusion of sap into the intercellular spaces, such as is well known to take place in the pulvini of *Mimosa* during movement response, denied that there is any extrusion of water by the cells in the upper moiety of the trap lobe, and BROWN denying the contraction of the upper face sees no necessity for such extrusion, but falls back on the expansion of the cells of the lower face. This makes it necessary to find a movement of water from a source sufficient for this expansion. The only source considered is the parenchyma of the upper face, in which, since the intercellular spaces are not flooded, water must pass from cell to cell; the movement would then resemble that of geotropism. An acknowledged difficulty is seen in the rapidity of the response which, though often slow enough, is at times and normally so rapid that complete closure is reached in the space of even less than a half second ($17 — 6$). This difficulty must be faced as also that arising from the attempt to account for the loss of water by some cells (those of the upper face) by changes in the substances present in the cells to less osmotically active ones, thus permitting the water to be drawn off into other cells (those of the lower face) to facilitate their expansion. How sufficient water can thus be moved to procure the recorded amount of expansion of the lower face, without causing a reduction (contraction) of the upper face in even greater amount (since the latter is shorter, if only slightly), is not clear.

This rapidity of movement seems to demand that there be a condition of unstable equilibrium resulting from growth and residing in the trap lobes. BATALIN advanced this idea but he was, it is recalled, committed to explain a shortening of the upper face. That tissue tensions do exist may be taken for granted (DARWIN), just as they exist in the valves of the fruit of *Impatiens*. In this plant the tensions are held in check by mechanical conditions, namely, the mutual adherence of the valves. This disturbed, the valves spring away by immediately curving in the same sense as the lobes of the *Dionaea* trap. In the latter the lobes maintain their form, unless stimulated, by the opposition of the two epiderms to their contiguous tissues. When stimulated, the balance of forces is upset and curvature immediately follows. That is, when stimulation takes place something happens to release the tensions. What this something is we do not yet know. If we might postulate chemical changes in the cell contents from sugar to starch in the upper surface of the trap lobes, it would serve us with a mechanism for changing the tensions, but sufficiently rapid changes are not known. BROWN's experiment in which he substituted xylene, in which sugars are insoluble, for water, are suggestive, but not convincing further than showing that tensions exist which might be released by such a mechanism. This is in essence the theory put forth by VON GUTTENBERG (1925) who believes that the movement is caused, not by any reduction of turgor in any tissues whatever, but by the drag of the parenchyma on the two epiderms (upper and lower), the upper being thicker and less extensible than the lower ($18 — 5, 6, 10$), as MACFARLANE also maintained. That this drag is positive, exerting a pull on the epiderms, is indicated by the fact that if the tissues of the upper epidermis and the contiguous parenchyma are partially robbed of water by the application of a plasmolyte to the upper surface, no closure can take place on stimulation (application of the plasmolyte to the base of the sensitive hairs was avoided). Indeed, any experiment in which the parenchyma is robbed of its turgor renders the valves incapable of closure. This positive drag therefore, present before closure, stretches the epiderms as much as it, previous to excitation, is capable. On stimulation this capacity is increased, the epiderms responding by expanding differentially, the upper scarcely at all, the lower 6–7%, in accordance also with measurements by Brown and others. Von Guttenberg then faces the questions, whence the water necessary to increase the volume of the parenchyma cells, and what conditions allow the momentary increase of water uptake? To the former he suggests that the water comes from the vascular tissues; to the latter that it may be due to the sudden changes of substances in the sap from a large molecular to a small molecular condition. Von Guttenberg extends this theory to the case of *Aldrovanda*, making the pertinent observation that, in view of the fact that this trap has only a single course of parenchyma cells, it is unthinkable that there exists a differential action in the tissues between the epiderms, of which more beyond.

Von Guttenberg's difficulties may, however, on theoretical grounds be avoided. If it be assumed that the response to irritability is confined to the epidermis, we might argue that this response consists only in the reduction of turgor. True, as von Guttenberg says, this would be removing one factor in tissue stretching, but as turgor expands the cells in every direction, the relative amount of extension depending on the lengths of the walls, its removal would allow the application of the energy of the turgid parenchyma to the flaccid epidermal cells, the longitudinal walls of which then would respond readily to the stretching effort, the amount of stretching depending only on the physical properties of the walls. In a word, the system would work like a bimetallic strip of metals of different indices of expansion, von Guttenberg's idea, but demanding simply loss of turgor in the epidermis only, and this, as von Guttenberg observes in regard to Ziegenspeck's theory, is easier physiologically than a rise in turgor in a mass of tissue. It should be added that the loss of turgor by the epidermis need not advance beyond an initial stage of relaxation, just sufficient to allow, without evident effusion of water, the stretching of the longer walls, which would otherwise be pushed out laterally by conditions of turgor. Thus the theoretical necessities are reduced to a minimum, and the movement of *Dionaea* brought into line with movements in general in sensitive plants. As to the bursting of fruits such as *Impatiens*, *Sicyos*, etc. we have to do with change of shape of parenchyma cells without change in turgor. In *Impatiens* the two epiderms are of unequal extensibility.

This seems to be the view advanced by Ashida (1934) which, prompted by his study of *Aldrovanda*, he applies "by deduction to the case of *Dionaea*." He cites Macfarlane's observations that the lower epidermis has a thinner cuticle than the upper, and is therefore more easily distensible, permitting curvature on the relaxation of the upper epidermis with the effect of closure.

What is the nature of stimulation is certainly not known. HABER-LANDT regarded the constricted cells at the base of a sensitive hair as sense organs which are activated by compression. BROWN found that the sensitive hairs do not respond to decompression procured by two successive movements of a hair which had previously been kept in an extreme bent position. Propagation of the stimulus cannot be dependent upon the vascular tissues, since they are absent from the trigger hairs; and in *Aldrovanda*, which has no vascular tissues except the single strand along the midvein, it is even more obvious that the path of movement must be found in the parenchyma, but whether of the epidermis alone or of the internal tissues also, is not yet known.

That response, an event following on stimulation, is accompanied by electrical disturbances BURDON–SANDERSON showed, and the char-acter of these permitted him to liken them to those which occur during muscular contraction, though this is not the same as iden-tifying the contraction, asserted by DARWIN and BATALIN, of the upper surface with muscular contraction (F. DARWIN, 1875), espe-cially when now such contraction has been questioned (BROWN). The molecular transposition measured by BURDON–SANDERSON might indeed be the expression of sap movements, and such sap movements need not be great quantitatively to upset an equilibrium and might constitute a trigger action to start the mechanism a-going.

Whatever the tensions in the open trap lobe may be, they must be duplicated in the similar trap of *Aldrovanda*, and when we look at this beyond, it is a help to comprehend what happens in *Dionaea* when such tensions are relieved.

For *Dionaea* we may at present say: —

1) During the open condition there are tensions present which are so distributed that they maintain the trap in an open position, the lobes standing at an angle as great as 80 deg. (DARWIN).

2) When stimulated the lobes close, the cilia becoming interlaced like the fingers of clasped hands. The lobes remain concavo-convex, inclosing a wide space between them. During this closure the outer face of the lobe expands, the inner remains unaltered, or at least it does not contract. If the stimulus is prolonged by chemical stim-ulation (as when an insect has been introduced), the lobes continue toward a greater mutual compression and thus obliterate to some measure the inclosed space (the "narrowing" of ASHIDA). BATALIN thought that this is due to a subsequent contraction of the lower face of this lobe. It might be due to a passive extension of the upper face resulting from rapid exudation of secretion, depleting the tissues of water. The edges of the lobes, which do not actively participate in the movements, become bent outwards and the cilia now extend less transversely, so that the two sets become more nearly parallel.

3) With the cessation of secretion and absorption, the lobes re-open, this being the result of increased growth of the upper faces, the expansion of the lower faces being maintained.

The mechanically stimulated trap closes, and reopens without nar-rowing in about 24 hours, when it will respond again. But repeated daily responses are followed by decreasing sensitivity, probably due to the completion of growth.

If closure follows trapping of suitable prey, narrowing (in the sense of ASHIDA) takes place. Reopening follows at the end of a period of days (5–10 or more) when there is evident a diminution of sensitivity, which however is regained in the course of time (some days, OUDEMANS).

Digestion. — During all this digestion and absorption have been taking place. DARWIN did a variety of experiments with various substances. We have seen that the upper surface of the lobes is crowded with many glands capable of secretion and absorption, as DARWIN stated. These glands remain passive unless some suitable material (insect, meat, etc.) is inclosed between the lobes. Then there is a copious secretion of a fluid which has the power of digestion, and which causes the dissolution of the substances acted upon. "It is so copious that on one occasion, when a leaf was cut open, on which a small cube of albumen had been placed 48 hours before, drops rolled off the leaf" (DARWIN). The secretion is acid, the presence of formic acid (BALFOUR) serving also for the inhibition of bacteria, so that, unless too great "portions" have been supplied, there is no odor of decay. BALFOUR found that a strip of meat placed partly within the closed valves and partly out, showed no bacterial action within, but did so without. When the rotted portion was placed in a fresh leaf, the odor of decay disappeared. This contravened the opinion of REES and WILL, whose experiment seems to have been done with abnormal plants (GOEBEL). There seems therefore to be no doubt of the digestive power of the secretion, though no *in vitro* experiments have been done with *Dionaea* secretion. According to DARWIN some substances are not digested (fats, fibro-elastic cartilage).

If not too great masses of material have been fed, when the trap begins to open the interior is found to be dry, and the fluid has been entirely absorbed. Experiments to show the usefulness of the absorption of proteins, such as those carried out by various authors on *Drosera, Utricularia*, have not been done. Our opinion on that must therefore rest on evident analogy.

FRAUSTADT thought that during the period when the trap is closed over an insect photosynthesis stops. But PFEFFER (1877) suggested that the lowering of the starch content observed by FRAUSTADT may be the accompaniment of a change in metabolism while at the same time photosynthesis may be proceeding. The work of KOSTYTSCHEW, if meagre, seems to deny FRAUSTADT'S belief (*see* under *Drosera*, p. 119).

Aldrovanda vesiculosa L.: — *Aldrovanda* is a small fresh water plant (*17* — 5) growing in quiet waters, floating just below the surface. It is quite rootless, and consists of a slender stem, clothed with whorls of leaves not distantly separated. Each whorl has eight leaves mutually attached at their bases. It branches infrequently, so that usually one finds only a single stem. The whole plant reaches a length of 10 to 15 cm. with a width of 2 cm. including the spread leaves which are reflexed in age. The tip of the shoot is especially conspicuous by the numerous bristles which jut beyond the general leaf profile. The flowers are supported on short stalks, bringing them just beyond the extent of the bristles. They measure about 8 mm. when widely open. The seeds are ovate, clothed with a hard shell (KORZSCHINSKI 1886).

This unique plant was first seen in India and was cited in 1696 by PLUKENET as *"Lenticula palustris Indica"* in his *Almagestum Botanicum* or *Phytographia* (4: 211, pl. 41, fig. 6). In 1747 GAETANO MONTI had received a collection of it made by an Italian physician, Dr. CARLO AMADEI, in the Dulioli Swamp, east from Bologna. It was named *Aldrovandia* by MONTI in honor of the Italian naturalist, ULISSE ALDROVANDI, who died in 1605. This plant was identified by J. J. DILLON with the PLUKENET one from India. In 1751 it was mentioned in a dissertation by L. J. CHENON (1751), a student of LINNAEUS, as *Aldrovanda* (probably a mistake in copying, thinks DUVAL–JOUVE, 1861) and finally published by LINNAEUS in the *Species Plantarum* 1753, p. 281, as *Aldrovanda vesiculosa*.

CASPARY points out on high philological authority that the Linnaean name is ungrammatical. The name *Aldrovanda* is now generally accepted in accordance with the International Rules of Botanical Nomenclature. Another plant from India was described as the species *verticillata* by ROXBURGH (*Flora Indica* 1832, 2: p. 113), but this was shown by T. THOMSON not to be distinct, but has been regarded as a variety. A plant from Queensland, Australia, once called the var. *australis*, is not distinguishable from the original species, though DARWIN found some difference in size, together with other minor ones, such as the number of serrations on the bristles.

Aldrovanda vesiculosa ranges from S. France to Japan, south to Australia, and in Africa to the southern tropics where it was found by Miss E. L. STEPHENS in the Chobe Swamp, 100 miles west of Victoria Falls. This material, together with living plants, has been studied by me, the latter having been obtained in Silesia and grown during the summer of 1933 in the Garden of the Botanical Institute of Munich. Beautiful herbarium specimens in all stages of fruiting and flowering from Mizoro Pond, near Kyoto, were sent me by Dr. JOJI ASHIDA.

The morphology and anatomy of the vegetative parts of the plant were first described by COHN in 1850, and more completely by CASPARY in 1859 and 1862. Further reference to details was made by GOEBEL (1891), FENNER (1904), and HABERLANDT (1901).

Like the leaves of *Dionaea*, those of *Aldrovanda* consist of a flattened petiole armed at its apex. This appears somewhat truncated, with four to six, or seldom even eight parenchymatous lobe-like bristles, surmounted by a nearly circular leaf blade, 4 mm. wide. When mature the petiole is wedge-shaped, broader at the apex, 6 mm. long and 4 mm. wide. The bristles extend another 5 mm. The midrib of the petiole with its vascular tissue continues into the blade, which has the form of a steel trap, as in *Dionaea*.

Seedling (*19 — 1–5*). — The elliptical seed has a snout at one end, plugged with a cap, under which lies the root end of the short hypocotyl. Surmounting this are the two broadly conical cotyledons pressing against the large endosperm, much as in *Dionaea* (SMITH). In early germination the hypocotyl protrudes, pushing off the cap and carrying it forward for some time, till indeed the hypocotyl reaches its fullness of development, with a length of 3 mm. ($19 — 1-3$). By this time the petioles of the cotyledons have emerged, and, just above the plumule, expand to form a sack-like expansion surrounding it. Above this they are suddenly constricted, the isthmus entering the seed and connecting with the expanded ends of the cotyledons which form a haustorium. The developing plumule breaks out of one side of the surrounding cotyledonary envelope and progresses toward forming the plant. The leaves of the first whorl are slender ligulate and taper to a fine point, or may be variously laciniate to some degree. There are usually five in the whorl. The next whorl, raised on an evident internode, shows still more laciniations, but does not yet produce traps ($19 — 5$). These, however, usually appear in the fourth whorl. Subsequently the mature condition is gradually established. The hypocotyl ends without forming a root cap, and initial cells appear never to be established after the primary condition has passed ($19 — 4$). This, KORZSCHINSKI, who described the course of germination, did not see, and this lack was indicated by GOEBEL. The structure of the seed and seedling in its primary condition is quite similar to that of *Dionaea*, as described by SMITH (1931), differing however in a few details, notably in the greater expansion of the cotyledonary petioles to embrace the plumule, and in the failure of root growth.

The leaf of maturity. — This consists of a wedge-shaped petiole (regarded by NITSCHKE as the leaf base (*fide* TROLL, 1939) and the narrow isthmus between it and the trap as the petiole, a view now regarded as untenable), somewhat truncated at the apex, where it bears four to six, occasionally more (eight, CASPARY) serrate bristles, and at its middle point a leaf blade in the form of a trap.

When four bristles only are present they appear to stand two on each side of the trap, but the inner two, as revealed during development, stand somewhat behind the insertion of the trap, and overlap it ($19 — 6$). If a fifth occurs, this quite evidently stands behind the trap, and therefore does not, as CASPARY noted, arise from the end of the petiole, but from its dorsal surface. The bristles cannot therefore be regarded as lobes of the leaf, as COHN thought, nor as stipular appendages (NITSCHKE, 1861), but rather as emergences.

The structure of the petiole ($19 — 9$) in general is that of water plants; there are wide intercellular chambers of pentagonal, hexagonal (along the midrib), or elongated form (along the margins), separated by partitions one cell thick. FENNER, who has more than anyone else described the minutiae of the plant's structures and their development, errs in showing large hexagonal chambers over the midrib, and in fact the figure of his transverse section does not consist with that of the leaf *en face*, the former being correct. The epidermis is scantily clothed with two-armed trichomes ($19 — 16$), standing on two very short stalk cells with cutinized walls, these in turn on two epidermal basal cells. The arms of these hairs may be short or, especially along the margins, twice as long. The bristles taper gradually from their broader bases and are serrated irregularly by projecting unicellular trichomes, ending in a similar spinous one.

The trap stands at the apex of the petiole, the midrib, carrying a single annular vessel with an ample phloem, being continuous from one to the other. But it always stands asymmetrically, resulting from a twist in the stalk, in such a manner that the mutually appressed lobes in the young trap are turned with their free margins to the left (as viewed from above) through an angle of about 90 degrees. In addition to this torsion, the trap is bent backwards (*i.e.*, to the right as seen from above) through an angle of 30 to 40 degrees (*17* — *5*). MONTI evidently refers to this posture when he said, "In barbularum medio folliculus oblique appenditur." It is thus brought about that, when the traps are open, their openings face outwardly away from the stem, instead of tangentially. The course of development of the leaf is here worth a glance (*19* — 6). In its earliest stage, the whole leaf consists of a mere conical protuberance from the stem apex. Soon it becomes apparent that the basal half is broadening to form the flat petiole, while the now more cylindrical end is to become the trap. Very soon this begins to show torsion which progresses until, when the leaf is approaching maturity, the trap comes to lie in its definitive position. In the meantime the bristles have developed, first the outer followed by the inner. At an early stage it can be clearly seen, as it was by CASPARY, that the trap and inner bristles do not lie in the same plane. In maturity, the bristles project much beyond the trap and so produce the bristly appearance of the plant.

The position of the mature traps resulting from torsion and bending may be regarded as a distinct adaptation, since their mouths, when open, are all placed so as to avoid obstruction from neighboring leaves, which in view of their numbers and crowding, is obviously advantageous for the easy approach of prey.

In describing the action of the trap, whose peculiarities of posture, much less pronounced but present in *Dionaea*, have just been described, a special terminology is required, proposed by ASHIDA. It is clear that if the trap is twisted 90 degrees to the left (in the sense above indicated) the one side or lobe of the trap must come to lie against the bristles (*19* — 5). This ASHIDA calls the *bristle-side lobe*. The other lobe is the *free-side lobe*. The importance of this distinction lies in the fact that both lobes are concavo-convex and lie dished the one into the other (*19* — 7). That is, the outer surface of the bristle-side lobe and the inner surface of the free-side lobe are convex, the other two concave. Since this has been brought about in the course of development, the two lobes acquire a different set, the effect of which will be clear when the action of the trap is described.

The trap has a unique structure, which we shall now describe. Morphologically it is a leaf blade, each half being nearly semi-circular, the circle being subjected to some degree of skewing. Each, of course, is attached to the midrib, which is the thickest portion. FENNER, CZAJA and others have called the midrib the "hinge," but as the proximal parts of the lobes do not move at any time, this is a misnomer. It is true that textbook figures taken from earlier authors would indicate the contrary, but they are certainly wrong, as ASHIDA has clearly shown.

Each lobe, when the trap is mature and is in the set posture (ready to catch prey), is concavo-convex from within out. But the curvatures are not simple spherical ones. It will be seen by the figures herewith that two oval zonal regions, one on either side of the midrib, are flat (*19* — 8, 21-23) and are subject only to slight curvatures under stress during the closure of the trap. From this flat middle region, the lobes spread with a maximum curvature along the transverse middle line. Here the curvature is much like that of the ribs of a vessel amidships. This is the principal region of motion during closure (2, *19* — 22-23). The next region is one of comparatively little inward curvature (5, *19* — 23) as far as the margin, which is sharply bent back inwardly to form a valve edged with a row of sharp teeth. The whole looks like a widely opened clam or mussel (*19* — 21*a*). This is what one sees looking merely at the outer form. When the thickness of the lobes is examined, the following is found. The inner half, along the midrib, is thick and relatively rigid. This half (the thick region) includes the place of greatest curvature, together with a measure beyond (again as seen in a transverse section normal to the midrib at its middle point) (1-3, *19* — 23). Anatomically it consists of three courses of cells, the two slender celled epiderms which are thin, enclosing a single course of very large thin-walled cells, the long axes of which run transversely the leaf (*19* — 10, 11). This structure is continued around the sharp bend of the motile region, which is somewhat thinner than elsewhere, into the sides of the trap somewhat less than half-way to the free margin. At this point the lobe suddenly thins, the middle course of large cells ceasing. The lobe then consists of a very thin membrane consisting of only the two epiderms juxtaposed, and so it continues quite to the inturned margin which forms the valve. The valve itself is thicker again, due to the enlargement of the epidermal cells, giving it a useful firmness to make it effective. Since only the middle transverse structure as seen in section has been examined, some details concerning the curvature of the lobe margins must be mentioned.

The stiff region of the trap wall along the midrib does not extend its full length, so that, beyond certain points, the proximal and distal parts of the walls are thin and, when the trap is closed, readily approach each other so as to lie juxtaposed. As the marginal valve does not reach the midrib — it becomes narrower as it approaches it and quite ceases 0.75 mm. away — there are left two spaces, one at the apex and one at the base of the blade, which, when the trap is closed, can allow the escape of water, while elsewhere the valve acts to prevent the escape of prey during the whole course of closure of the trap. This escape of water is necessary to permit the two thin regions of the lobes to approach and to become mutually appressed. This is possible because the thin region of the free-side lobe inclines to bend when pressed against the bristle-side lobe, due to its set acquired during development, so that when the trap is fully closed, the thin regions of the two lobes dish into one another as during development (*19* — 21, 22), crowding the prey, if caught, into the digestion cavity. Before the act of closure is looked into more carefully, further details of anatomy will be examined. The thick region, as above said, is composed of three cell layers, the two thin epiderms sandwiching a middle course of large thin-walled cells of cylindrical form. In these three courses the cells are elongated at right angles to the midrib, and have straight walls, excepting that the outer epidermis beyond the motile zone, to be delimited later, has wavy-walled cells. In passing over into the thin region of the lobe, the middle course of cells ceases entirely, so that there remain only the two epiderms juxtaposed (*19* — 19). In the inner zone of this region the cells are elongated and have straight walls, but there is a gradual transition to irregularity, when the walls become wavy. The thinnest part of the valve is toward the outer edge, where it is reduced to 0.5 mm. and is here only one cell in thickness. This is accounted for by the fact that, as COHN and CASPARY observed, the cells of the two epiderms become mutually intercalated, the cells of the inner course protruding between those of the outer course to occupy part of the general outer surface and vice versa (*19* — 12, 13, 17). The margin of the thin region is reflexed to form the valve and has a greater thickness, namely about 1 mm. Along the edge of the valve stands a row of sharp, stiff, unicellular hairs which, when the trap is closed, intercross to prevent any escape of prey between the valves (COHN) (*19* — 18), recalling the analogous arrangement in *Dionaea*, but in a reverse sense. This the trichomes accomplish more by numbers than by strength, which is indeed not great, as DARWIN observed. His doubt on the usefulness of the device is, however, scarcely justified.

The cells of the two epiderms of the thick regions differ in size. The outer epidermis per unit of measurement is composed of more and therefore more slender cells, than the inner, in the ratio of about 7:5. The cells of the middle course are longest near but not next the midrib. The structure of this is seen in *19* — 10, 11, 23.

The inner and outer surfaces of the trap are supplied with a variety of trichomes with various functions. On the outer surface there are squat, two-armed hairs (*19* — 16) similar to those found over the general plant surface. Their capital cells are devoid of cuticle, and they secrete mucilage. On the inner face of the lobes are to be found three kinds of hairs. On the surface of the distal zone of the thin portion there are four-armed hairs resembling superficially the "quadrifid hairs" (so called by DARWIN) in the interior of the traps of many species of *Utricularia* (*19* — 15). Aside from having four arms, which lie prostrate against the surface of the leaf, they are otherwise of the same structure as the two-armed hairs, and like them are devoid of cuticle, and secrete mucilage (GOEBEL). They are distributed in a broad zone lying adjacent to the valve (*19* — 8). The innermore region is devoid of them. On the inner surface of the thicker region of the lobe occur bun-shaped glands which may be regarded as digestive and absorptive in function (*19* — 14). They arise from two (FENNER) epidermal cells, on which stands a short stalk of four cells which expand into balloon shaped upper ends, clothed with a dozen or more cells to form the capital. They too lie in a zone of much density toward the outer margin of the thick region, and are few and more scattered nearer the midrib, on which, however, there is a dense row of them. DARWIN regarded the "quadrifid" or cruciform hairs within the trap as absorptive, but DUVAL–JOUVE (1876), because of their occurrence on the outer surfaces of the petiole, etc., considered them as of identical nature with the latter.

In this region, to which, thought MORI (1876), irritability was confined, there are also about 40 (20 on each lobe) long, very slender hairs, described by GOEBEL, HABERLANDT and FENNER, analogous to the normally six sensitive bristles which occur on the lobes of the Dionaea trap. In Aldrovanda, however, they are of a much simpler though equally effective structure. They are about 1.3 to 1.5 mm. long and 0.05 mm. thick except at the base, where they are a bit wider. They are very slender shafts, arising from a four-celled base lying in the epiderm, and projecting slightly therefrom. On these is surmounted a length of two courses, each of four long, slender cells. These bear the super-sensitive cells, four in number, though sometimes there appear to be only two. HABERLANDT does not state the number. They are short, thin-walled and form a sort of joint or hinge where the otherwise stiff hair can bend sharply, thereby compressing the cells on the concave side (GOEBEL, 1891). Above there are two courses of slender cells of two each, gradually tapering to a sharp, sometimes forked, end (19 — 20). They are arranged and postured in such fashion that, contrary to the impression given by some authors, they are not bent on the closure of the trap. They stand upright on the flat region of the trap on either side of the midrib, where they have plenty of head-room when the trap is fully closed, but obliquely on the sides so that, though long enough to reach beyond the fully closed digestion chamber, they lie sandwiched between the thin regions when approximated without being bent. Disturbing these hairs results in the closure of the trap, one touch of a bristle of a young leaf sufficing, but as the leaf grows older two or even many more become necessary. Quite old leaves, appearing at first to be beyond response, showed action when a lot of the sensitive hairs were disturbed by a sweeping motion of a needle a considerable number of times.

But though I did 300 experiments I found it difficult to make a very definite rule. There is a good deal of difficulty, of course, in getting a clear-cut result when one is dealing with so small an object as the Aldrovanda trap which has so many delicate bristles close together. In cases where the results were quite clear-cut, the data were contradictory. Thus in one case a young trap responded to one touch of a single hair while another one, of similar age and apparently ready for action, being widely open, required seven stimuli applied to a single bristle. Another required even more, caused by a sweeping of a number of hairs after six single stimuli. In somewhat older leaves, two stimuli only were frequently required to effect closure, but this also was by no means constant. Older traps behaved often in a singularly refractive fashion, but yet were found to respond at last. One case only: a single inner (on the flat region) bristle was bent 10 times; a second was bent 10 times; several bristles were then bent by a sweeping motion 10 times; then several outer bristles were swept ten times, and finally a single inner bristle was bent twice, followed by the closure of the trap. On the other hand an old trap closed with one stimulus only, seen by Dr. E. MERL and myself, as we were working jointly at the time. Another distinctly old trap responded to the eleventh stimulus, ten on one hair, the eleventh on another. Many did not respond at all. ASHIDA made quite similar observations. DE LASSUS (1861) had already observed that young traps are somewhat more sensitive than older ones. It became apparent that this lack of uniformity, while a fact, does not mean lack of dependability of the trap in nature, since the prey which ventures into an open trap must needs stimulate many hairs many times if it moves about. If the trap closes partially (see below) so that the prey cannot escape, the continued movements insure a further stimulation, and complete closure is assured.

The mode and mechanics of closure may now claim our attention. We have seen that each lobe displays two concentric regions, an inner thicker, and an outer very thin and pliable, and edged with a valve. If a relatively weak stimulus is applied, the lobes close till their free edges meet. Unless additional stimulus is added, in the course of a short time (20 to 30 min.) the lobes begin to open, and shortly resume their original postures, at some 45 or 50 degrees from each other. If, however, a sufficiently strong stimulus, or repeated stimuli be used, the lobes continue to close still further. This is possible because the free-side lobe flexes under pressure against the bristle-side lobe, at first just inside the valvular edge, the flexure extending until most of the two regions are mutually appressed ($19 - 21$). The two marginal valves become bent under this mutual pressure, the teeth intercrossing so as to prevent prey from escaping when the lobes are first closed. Resulting from the whole movement, the thick regions have moved together and a space has been inclosed by the meeting of their outer limits, forming a smaller but more inescapable prison ($19 - 22$). Here the digestive glands begin their work of digestion, and in the course of time the prey is disintegrated and the products absorbed. If a plant is lifted out of the water, the water films stimulate the traps to closure, and in closing, air is entrapped. The idea that the traps were hollow, closed organs, held by MONTI, led him to use the descriptive name *"vesiculosa."* COHN (1850) and DE LASSUS (1861) found this to be a mistake.

The mechanism of movement. — The sensitivity of the trap was first observed by AUGÉ DE LASSUS, who was cognizant of the facts regarding *Dionaea* and *Drosera* in 1861. The fact was rediscovered by B. STEIN in 1873 (mentioned by COHN in 1875) who found that it is the slender hairs which are capable of receiving stimulus, and recognized the analogy in this detail with *Dionaea*. Additional confirmation was offered by MORI (1876). GOEBEL showed more completely this analogy by demonstrating the hinge of the sensitive hair. CZAJA (1924) studied the effect of various kinds of stimulation. He incorrectly regarded the midvein as a hinge about which the valves rotate to approach each other in closure.

It has remained for JOJI ASHIDA to make a studious attempt to elucidate the mechanism of response, following that of BROWN and SHARP for *Dionaea*. ASHIDA first made clear where the exact region of active bending is. To determine this, he devised a method of imbedding the open trap in agar jelly, transferring it from warm water to still fluid agar at the same temperature, low enough to do no harm. On setting, the agar with its imbedded trap could be cut. It was noticed that on cutting the leaf it would react, and in doing so, it would withdraw from the agar on the outside, so indicating the zone of maximum bending. This was found, as already shown above, to be in the flanks of the thick region, between the flat part next the midrib and the outer rib-like region (2, *19 — 23*). How is this movement accomplished? In a complete response the amount of movement is sufficient to bring the edges of the thick regions in mutual apposition, thus inclosing an ellipsoidal shut-off space. Meanwhile, as already said, the thin regions dish the one into the other as the result of mutual pressure brought about by the thick regions.

Precisely what happens to procure the bending is more obscure. An observation made by ASHIDA is, if substantiated, of prime importance. It is that the outer epidermis of the motile zone, when in the state of open rest, is undulated, and in this condition not in a state of extension, whereas the inner epiderm is, if not fully extended, at least more so than the outer, since very light, if any, undulation is to be seen. During closure the undulations disappear, due to stretching of the tissues. As I have already suggested (1933), the two epiderms act after the fashion of a bi-metallic spring. Assuming this to be the case, two questions arise. What condition of the tissues operates to keep the outer epidermis lax? And what happens to procure the changes from the lax to the taut condition?

In addition to this undulation of the outer epidermis, the motile region is thinner than the non-motile parts of the thick region. And if the opposing lobes are cut away so as to exclude their mutual pressure during closure, it is ascertained that the lobes can curve far more than they do otherwise, as is the case in *Dionaea;* and further, that the free-side lobe bends, during closure, more than the bristle-side lobe. ASHIDA has also demonstrated to his own satisfaction that the outer epidermal walls are the more easily extensible, the outer subepidermal walls less easily, while the two inner walls are least extensible. This conclusion is regarded as flowing from the observation that, if a trap is plunged in acetone or alcohol, under the internal pressures induced by the entrance of these fluids into the cells, vesicles arise, but only on the outer face of the motile zone. The vesiculation is caused by the rising of the cuticle and the breaking of the radial walls of the epidermis. Evidently the outer epidermal walls are readily extensible, but, since they do not retract when the vesicles are reduced, they are thrown into folds. ASHIDA argues that the walls are plastically, not elastically, extended. That the motile zone is weaker than the lobe is elsewhere was shown by a tearing test, the result being that the lobes always tear at the motile zone. Again, from observing the movements of the intercellular air on the entrance of alcohol, the inference was drawn that the walls in the motile region are more readily penetrated than elsewhere.

Before discussing the mode of operation of the motile mechanism in *Aldrovanda*, for the purposes of comparing it with that of *Dionaea* (there is a definite analogy between them), ASHIDA draws the following parallel between them. The motile zone of *Aldrovanda* is but three cells in thickness; that of *Dionaea* composed of several to many cells in thickness, according to age of plant.

Aldrovanda	*Dionaea*
	The outer epidermis
The outer epidermis	The mass of parenchyma beneath (either one or both)
The middle course of parenchyma	The parenchyma as a whole
	The inner epidermis
The inner epidermis	The parenchyma beneath (either one or both)

The actual leaf movement embraces two phases of motion which ASHIDA calls (*a*) the shutting movement, to the "shut" stage, when the rims of the lobes just meet; (*19 — 21b*) and (*b*) the narrowing movement leading to the "narrowed stage" (*19 — 21d, 22*). In recovery the opening passes through the "rebulging movement" from the narrowed stage to the merely shut stage and the reopening movement, completing the opening. To avoid confusion these terms will be used.

In the shutting movement the margins of the thick region approach sufficiently to bring the margins of the thin regions together. This follows on the application of a weak stimulus, but proceeds no further. In time reopening occurs. If, however, the stimulus is sufficiently strong, this posture is passed through, the edges of the thick region approach mutually still further, the thin regions press on each other mutually, and the free-side lobe buckles, dishing itself in against the more rigid bristle-side lobe. ASHIDA maintains that these two movements are not simply a continuation the one of the other, as will be seen.

The rapid shutting movement is caused by the loss of turgor by the inner epidermis. This allows the other two layers to expand and the curvature ensues mechanically. The membranes of the outer epidermis are stretched irreversibly. The undulations described by ASHIDA disappear, having previously been maintained by the outward pressure of the inner epidermis. The posture thus attained now changes to that of the narrowed posture by the narrowing movement. This is a slow movement, accomplished by the slow elongation of the outer epidermal cells, that is, by growth. Resulting is the mutual appression of the two thin regions, during which water must escape from the inclosed space. ASHIDA tried to determine by means of colored fluid where the water escapes but did not get any very convincing evidence. It has been suggested above that the escape is between the non-valvular parts of the lips at the forward and rear ends of the margins. ASHIDA, by means of ingenious optical apparatus, was able to record photographically the advance of the whole movement. The shutting movement is very rapid, occupying about one fiftieth of a second, following on a latent period of 0.09 seconds. This rapid movement involves the expulsion from the trap of water, the pressure of which must be overcome. As in the case of *Utricularia*, the energy expended is sufficient to cause a trap lying free in the water to close with a sudden jerk, displacing it, just as a *Pecten* swims. There seems to be a slight difference in the behavior of the two lobes, the free-side lobe moving a bit more rapidly than the other. The difference is very little, however.

Advance from the shut to the narrowed posture is slower, more irregular, complicated by conditions. The slowness depends in the first place on the slowness of the mechanism causing it, namely the absorption of water and extension by growth of the outer epidermis. It seems not unlikely, however, that closure is impeded by the prevention of the escape of water by the mutually appressed valves of the lobe margins and the probably tight appression of the non-valvular portions. This, of course, insures in nature the retention of prey. To test this point, Ashida made a hole in the bristle-side lobe to allow the free escape of water, when the record indicated that the inclosed water in an uninjured trap does indeed offer impedance to narrowing. The free-side lobe, however, due to its measurable rigidity offers resistance to buckling and by itself produces irregularities in the rate of narrowing, which commences in any event, if the stimulus is sufficient, in about 30 min. after the shut stage has been reached. The narrowed condition in the case of strong stimulation, but in the absence of prey, is maintained for a period of from 6 to 12 hours.

In the return to the widely open condition, the trap passes through the reverse of the two phases of movement seen during shutting and narrowing, that is, during a first period the rebulging of the free-side lobe takes place, followed by the reopening of both lobes when the trap is again ready to react if stimulation is applied. All this is ascribed to the growth of the inner epidermis. During its progress irregularities of rate of movement can be ascribed to the resistance to the inflow of water into the narrowed trap and the elastic action of the thin regions added to the action proper to the thick regions. It is not known just how the water enters, but it may again be suggested that the valve-free parts of the lips of the thin regions may be the place of entrance, as well as of exit.

To recapitulate. — The rapid shutting movement is caused by the response of the inner epidermis of the thick region in loss of turgidity. The slow narrowing movement is brought about by the growth of the outer epidermis, following its stretching in the curving of the lobe. The movements of recovery are due to the growth of the inner epidermis, following the restoration of turgidity. The shutting movement is facilitated by the circumstance that the walls of the outer epidermis are at open rest, not stretched to their full capacity, and that these walls can be stretched plastically. A feature peculiar to *Aldrovanda* is the fact that the loss of turgor by the inner epidermis causes curvature of the single large celled middle layer, the walls attached to the inner epidermis shrinking and those to the outer expanding. In a more anatomically complex organ, such as the trap of *Dionaea*, the same must be true of all the parenchyma, but the difference of extension between the outer and inner walls of any individual cell must be less, since the total difference as between the inner and outer epidermis is distributed throughout the tissue of, it may be, some dozen cells in thickness. It is quite possible, therefore, to extend the explanation given above for *Aldrovanda* to *Dionaea*, at the same time excluding the loss of turgidity from the parenchyma, and refer the whole movement to the action of the epidermis alone. This, of course, does not square with BROWN's explanation, but it nevertheless deserves consideration.

Reference has already been made to the fact of sensitivity, its seat and the varying response of leaves of various ages. We inquire now more particularly into the responses to various types of agents, whether stimulatory or otherwise. Under conditions of nature, within the ordinary limits of temperature during the growing season, it has been found that stimulation through pushing against the sensitive hairs by animals, such as water fleas, spiders, etc. of small size, procures closure (shutting and narrowing). The trap then usually has caught a small total amount of food material which is digested. In the course of a few days (5–6, CZAJA 1924) the traps reopen and are ready to act again. This may be repeated by the same trap several times, the number depending on the size of the prey caught and the amount of undigested remains. The possible activity in repeated response and reopening is certainly not so limited as thought by FENNER.

If, however, the prey is large and fills the digestion cavity (CZAJA used for experiment pieces of flatworm), the trap may never open again. This may be due to the time involved, so that the trap passes through its growth period and loses its sensitivity, or the production and accumulation of substances having a poisonous effect. Too much feeding is known to have a deleterious effect in other carnivorous plants. This argues little or nothing in regard to the total value of the process, since one long feeding may be of as much use to the plant as several short ones.

The observation of BURDON–SANDERSON on *Dionaea*, that response can be obtained by electrical stimulation, was the beginning of a number of studies of interest in the field of general plant and animal physiology, leading to the examination of various agents on the activity of the trap. By means of the electric current it has been possible to analyze the response into time phases. CZAJA determined the intensity of threshold stimuli to be $0.91 \cdot 10^{-6}$ Coulomb for an opening shock, and $0.24 \cdot 10^{-5}$ for a closing shock. By repeated application of smaller shocks he found that there is a summation of stimuli. ASHIDA used this method for further analysis of the response, and found that for fully opened leaves the direction in which the current engages the trap has its effect, which is greater when applied transversely than longitudinally, from which it is inferred that the stimulus is more effective when running parallel to the long cells of the motile zone, than across, and that the latter is more sensitive to this stimulus than are the sensitive hairs themselves. This may be related to the various resistances offered by the tissues concerned and the direction of the current through the individual cells. The possibility of controlling the intensity of stimulation by means of the electric shock has further permitted the examination of the behaviour of the trap under special conditions of temperature.

Within the permissible temperature limits (extreme temperatures, it goes without saying, are finally damaging) CZAJA found that sensitivity increased with higher temperatures, as determined by observation between 15 to 35 deg. C. Raising the temperature gradually to 45 deg. was followed by spontaneous closure of nearly all the traps (that is, excepting some of the oldest). Opening again on reduction of temperature to 20 deg. they again closed on gradual lowering to 10 deg., the older traps responding in this way on reducing the temperature further to 5 deg., all due to the reduction of sensitivity, as shown by appropriate trials (CZAJA 1924).

ASHIDA went further, and found that sudden changes of temperature (he used changes of 10 deg. C.) in either direction would cause closure. From his data the curious fact emerges that sudden reduction of temperature beginning with any workable levels from 10 to 40 deg. C., is more effective than sudden rise in temperature at these levels. Further, the higher the initial level of temperature the more sensitive is the trap to rises, and the less sensitive to drops. Examples of stimulation to both rise and fall of temperature are not lacking, e.g. changes in the growth rate of coleoptiles (SILBERSCHMIDT), nastic movements of leaves (STERN and BÜNNING), the curling of tendrils (MACDOUGAL), cited by ASHIDA, offer some analogy. Protoplasmic movement is retarded only by a fall in temperature, the *Aldrovanda* trap being stimulated by both rise and fall, but more by the latter. *Aldrovanda* appeared therefore to ASHIDA to be unique in the quantitative aspects of behavior in this regard. METZNER (1920) had, however, already shown that bipolar-flagellated *Spirillum* sp. show a reversal of movement due to thermotaxis both on increase and decrease of temperature. But such rises and falls of temperature as can be experimentally imposed can scarcely be expected in nature except as slow changes; they can hardly be regarded as affecting appreciably the general economy of the plant.

In a third paper ASHIDA has given the results of studies of response of *Aldrovanda* traps of different ages to weak and strong stimulation applied in the form of constant currents of 30.6 and 70.1 volts. With the strong current all traps of various ages and at different temperatures (10 to 40 deg.) close promptly in the same time interval. With the weak current, however, the responses were scattered, a frequency polygon expressing the results having its highest node at about the same position as in the case of the strong current stimulation, with secondary nodes scattered to the right of gradually lessening height. The explanation of the delayed responses lies, ASHIDA believes, in the distinct and different sensibility of the hairs and the motile zone, diverse excitability of different cells and other possible causes.

Responses to chemical stimuli. — Both CZAJA and ASHIDA have studied the behavior of *Aldrovanda* to a series of chemical agents: narcotics, electrolytes (acids, alkalis, salts), non-electrolytes (sugar, glycerine).

Sugar, glycerine. — It is difficult because of the impenetrable cuticle to plasmolyze the cells of the trap unless a cut is made to allow the approach of the plasmolyte, as CZAJA also found for *Utricularia*. At the most, the cells display a systrophic contraction, but there is no quantitative relation to the concentration of the plasmolyte (ASHIDA). By watching the creeping in of the plasmolyte through the cut ends of cells, CZAJA estimated the osmotic equivalent to be about m/3 KNO₃.

A plasmolyte has the effect of immobilizing the trap by the withdrawal of water. For sugar (sucrose) immobilization occurs in from 40 seconds to 7.5 minutes for solutions of the concentrations 0.50 M. to 0.11 M. according to the age of the leaf, the younger being more easily affected. They react on stimulation till immobilization sets in. On immersion in the solution (0.2 M. sucrose), the trap opens a little beyond the normal, due perhaps to the withdrawal of water weakening the bending force of the outer epidermis and the middle layer. The springiness of the walls is, however, retained to some extent, and they will spring open if closed by force, unless too far. When left for some hours (six) in a 0.15 M. glycerine solution the power of movement is recovered, due perhaps to the penetration of the solute into the cells. Rapid changes of concentration in either direction can stimulate, causing partial closure, but it is evident that the immobilising effect and that of stimulation are antagonistic. Only traps which are not completely immobilized can react at all.

Neutral salts. — CZAJA found only a "narcotizing effect." ASHIDA, however, found also that salts in solution can stimulate, for, though strong solutions may quickly immobilize, their first effect is stimulation and the traps close. Even in a saturated solution of KCl the traps reacted within 1.6 to 2.6 seconds according to the age of the trap, the younger the quicker. Similar behavior was found for some other salts.

Acids and alkalis. — When ASHIDA exposed traps to low concentrations of acetic acid and of HCl (0.005 to 0.05 N.) they closed after various rather irregular periods from 29 to 2 minutes, respectively. Since osmotic pressure is regarded as not entering in, ASHIDA tried combining an acid with a non-electrolyte (acetic acid with sucrose) and found that the reaction time was reduced, and that the more sucrose is present, the shorter the reaction time. Two possible explanations present themselves. Sucrose, even much below the concentration which can stimulate osmotically, may help the stimulating effect of the acid, an additive effect; or the permeability of the protoplast to acid may be increased during partial plasmolysis. ASHIDA favors the latter alternative, for the additive effect is not observed in young traps, in which osmotic and chemical stimulation alone procure quicker responses. The second alternative also receives support from the observations of SCARTH (1927) that acid dyes penetrate *Spirogyra* cells more readily when the protoplast is changing its volume during plasmolysis.

Where now is the stimulus perceived? From applying acid to the different leaf surfaces, ASHIDA found that when it was put on the upper surface the response was obtained more quickly, indicating that the joint cells of the sensitive hairs are the points of perception, though the difficulty of confining the acid to the hairs alone, which is obvious, throws some doubt on the conclusion.

Other organic substances: — When exposed to commercial formalin, the trap becomes immobilized in 35–45 seconds. During this period, if stimulated mechanically the traps will close. In some cases the traps close on direct stimulation by the reagent about 15–30 seconds after immersion. Because overtaken by immobilization, the closure is never complete. In dilute formalin, the closure may be complete, since immobilization does not overtake the traps quickly enough. This is explained by the toxic effect overtaking the epidermis cells before the reagent can enter by way of the sensitive hairs. Ashida also reports the recovery of sensibility in 20 minutes after immobilization by exposure to concentrated formalin for 45 seconds, indicating that the injury to the epidermal cells is to some extent reversible. Such traps may close and narrow, perhaps as an after effect of adherent formalin for 1 minute, hence completely immobilized traps close and narrow in water 5–10 minutes later in spite of complete immobilization. If entirely killed by longer exposure, no movement occurs.

Such experiments are puzzling, but indicate at least that the toxic effects are realized somewhat slowly, and that the stages of turgor reduction realized in the meantime are such as to allow the working of the mechanism of closure, partially or completely. The slow penetration must be due to the resistance of the cuticle. Ashida recognizes two effects, stimulation and immobilization, on the rate of the latter depending the ability to respond, through the action of the sensitive hairs, into the hinge cells of which the reagent can penetrate more quickly.

In ethylalcohol 10–40 percent by volume, traps close spontaneously in from about 1 to 90 minutes, according to age. Curiously enough, in solutions stronger than 40% closure occurs in two steps, both sudden, separated by a pause.

In saturated chloroform-water, most traps close within 1 minute, some quickly, some slowly and some irregularly. Restoration to water procures no further activity, and they die. Czaja had previously obtained similar results. He found also that, after treatment with ethyl ether at similar concentrations, return to water restored the normal activity. The effect of narcotics, he says, is at first stimulative, then destructive. He obtained similar results with methyl and ethyl alcohols.

The addition of peptone or egg-albumin to the culture medium causes the traps to close and narrow, as also if a fragment of fish or meat is fed to the trap. Closure follows then from mechanical stimulation, and narrowing results from the chemical stimulation. Gelatin and coagulated egg-albumin do not stimulate beyond the shutting stage, since they do not stimulate chemically (Ashida).

Digestion and absorption. — There is not much doubt that *Aldrovanda* digests prey and absorbs the products of digestion. All observers have seen that the bodies of prey, except the hard parts, disappear, and Darwin did a few experiments which convinced him that absorption takes place. The evidence is, however, not complete, and we base our opinion with DARWIN on the obvious analogy with *Dionaea*. The closure of the trap into the narrowed posture reduces the volume of fluid containing the digestive ferment, if present, thus rendering it more effective (DARWIN). FERMI and BUSCAGLIONE (1899) offered some evidence that *Aldrovanda* is capable of digestion by placing traps on sterilized gelatin, and finding that it was rendered fluid.

To the earliest observers the traps of *Aldrovanda* were thought to be vesicles. The lifting of the plant from the water released the traps so that air was inclosed, as in the case of *Utricularia*, but, as COHN pointed out, this air was purely accidental. That it enabled the plant to float in the water, or at least assist in this when the plant becomes loaded with prey (FENNER), in view of the fact that it floats whether air is present in the trap or not, was seen to be a gratuitous explanation. More recently FENNER advanced the idea that gas is present as the result of chemical activity (digestion of one kind or another). But this also has been questioned (CZAJA 1924). That the presence of an air bubble assists in digestion by reducing the water content of the digestion cavity, thus procuring a more concentrated solution of ferments, that the water is absorbed by the epidermis cells, and that the air bubbles assist in opening by outward pressure (FENNER), are ideas which are superfluous in view of the fact that adequate observation shows that the inclusion of air is accidental. FENNER reports also that in vigorous leaves, after the capture of prey, not only do the digestive glands, but also the valve trichomes and the quadrifid hairs show signs of activity by exhibiting changes in their contents. This requires further examination. It is true that DARWIN had made similar observations indicating, it seemed to him, that the valve teeth and quadrifids do absorb, but this evidence was regarded only as indicatory.

When small prey are captured, the trap, stimulated by the vigorous movements in the attempt of the prey to escape, remains closed for some time according to the mass of the substance to be digested. If the trap is overfed, as when supplied with large pieces of a flatworm (CZAJA) it remains permanently closed, possibly because poisoned by the overplus of deleterious products, or perhaps because growth had ceased. Reopening may be repeated several times under favorable conditions of sufficiently meagre feeding. As already said heavy feeding may, however, advantage the plant as much as several smaller feedings.

According to SCHENK (on the authority of CRAMER, 1877) *Aldrovanda* was grown by him for two years in an inorganic salt solution without, apparently, any deleterious effect. PFEFFER cites this in support of the non-obligate character of carnivory in this plant. This experience of SCHENK's is surprising in the light of the experiences of ASHIDA, who found it very difficult to grow the plant except under rather special conditions. "No inorganic culture medium could be found which would keep the plant in the normal form even for a week". *Aldrovanda* grows in shallow water between the stems of *Typha*, *Zizania*, *Phragmites*, etc., which HAUSLEUTNER regarded as merely protection against sun and wind. ASHIDA took a hint from these relations, and found that by introducing into the water remains of the associated plants mentioned above, *Aldrovanda* can be made to grow quite satisfactorily even to flowering and seeding.

Literature Cited:

ASHIDA, JOJI, Studies on the leaf movement of *Aldrovanda vesiculosa* L., I. Process and mechanism of the movement. Mem. Coll. Sci., Kyoto Imp. Univ. B. 9:141–244, 1934; II. Effects of mechanical, electrical, thermal, osmotic and chemical influences. *Ibid.* B. 11:55–113, 1935; III. Reaction time in relation to temperature. Bot. Mag. Tokyo 51:505–513, 1937.

BALFOUR, T. A. G., Account of some experiments on *Dionaea muscipula* (Venus's Fly-Trap). Trans. Proc. R. Soc. Edin. 12:334–369, 1875.

BATALIN, A., Mechanik der Bewegung der insectenfressenden Pflanzen. Flora 35:54–58; 105–111; 129–154, 1877.

BROUSSONET, P. M. A., Hist. & Mém. de l'Acad. des Sci. 1784, p. 614.

BROWN, WM. H. & L. W. SHARP, The closing response of *Dionaea*. Bot. Gaz. 49:290–302, 1910.

BROWN, WM. H., The mechanism of movement and the duration of the effect of stimulation on the leaves of *Dionaea*. Am. Journ. Bot. 3:68–90, 1916.

BURDON-SANDERSON, J., Note on the electrical phenomena which accompany stimulation of the leaf of *Dionaea muscipula*. Proc. R. Soc. London 21:495–496, 1873.

BURDON-SANDERSON, J., Venus's Fly-Trap (*Dionaea muscipula*). R. Inst. Lecture, 5 June, 1874. Nature 10:105–107; 127–128, 1874.

BURDON-SANDERSON, J., On the electromotive properties of the leaf of *Dionaea* in the excited and unexcited states. Phil. Trans. Roy. Soc. London 173:1–53, 1882. Second paper, *ibid.* 179:417–449, 1888.

BURDON-SANDERSON, J. & PAGE, Paper read before the R. Soc. London,. 14 Dec. 1876 (*n.v.*). Results set forth in BURDON-SANDERSON, 1882.

CANBY, W. M., Notes on *Dionaea muscipula* Ellis. MEEHAN'S Gard. Mo.: 229–231, 1868.

DE CANDOLLE, C. P., Sur la structure et les mouvements des feuilles du *Dionaea muscipula*. Arch. Sci. Phys. Nat. 55:400–431, 1876.

CASPARY, R., *Aldrovandia vesiculosa* Monti. Bot. Zeitung 17:117–124; 125–132; 133–139; 141–150, 1859.

CASPARY, R., *Aldrovandia vesiculosa*. Bot. Zeitung 20:185–188; 193–197; 201–206, 1862.

COHN, F., Über *Aldrovandia vesiculosa* Monti. Flora 43:673, 1850. (*through* COHN 1875).

COHN, F., Über die Function der Blase von *Aldrovandia* und *Utricularia*. Cohn's Beiträge Biol. d. Pflanzen 1(3):71–92, 1875.

COKER, W. C., The distribution of Venus's Fly Trap (*Dionaea muscipula*). Journ. Elisha Mitchell Sci. Soc. 43:221–228, 1928.

COKER, W. C., A new locality for the Venus' fly-trap (*Dionaea muscipula*). Science 88:188, 1939.

CRAMER, C., Über die insectenfressenden Pflanzen. Lecture, Zurich 1877.

CURTIS's Botanical Magazine, Vol. 20. *Dionaea muscipula*. Venus's fly-trap. Plate 785 and description, 2 pp., London, 1804.

CURTIS, M. A., Enumeration of plants around Wilmington, N. C. Boston Journ. Nat. Hist. 1, 1834 (*Dionaea muscipula*, pp. 123–127).

CZAJA, A. TH., Reizphysiologische Untersuchungen an *Aldrovandia vesiculosa* L. Arch. f. d. gesamte Physiologie d. Menschen u. Tiere 206:635–658, 1924.

DARWIN, C., Insectivorous Plants. London 1875.

DARWIN, E., The Botanic Garden. London 1791.

DARWIN, F. in DARWIN, C., 1875, ed. of 1888, p. 257.

DIDEROT, DENIS, Oeuvres de DIDEROT. Ed. by Assézat, 1875. (*re Dionaea*, 9:257) (*through* É. MORREN, see under *Drosera*).

DIELS, L., *Droseraceae*. Das Pflanzenreich, IV, 112:1–136, 1906.

DILLWYN, LEWIS W., Hortus Collinsonianus. An account of the plants cultivated by the late PETER COLLINSON, Esq., F. R. S. arranged alphabetically according to their modern names, from the catalogue of his garden and other manuscripts. Swansea, W. C. Murray and D. Rees, 1843.

DUVAL-JOUVE, J., Letter to DE SCHOENFELT. Bull. Soc. Bot. de France 8:518–519, 1861.

DUVAL-JOUVE, J., Note sur quelques plantes dites insectivores. Bull. Soc. Bot. France 23:130–134, 1876.

ELLIS, JOHN, Directions for bringing over seeds and plants from the East Indies and other distant countries in a state of vegetation together with a catalogue of such foreign plants as are worthy of being encouraged in our American colonies, for the purpose of Medicine, Agriculture and Commerce. To which is added The Figure and Botanical Description of a New Sensitive Plant called *Dionaea muscipula* or Venus's Fly-trap. London, 1770. Sub-title: A botanical description of the *Dionaea muscipula* or Venus's flytrap; a newly discovered sensitive plant: in a letter to Sir CHARLES LINNAEUS

Knight of the Polar Star, Physician to the King of Sweden, and Member of most of the learned societies of Europe, from JOHN ELLIS, Fellow of the Royal Societies of London and Upsala (with a colored plate of *Dionaea muscipula*).

FENNER (*see* under *Nepenthes*).

FERMI & BUSCAGLIONE (*See* under *Utricularia*).

FRAUSTADT, A., Anatomie der vegetativen Organe von *Dionaea muscipula* Ellis. Cohn's Beiträge Biol. d. Pflanzen 2:27–64, 1877.

GARDINER, W., On the changes in the gland cells of *Dionaea muscipula* during secretion. Proc. Roy. Soc. London 36:180–181, 1883.

GOEBEL, K., Pflanzenbiologische Schilderungen. S. 57–72, Marburg 1891.

GOEBEL, K., Organographie der Pflanzen. S. 741–742, 1898–1901.

GUTTENBERG, H. VON, Die Bewegungsmechanik des Laubblattes von *Dionaea muscipula* Ell. Flora 18–19:165–183, 1925.

GUTTENBERG, H. v., Zur Kenntnis lebender Bewegungsmechanismen. Planta 1:666–678, 1926.

HABERLANDT, G., Sinnesorgane im Pflanzenreich. S. 108–117, Leipzig 1901.

HAUSLEUTNER, Cultur der *Aldrovanda*. Bot. Zeitung 1850, S. 831 (*through* ASHIDA).

HEINRICHER, E., Zur Kenntnis von *Drosera*. Ferdinandeum Zeitschr. Innsbruck 46:1–25, 1902; 47:300–307, 1903.

HOLM, T., Contributions to the knowledge of the germination of some N. American Plants. Mem. Torr. Bot. Club 2:57–108, 1891.

HOOKER, J. D., Address to the Dept. of Bot. and Zool., B. A. A. S. Belfast meeting 1874. London 1875, pp. 102–116 (*Dionaea*, pp. 103–105).

JONES, FRANK MORTON, The most wonderful plant in the world. Natural History 23:589–596, 1923 (Contains a facsimile of part of a letter from CHARLES DARWIN to WM. M. CANBY, in which the phrase forming the title of JONES' paper is quoted. The letter was dated from Down, Kent, Feb. 19, 1873).

KORZSCHINSKI, S., Über die Samen der *Aldrovandia vesiculosa* L. Bot. Centralb. 27:302–304; 334–335, 1886.

KOSTYTSCHEW, S., Die Photosynthese der Insektivoren. Ber. d. D. Bot. Ges., 41:277–280, 1923.

KURTZ, F., Zur Anatomie des Blattes der *Dionaea muscipula*. Arch. Anat. und Physiol., Lpz. 1876:1–29.

DE LASSUS, AUGÉ, Analyse du mémoire de GAËTAN MONTI sur l'*Aldrovandia* suivie de quelques observations sur l'irritabilité des follicules de cette plante. Bull. Soc. Bot. de France 8:519–523, 1861.

LINDLEY, JOHN, An introduction to botany. 4th Ed., London 1848.

LLOYD (*See* under *Heliamphora*).

MACDOUGAL, D. T., The physiology of tendrils. Bot. Centralbl. 66:145, 1896.

MACFARLANE, J. M., Contributions to the history of *Dionaea muscipula* Ellis. Contrib. Bot. Lab. Penna. 1:7–44, 1892.

METZNER, P., Die Bewegung und Reizbeantwortung der bipolar begeisselten Spirillen. Jahrb. wiss. Bot. 59:325, 1920.

MEYEN, F. J. F., Neues System der Pflanzenphysiologie 3:543–550, Berlin 1839 (*through* v. GUTTENBERG).

MONTI, GAETANO, De *Aldrovandia* novo herbae palustris genere. Comment. de Bononiensi Scient. et Art. Instituto et Academia 2(3):404–411, 1747. MONTI'S paper itself bears no date, but must have appeared between 1737 (it contains a quotation from LINNAEUS which appeared in that year) and 1747 (DE LASSUS, 1861). A translation into French appeared in the Collection Académique 10:401–407 (foreign part), Paris 1773 (*through* DE LASSUS).

MORI, A., Nota sull'irritabilitá delle foglie dell'*Aldrovandia vesiculosa*. Nuov. Giorn. Bot. Ital. 8:62, 1876.

MUNK, H., Die electrischen und Bewegungserscheinungen am Blatte der *Dionaea muscipula*. Arch. f. Anat., Physiol. u. wiss. Med. 1876:30–203.

NITSCHKE, 1861 (*See* under *Drosera*).

OUDEMANS, C. A. J. A., Over de prikkelbaarheid der bladen van *Dionaea muscipula*. Versl. Mededeel. K. Akad. Wet. 9:320–336, 1859.

PFEFFER, W. (*see* under *Drosera*).

PLUKENET, L., Almagestum Botanicum seu phytographiae Plukenetianae onomasticon etc. London 1696. 2d. ed., London 1769:211–212.

REES and WILL (*See* under *Nepenthes*).

SANDERSON, J. BURDON, *See* BURDON-SANDERSON.

SCARTH, G. W., The influence of internal osmotic pressure and of disturbance of the cell-surface on the permeability of *Spirogyra* for acid dyes. Protoplasma 1:204, 1927.

SCHENK, cited by CRAMER, 1877.

SILBERSCHMIDT, K., Untersuchungen über die Thermowachstumsreaktion. Ber. d. D. Bot. Gesell. 43:475, 1925 (*through* ASHIDA).

SIMS, JOHN, *Dionaea Muscipula*. *See* Curtis's Botanical Magazine.

SMITH, CORNELIA MARSCHALL, Development of *Dionaea muscipula*, I. Flower and Seed.

Bot. Gaz. 87:507–530, 1929; II. Germination of seed and development of seedling to maturity. *Ibid.* 91:377–394, 1931.

SOLEREDER, H., Systematische Anatomie der Dicotyledonen. Stuttgart 1899.

STEIN, B., 1873. Mentioned by COHN, 1875, p. 73.

STERN, K. & E. BÜNNING, Über die tagesperiodischen Bewegungen der Primärblätter von *Phaseolus multiflorus*, I. Der Einfluss der Temperatur auf die Bewegung. Ber. d. d. Bot. Gesell. 47:565–584, 1929 (*through* ASHIDA).

THOMSON, T. and J. D. HOOKER, Praecursores ad Floram Indicam. Journ. Proc. Linn. Soc. Bot. London. 2:83, 1858.

TROLL, 1939. *See* under *Nepenthes.*

YOUNG, WM., Catalogue des Arbres, etc., d'Amérique. 1783, p. 34 (n.v. *through* COKER).

ZIEGENSPECK, H., Über Zwischenproducte des Aufbaues von Kohlenhydrat-zellwänden und deren mechanische Eigenschaften. Bot. Arch. 9:297–376, 1925 (*n.v., through* v. GUTTENBERG, 1926).

Chapter XIII

UTRICULARIA, BIOVULARIA AND POLYPOMPHOLYX

Form, habit and habitat. — Distribution. — Embryology. — The various types arranged according to the character of their traps. —The vulgaris type (Freely floating forms. Semi-submersed, submersed but anchored forms. Terrestrial and epiphytic forms). — *Biovularia*, a floating type. — The purpurea type, a floating form. — The dichotomamonanthos type (Floating form. Terrestrial. *Polypompholyx:* annual, monaxial). — The cornuta type. — The caerulea type. — The capensis type. — The orbiculata type. — The longiciliata type. — The globulariaefolia type. — The nana type. — The Lloydii type. — The Kirkii type. — The simplex type.

Of the *Lentibulariaceae* there are recognized by KAMIENSKI five genera, *Pinguicula*, *Genlisea*, *Polypompholyx*, *Utricularia* and *Biovularia*. The first two, *Pinguicula* and *Genlisea* have already been considered. It now remains to treat *Utricularia*, *Polypompholyx* and *Biovularia*. These plants are freely floating or anchored aquatics, or are epiphytic, in wet moss, or are terrestrial in wet to moist sandy soils. The largest of these are among the aquatic and epiphytic forms. The former are well exemplified by *U. vulgaris*, among the best known, which is a lax floating plant of several feet in extent, but of little mass. The epiphytic *U. reniformis* is more massive and makes a brave showing as a greenhouse plant, frequently found in the good company of the orchids because of the similar habitat requirements and the showiness of their flowers. It is indigenous in Brazil. One species, *U. nelumbifolia*, finds its home habitually in the water-containing leaf rosettes of large Tillandsias, whence it sends out runners which reach into the urns of neighboring rosettes (GARDNER 1842, ULE 1898). Showy species are *U. Humboldtii*, *U. longifolia* (both S. America), *U. Endresii* (Costa Rica) and the related *U. Dusenii* which, though small, has a flower of the same type. Other of the larger species are the tropical American terrestrial *U. globulariaefolia* and *amethystina* (Trinidad), and a few others chiefly noticeable because of their tall inflorescences. But among the aquatics are found also the smallest species, as *e.g. U. cymbantha* (Africa) and a related unnamed species of still smaller size, the flower being only 2 mm. long, and the stolons mere threads, collected by Miss E. L. STEPHENS in Portuguese East Africa. As small are the two species referred by KAMIENSKI to *Biovularia*, *B. minima* and *B. olivacea*. With a few exceptions such as those above noted, the terrestrial species are small. When in flower and in numbers, they are conspicuous enough, but if not in flower they may be found only with very assiduous hunting. How one would find *U. simplex* (S. W. Australia) unless in flower is past guessing, so minute are the leaves.

But large or small, massive or delicate, perennial or evanescent annuals, they present a complex and puzzling morphology. They are entirely rootless, even in the embryonic condition. The distinction between stem and leaf is vague. Only in the inflorescence and in certain shoots (air-shoots of *U. vulgaris* etc.) is the morphology easily recognizable. But most to be wondered at are the traps which present an astounding degree of mechanical delicacy depending on a fineness of structure scarcely equalled elsewhere in the plant kingdom. Moreover they occur in an unexpected variety of form. But withal they are small, the largest scarcely exceeding 5 mm. in greatest extent, the smallest 0.3 mm. The prey caught by these traps are small — water fleas, minute larvae often of mosquitos, very young fish (DEAN) and small tadpoles, fish and tadpoles, however, being ensnared only by being caught by the tail or head in the mouth of the trap but not entirely engulfed as is smaller prey (DEAN, LLOYD). Larger prey may, however, be finally "entirely absorbed" according to MATHESON (1930), as e.g. in the case of the larva of Brachydeutera argentata. MATHESON sees the difficulty of explaining this, since the greater mass of the animal's body is outside of the trap. An explanation is, however, at hand and will be later offered.

The observation that mosquito larvae are often caught in the traps has led some investigators to hope that the floating large trapped species of Utricularia would be useful in aiding to control those pests (MATHESON 1930). It is well enough known that multitudes of mosquito larvae are in fact captured, the number being limited only by the number of traps available (FRANÇA).

The flowers are of the personate type, two-lipped, the throat usually closed by a palate, and the lower lip provided with a spur of various shape, except in a few species, in which it is a saccate enlargement, as in Biovularia, in U. cymbantha, U. Stephensae (Ms. name), and in U. minor, a fact which tends to invalidate KAMIENSKI's genus. U. purpurea and its co-species have flowers with a peculiarly laterally saccate lower lip. Most extraordinary are the two species U. capilliflora F.v.M., and U. Dunstani Lloyd (LLOYD 1936c) (TEXT FIG. 5). The former has the upper lip drawn out into two very long attenuate lobes, the lower lip into five slender finger-like lobes. In U. Dunstani, the upper lobe is rounded and entire while the lower lip is five lobed, the middle adjoining two lobes small, and the two lateral lobes very long and attenuate and to the casual observer identical with the long tips of the upper lip in U. capilliflora. The flowers are very small; had they been large they would have excited as much admiration as the flowers of some orchids or that of an Aristolochia with long appendages. The showy flowers of some S. American species have been mentioned. These are large and are rendered conspicuous by the wide lateral lobes of the lower lip particularly. Yellow is the most prevalent color, but white to purple flowers are also frequent with admixtures in the form of yellow or reddish markings on white or blue grounds; or red on yellow, especially on the palate, are often met with. Generally the pistil has a unilocular, globular ovary with a two lipped stigma, the lower being considerably larger than the upper. The seeds are usually numerous on a globular basifixed placenta. In certain species, however, two to three seeds only are produced on a rounded placenta (U. cymbantha) or two only, back to back, in Biovularia, the placenta reduced. The release of the seeds may be by circumcissile or irregular fracture, by a triangular window (*U. subulata*), or by a longitudinal slit (*U. orbiculata*). There are only two stamens bending upward along the curve of the ovary wall.

The sepals are usually two in number, upper and lower. In *Polypompholyx* there are four, hence DE CANDOLLE'S justification of his name *Tetralobus*, of slightly later date than and therefore superceded by *Polypompholyx* Lehmann. *Polypompholyx* as a generic name should, according to BARNHART, be in turn superseded by *Cosmiza* Raf. 1838, since both *Polypompholyx* Lehmann (Feb. 1844) and *Tetralobus* DC. (Mar. 1844) are later names. LEHMANN'S name is at the moment generally used.

U. fimbriata superficially resembles *Polypompholyx* in having its

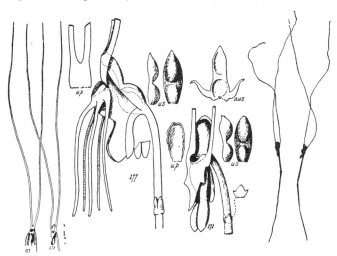

FIG. 5. — *Utricularia capilliflora* (277) and *U. Dunstani* (272); *up*, upper corolla lobe; *us*, upper sepal; *aus*, abnormal upper sepal. The two figures on the right are shadow prints from herbarium specimens, natural size.

two fimbriate sepals backed up by two fimbriate bracts, and has been incorrectly referred to *Polypompholyx*. BARNHART calls it *Aranella fimbriata* (BARNHART 1916).

The *Utriculariae* are of world wide distribution. Of the widest distribution are the submersed or semi-submersed plants of the type of *U. vulgaris*. They are found occupying a circumboreal zone characterized by certain species peculiar to it, throughout N. America including Greenland, Europe and Asia. Related species extend throughout the tropics and into S. America, S. Africa, Australia and New Zealand. The submersed floater *U. purpurea* and its co-species are purely American, extending from Maine, possibly Newfoundland, down the Atlantic Coast, west, to Indiana, and into E. South America. Another submersed form, *U. tubulata*, which is related to quite another group peculiar to Australia (the *U. monanthos* type), is found in N. E. Australia (Queensland).

The terrestrial forms are widely distributed in the tropics of the

Old and New Worlds, with northward extensions along the Atlantic coast, through Central America, and along the Pacific Coast of Asia. These include a considerable number of distinct types, some of which are peculiar to America, others to the Old World, and still others common to both (*U. subulata*). They are to be found also in Australasia.

So far as is known, *Utricularia* is not found on oceanic islands.

Embryology. — The embryological story of *Utricularia* has not yet been worked out in its fullness, but certain striking features have been observed and have been recorded by LANG, MERL (*Genlisea*), MERZ, and WYLIE and YOCOM. MERZ pointed out that the vascular tissues supplying the large placenta end there and do not enter the funicles of the ovules. As a compensation for this, it would appear, special masses of nutritive tissue arise in the chalaza and in the placenta (*Utricularia vulgaris*, etc.) or what amounts to the same thing, in a "funicular hump" (to quote WYLIE) (*Polypompholyx* Lehm.). These islands of food materials are made use of for the embryo by the penetration into them of peculiar haustorial extensions of the endosperm. Transitory starch appears in these haustoria. These nutritive masses are finally cut off from the ovule, as the embryo approaches maturity, by the development of diaphragms of suberized cells. Since according to MERZ the end of the suspensor extends into the placental nutritive tissue, this is cut off at the same time. WYLIE and YOCOM do not support this. In the related *Genlisea*, nutritive islands occur entirely within the ovule (MERL).

The ovule has but a single integument, which is common enough among the sympetalae, from the outer cell course of which a thin testa is derived. The tegmen, membranous and delicate, may represent the remaining tissue of the integument, since the nucellus is absorbed (MERZ). The mature embryo has neither root nor *punctum vegetationis* (MERL, LLOYD).

Seed, embryo and seedling. — The seeds, in most cases, develop on a large globular, central placenta, and are crowded sufficiently in some species so that by mutual compression, they become angular, approximately hexagonal, with flattish outer chalazal and inner micropylar surfaces, the latter the smaller (WARMING, WYLIE). The planes of the sides radiate as if from the center of the placenta (*U. vulgaris, U. resupinata*), or the ovules overlap and become winged with circular wings (*U. oligosperma, U. exoleta*) the whole dished into a concavo-convex lens shape. In other species, chiefly terrestrial, the seeds are minute (down to 0.2 mm. in diam.) and globular or oval, occasionally lobulate (*U. reniformis, U. Dusenii, U. purpurea*) or have polar clusters of trichomes (*U. brachiata*) (COMPTON) or scattered glochidia covering one end (*U. orbiculata*).

The testa is composed of an epidermis of darkened (reddish or brown), relatively large cells with their inner and radial walls thickened, the outer thin and collapsed in maturity. Their shape varies from round angular to elongate, many and relatively small or few and relatively large. In a few instances they become mucilaginous when wet, in species which grow with the vegetative parts submersed and attached to a stony substrate in running water (*U. rigida*, and probably *U. neottioides*). In a very few instances the seed has no hard testa, but simply a thin lax membrane easily torn, and the seed seems to be released by the rotting away of the capsule (*Biovularia*).

Embryo. — The embryo is a mass of scarcely differentiated cells containing much starch and oil, and is either bun shaped with a depression at the vegetative pole (*U. vulgaris*) (WARMING) (*21 — 6*) or flattened by lateral compression, with the growth pole on its edge (*U. emarginata* and *exoleta*) (*21 — 7*), this position and form being due, according to MERZ, to rotation of the embryo-sac and embryo through 90 deg. following the abscission of the egg-pole endosperm; or again more or less oval or spindle shaped (a host of species, *e.g. U. bifida*) (*22 — 1, 18*). In a few there is a depression at the root pole (*Polypompholyx*) (*22 — 26*). Its structure is very simple: it is a mass of rounded parenchyma clothed with an epidermis, the cells of which covering the growth pole are small, columnar and highly protoplasmic. The primary organs usually originate at this pole, but may occasionally appear elsewhere (*U. bifida*) (*22 — 19–22*). There is an entire absence of a root. Even at maturity the embryo has as yet no lateral organs. GOEBEL reported them in the embryo of *U. orbiculata*, but I have failed to find them. In *U. reniformis* and *U. nelumbifolia* primary leaves have been seen, and these species may display vivipary (MERL).

While the growth pole produces lateral organs, two in many cases (cotyledonoids) or various numbers in others, a *punctum vegetationis* (the primary primordium of a shoot) is never present in the embryo, nor is ever developed. Shoots when present in the plant are always produced as lateral organs.

Germination (*22 — 1–28*). — The events of germination show that there are three types of seedling: (1) a simple, in which there are two cotyledonoids (since one of these is a stolon); and (2) a complex, in which there are 6 to 13 (WARMING, JANE) cotyledonoids, or indeed only two; and (3) a type in which there are no cotyledonoids at all, with three primary shoots only. The simple type is displayed by all the terrestrial species (so far as known), such as *U. capensis*, *U. bifida*, *U. monanthos*, *Polypompholyx*, which have been studied. The complex type is seen in *U. vulgaris* (with many cotyledonoids) and in *U. exoleta*, *U. emarginata* etc. (with two cotyledonoids). *U. capensis* among others has been studied by myself (*1937b*). The seed is minute and oval in shape. From the growth pole emerges at first a leaf followed shortly by a stolon. Between them in the expected position there is no *punctum vegetationis*. The leaf extends upwards, the stolon downwards. The first evidence of further growth is the appearance of a trap, on the base of the stolon, a little away from the middle line (*22 — 14*), or rarely, as in *U. cleistogama*, asymmetrically near the leaf base. At the base of the trap-stalk a bud arises which produces an ascending stolon with more or less crowded leaves. This becomes thicker with upward growth, finally becoming an inverted cone, a protocorm bearing leaves, traps and stolons. Their vascular tissues form within the protocorm a loose stem-like structure, similar to that described by WARMING for *Genlisea* and by myself for *Poly-*

pompholyx. At its top is formed at length a large radially symmetrical bud, which becomes the inflorescence (*22 — 11, 25*). Of the stolons, some are anchoring in function (rhizoids) while others become runner stolons, bearing leaves along the upper surface, and facing toward the corm, in the adaxial axils of which other scapes may arise. Thus is produced a spreading plant. Scapes may also arise from buds adventive on the leaves, this among many irregularities of growth. Sometimes the primary leaf may produce a number of traps in the adaxial axils of which buds are formed, as in the case of the axils of leaves produced on stolons.

This course of events, thus briefly stated, is followed by all other species studied: *U. bifida*, *U. monanthos*, with evidence from a considerable number of others. *U. bifida* was also studied by GOEBEL who seems to have thought that the first bud was between the cotyledonoids, and suffered later displacement, as his drawings indicate. But the statements of both GOEBEL and MERL (*U. longifolia*) admit an asymmetrical position. My own studies of *U. bifida* have revealed a strong tendency on the part of the embryo to produce at first a leaf only, raised more or less on an elongate extension of the upper part of the embryo body (a podium) and for the primary stolon to be produced at its base from a distinct bud there seen (*22 — 1-11*).

If the protocorm produces no runners, as in *U. capilliflora*, *U. violacea*, *U. Hookeri*, *Polypompholyx*, an inflorescence can be produced only from the top of the protocorm (*22 — 25, 26*), or by secondary branching from the scape itself. This development is called abrupt. Such plants do not spread by runner stolons. The behavior of *U. capensis* etc., which spreads by runners, is diffuse.

In all these forms, especially in the abrupt kind of germination, the primary bud arising from the first stolon can elongate very considerably to form a naked ascending stolon producing leaves only at length. The curious asymmetrical relations of embryo and its primary organs than becomes quite apparent. I have seen this in *U. violacea*, *U. Hookeri* and *Polypompholyx*, in which the events of germination are preserved in the mature individual, for the embryo may persist throughout the life of the plant (*22 — 26*).

The complex kind of germination is displayed by a lot of species represented by *U. vulgaris*, which has been the subject of much study by WARMING, PRINGSHEIM, KAMIENSKI, GOEBEL, JANE and LLOYD, and by *U. oligosperma* (GOEBEL). The condition found in *U. exoleta* (GOEBEL) and *U. emarginata* though simple in the sense indicated by the number of cotyledonoids, is merely a special case evidently related to the *vulgaris* condition.

In *U. vulgaris* the embryo is a prolate spheroid. From a low dome arise several leaf buds in an outer circle, within which several other primordia stand, with no apparent order, though it has been stated otherwise (GOEBEL). The outer, and some of the inner primordia become awl-shaped leaves, but to pick out two of these as cotyledons is impossible (GOEBEL). Occasionally one of them ends in a trap (GOEBEL; JANE). Of the inner primordia, some become leaves, usually one a dorsiventral shoot, and one a primary trap. Sometimes leaves are produced which are evidently partly shoot in structure, the distinction between leaf and shoot being here vague. The apex of the dome never develops (*21 — 1-5*).

In *U. exoleta* and *U. emarginata* the embryo is laterally compressed so that the growth pole is on the edge. Here two leaves are produced. These may occasionally become shoots (*21 — 7*D). Near their bases, but displaced to one side are usually two buds, sometimes a third. These become dorsiventral shoots.

Aberrancies of development are not at all unusual. For example, one embryo of *U. vulgaris* produced only two leaves and two shoots which became at once dorsiventral "water shoots."

In *U. nelumbifolia*, otherwise similar to *U. vulgaris*, the primary leaves are widely forked (MERL) and those of *U. reniformis* are broadly spatulate (GOEBEL). According to GOEBEL, the embryo of *U. montana* has no primordia before germination, and on it there are produced two primordia (the cotyledonoids) of which one becomes a spatulate leaf, the other a trap, on the side of the "vegetation point" which grows directly into a radial structure from which stolons etc. grow. The interpretation here is to be questioned, as it is doubtful if GOEBEL's identification of the vegetation point is correct.

The third type of germination is seen in *U. purpurea*. The embryo is ovate, with a flattened broad end. From this there normally arise, in succession, three shoot buds standing in a triangle with respect to each other. The first is dominant in growth; the second to appear may form at first a close second, but at length lags behind in growth; while the third may not do more than put in an appearance, and then fail to develop (TEXT FIG. 6, 1-7). In one case a fourth shoot bud appeared early (TEXT FIG. 6, 4 and 5), but its subsequent development showed it to be a branch at the base of the first bud, and in other seedlings it appeared later, but constantly. The development of the first shoot has been followed until it produced five whorls of branches (leaves in the taxonomic texts). The earlier two whorls have but two members bearing traps, placed symmetrically attached to the upper moiety of the stem. On the upper surface of the stem as a member of the whorl may appear a bud of unlimited growth, destined in its turn to produce whorls of secondary members (TEXT FIG. 6, 7). In the third to fifth whorls, two additional members, placed in the wide dorsal space, appear. These, however, do not bear traps. In the fourth whorl, in one case observed, one of the ventral pair produced a branch which, however, bore no trap. In one instance a seedling was found in which the first and second buds were fasciated (TEXT FIG. 6, 6). It is evident that in this type the seedling at once takes on the morphological character of the mature form, which, however, has whorls of four (*U. elephas*) or six (*U. purpurea*) branched members.

It would be most interesting to know the course of germination of *U. tubulata*, but of this we are yet ignorant.

Types of Utricularia. — In the following account, the various species, so far as they are here included, are arranged according to the character of their traps.

1. *The Utricularia vulgaris type.* — All the plants of this type have traps which are closely similar in the mechanical details of structure

to those of *U. vulgaris*, differing among themselves only as regards non-essential, small details. A description of the trap is deferred till later.

Freely floating forms. — *U. vulgaris* itself is the best known and most widely distributed, and will serve well as the type of numerous species, world wide in distribution.

The plant consists of a cylindrical or laterally compressed axis which may reach a length of 300 cm., probably more, supporting two lateral rows of divided "leaves," and dying off behind as it grows from the tip. The leaves are very crowded toward the growing circinate end. The whole plant is lax and lies in the still water in which it grows entangled, one plant with another, forming often dense mats. Toward the end of the growing season the more terminal internodes become very short and the leaves densely packed to form a resting bud (turion), which sinks or floats, according to circumstances, and may be frozen in the ice. In spring the tips of the leaves or the chief axis proliferate, giving rise directly to new plants with leaves of simpler structure at first.

A leaf arises from a single lateral outgrowth from the prostrate stem, remaining single in *U. oligosperma*, or forking as it develops (Pringsheim, Goebel) to form two lobes (*21 — 8*), at whose bases may arise secondary outgrowths, one on each of which can develop into additional lobes. The third and fourth lobes are not at all or only weakly developed in some species (*U. vulgaris*) but are strongly developed in others, e.g. *U. Thonningii*. In others fifth and sixth small lobes are formed laterally to the third and fourth, and are known as auricles. In *U. Thonningii* (Angola) the auricle is a fan shaped production, with many rays from its edge, all armed with stiff bristles, occasionally bearing a trap. In *U. stellaris* (Asia, Africa) and *flexuosa* (Singapore) the auricles are deeply subdivided, the divisions more or less curved and crowded upon each other. Each leaf lobe is pinnatifid, the pinnae being, however, alternate, the internodes so placed as to produce a zigzag axis, appearing monopodial (*20 — 1*). The lateral divisions (pinnae) have the same disposition of parts. The ends of the divisions are usually armed with stiff bristles, either singly or in bundles, and these afford a taxonomic character.

The traps are borne on the leaves in such position as to suggest that each represents a leaf division (Goebel, Meierhofer). The details of the structure of the trap will be given fully beyond. Here is only to point out that the trap is always placed with its sagittal section transverse to the plane of the leaf, the mouth facing the apex of the shoot (*20 — 1*). The interior surface of the trap is morphologically the upper surface of the leaf division which it represents (hypopeltate, Goebel). In some species only one lobe of a leaf produces traps, the other (upper) half being wholly photosynthetic in function.

In certain species leaves of a highly specialized kind occur on the basal part of the flower stalk. In these the midrib is much inflated by the enlargement of intercellular spaces while the lateral divisions are much reduced. These are disposed in a whorl ("false whorl") and act as floats to support the inflorescence above the water surface (*U. radiata, U. inflata, U. stellaris*) (*20 — 12*). The size and shape of these floats are characteristic of different species possessing them. In *U. stellaris* they are short and of relatively wide diameter. In *U. inflata* they are long (4–5 cm.) and clavate.

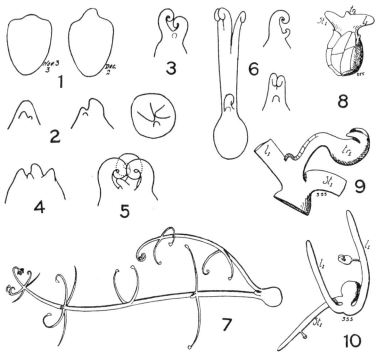

FIG. 6. — 1–7, *Utricularia purpurea.* — 1, Early stages of germination of a seed (3.3 mm long) from which only one growing point arose (to be followed by others later in all probability); 2, Three figures in a row, three views of an early stage of germination, a later stage of which is shown in 3, in which two young growing points show circination; 4 and 5, Two following stages in the germination of a seed which produced three growing points all of nearly the same age, with a fourth, secondary to the middle growing point; 6, A case in which fasciation occurred, the two figures on the right show an early stage of germination, a much later stage is shown on the left, in which it is seen that one of the growing points had divided, an abnormality; 7, An advanced stage in germination (15 mm long), one of the three growing points still quiescent; five whorls of branches (the maximum seen) were produced, as shown on the longer stolon of this figure. At the first whorl of this, the bud of a branch stolon of indefinite growth is seen. No traps are produced on the two dorsal branches of the third and fourth whorls.

8–10, *Utricularia cleistogama.* — 8, Early stage of germination showing primary stolon and primary leaf, with the primary trap on the leaf near its base; 9, A later stage in detail showing the origin of the trap from the leaf base; 10, A more advanced stage of the seedling in which a second leaf arose in the place of a primary trap.

Still another form of leaf occurs on short stolons at the base of the scape of the inflorescence (BUCHENAU 1865), the so-called rhizoids, several of which are usually present. Their leaves are much reduced in size and have very small pinnae which are curved and crowded into claw-like masses. More or less of each pinna is densely covered with mucilage glands quite like those scattered over the whole plant surface (*U. vulgaris*, etc.).

In the species *U. oligosperma* there is a pronounced dimorphism of leaves, each kind occurring on separate branches. Those of one kind bear none, or very few poorly developed traps. They are finely divided with very long terminal divisions in the form of flat, ensiform divisions, and are very crowded, so that the leafy branches appear as dense tufts strongly contrasted with those which bear the second kind of leaves which are trap bearing. The traps are very numerous and crowded, and the leaves which bear them have only a single lobe, whose divisions all lie in the plane of the axis which bears them.

The leaves in this and similar species (*e.g. U. mixta*) are provided on one side only with a small foliose appendage consisting of about four radiating accuminate members each bearing a trap, the whole having a stipulate appearance (*23 — 3*). These may be similar to the minute axillary shoots mentioned by PRINGSHEIM in *U. vulgaris* (*21 — 10*), different only in position.

A pair of similar appendages (we may call them tentatively dwarf shoots) occurs also at the sides of the base of the air shoot, but here they often have more divisions, each carrying a trap (*23 — 2, 6*). They are found also in *U. mixta*. To the unaided eye in such cases there appears at the base of the air shoot a tight grape-like cluster of as many as a dozen, or as few as two to four traps. Without careful examination it would seem as if the air shoot were supplied with stipules, but the organs in question arise directly from the axis. They, however, derive their vascular strands as branches from the main strand entering the air shoot, though exceptions have been noted. So far as I am aware these peculiar dwarf leaves are to be found only on those species which have strap-shaped stolons, the greater longitudinal plane being vertical, the upper edge somewhat narrower than the lower. They cannot readily be homologized with the auricles of some species because of the distinct origin from the stolon.

A large number of species of the *U. vulgaris* type (*U. exoleta, emarginata, gibba, cymbantha,* etc.), plants with thread-like stolons, have leaves which may be no more than a single fork, two slender segments arising from the base, only the lower one bearing a single trap (*21 — 17, 18*); or they may be variously more complex, but always much simpler than in *U. vulgaris*.

Branching; origin of the inflorescence. — It was quite apparent to the earlier observers (IRMISCH 1858; BUCHENAU 1865) that branching in *Utricularia* does not follow a pattern common to the flowering plants. The observations of these students, with those of PRINGSHEIM (1869) and GOEBEL (1891), afford the available basis for description to which my own studies have been added. From these there emerges in fairly clear form the pattern peculiar to these very aberrant organisms. We consider *U. vulgaris* which PRINGSHEIM studied developmentally, in contrast with IRMISCH and BUCHENAU who examined only the mature condition.

U. vulgaris. — The growing point (*21 — 8*) of the horizontal shoot shows upward circination (PRINGSHEIM, GOEBEL) and that (1) a row of peculiar branches arises in a line on the upper surface of the stolon in no relation to the leaves except that they are usually nearer the nodes than to the middle of the internode, and either in front or behind them. They do not arise in a leaf axil. These, first seen by BUCHENAU and thought by him to be roots, are the "tendrils" of PRINGSHEIM and "air shoots" of GOEBEL ($23 - 1$). GLÜCK questions their usefulness as air shoots. They are long and very slender with two lateral rows of "mussel-shaped" leaves with stomata, and are circinate forwards. They are absent from many species, including all of the *U. exoleta* type. They have the ability to transform themselves by apical growth into ordinary shoots (GOEBEL, GLÜCK). (2) Lateral branches (st_2) arise near the upper edge of the oblique leaf insertion, but not in the leaf axil. They are of occasional occurrence only ($21 - 8$, st_2). (3) The inflorescence (sc) arises in association with a third stolon branch (st_3) in the axil of st_2, the latter being the larger at first, the scape arising from its base. As GOEBEL observed in *U. flexuosa*, "Never does one find the inflorescence isolated, but always combined with a leafy branch springing from its base." The question which of the two is primary cannot at the moment be settled. (4) In some leaf axils ("older ones," PRINGSHEIM) buds may arise, which do not center on the middle of the leaf axil. Here again are two, one arising from the base of the other, and they are a leafy shoot and a scape (the smaller) just as when an st_2 branch is present, but now in a leaf axil, not in the branch axil ($21 - 9$). PRINGSHEIM calls them dwarf or aborted shoots. (5) In the axil of most leaves there is a cluster of about 4 traps arising at the middle point. GOEBEL interpreted PRINGSHEIM's observation and drawing to mean that this group of traps arises from a short branch, while PRINGSHEIM thought that the branch arises from a trap stalk. GOEBEL is probably correct ($21 - 10$).

U. stellaris, *U. inflata* and the like appear to conform to the above description. In *U. oligosperma* and *U. mixta* somewhat more special conditions prevail. Instead of one branch of st_2 rank, there are two, coordinate in development, one opposite the single leaf (undivided at the base) and one below the axil. The lower of these (*U. oligosperma*) bears leaves with very many traps, the upper is almost devoid of traps. Above the axil of the upper branch arise the twin branches, one a leafy branch, the other a scape, conjoined at the base ($21-11$). Thus in maturity there is a cluster of stolons radiating from the base of an inflorescence, the forward and backward extensions of the chief stolon, and three leafy branches. In both species the air shoots are prominent and have laterally placed at their bases clusters of traps which have been referred to already as dwarf leaves. They occur also at the leaf bases, either axillary or at one side. There is evidence that these are dwarf shoots (GOEBEL) bearing traps with broadened stalks, not trap stalks bearing shoots, as PRINGSHEIM thought.

U. minor ($21 - 16$, 17) was studied by IRMISCH and by BUCHENAU. It is a smaller and more slender plant, the leaves, in lateral rows, being placed aslant, facing upward, the upper edge being therefore farther from the apex than the lower. The branching is essentially as in *U. vulgaris*, with the difference that the chief branch (st_2) arises at the lower edge of the leaf, and is circinate upwards. In the axil of the leaf there are two shoots, a leafy one (st₃) circinate towards st₂ and a scape (sc) circinate towards sc₃. sc₃ and sc may, however, occur without sc₂ which is much less frequent in incidence. In the normal condition therefore when the scape is developed there are at its base two stolons, one from the chief axis and one from the base of the scape. An additional one, apparently seen by BUCHENAU, may arise from the scape base. My material came from Eire through Professor H. H. DIXON.

In *U. gibba* (*21 — 12*, 20), on the other hand, the first branch arises at the *upper* edge of the leaf base. A pair of mutually facing and circinate branches then arise, as in *U. minor*, to produce a second branch and scape. Secondary scapes arise in close apposition to the primary as branches of the bearing stolon. A plant sent me by Dr. F. W. WENT from Pasadena behaves similarly as do also *U. emarginata* and *U. exoleta* (*21 —* 18, 19). In these species the scape produces near its base numerous branches, not in any leaf axil, which bear much reduced and very glandular leaves. These are rhizoids (*23 —* 8). Secondary scapes may also arise in the axils of these (*21 —* 20).

It is apparent that in the *vulgaris* type of *Utricularia* the branching has distinct peculiarities. One sort of branch, the air-shoot, never arises in any relation to a leaf. The chief stolon branch (st₂) arises near one edge of a leaf base, more or less overlapping the axil, but never centered on it. At its base, opposite the leaf axil, arise two buds, one a stolon and the other, on or near its base, an inflorescence. In some species a dwarf shoot bearing only traps arises in the leaf axil, behind the scape and its companion shoot.

The rhizoids are absent from some species. They are regarded as anchoring in function, but are only very ineffectively so in the floating species (GLÜCK). They are much better developed and are much more numerous in the *exoleta* type.

In the mature condition the original position of the primordia is usually completely obscured by the enlargement and mutual distortion of the adjacent parts. The embryonic condition was studied by PRINGSHEIM and by GOEBEL, both of whom recognized the origin of the "tendrils" or "air-shoots" and of the chief stolon branch.

The immediately above mentioned species (*U. gibba, exoleta,* etc.) are, in contrast to *vulgaris*, very slender plants with thread-like stolons and simple leaves, once or twice divided, or even thrice (*U. emarginata*) (*20 —* 2). The internodes are long. Obviously closely related to these are two African species, *U. cymbantha* Oliver and *U. Stephensae* (in Ms.) which deserve special mention. These are minute plants with single flowered scapes. The method of branching is simple. A stolon branch (st₂), always single, and without axillary buds, arises near the upper edge of a leaf, but more or less axillary, while the scape arises from or near to the upper surface of the stolon, and near or somewhat distant from a leaf and certainly in no definite relation to it (*23 —* 12, 13, 21, 22).

Submersed, semi-submersed but anchored forms of the vulgaris type. — These fall into two groups: those which grow (1) submersed but send out shoots of two kinds, one chiefly trap-bearing; or (2) on the surface of the wet substrate, sending out branches which penetrate the substrate, bearing traps and reduced leaves. These emerge eventually. To the former belong such species as *U. ochroleuca, U. Bremii* (Europe) and *U. minor* (in both hemispheres). To the latter belongs *U. intermedia* (20 — 4; 21 — 13, 14). According to GLÜCK they exhibit a good deal of polymorphism in response to environmental differences. So far as they have been investigated the method of branching shows no peculiarities. For full accounts the reader may be referred to GLÜCK'S book.

Here may be mentioned the peculiar *U. clandestina* Nutt. (23 — 1). This is a lax floater of the general appearance of an undernourished condition of *U. vulgaris*. It is provided with special branches with reduced foliage and traps, these occurring sparingly if at all on the leaves of the main stolons. The scape of the inflorescence arises in connection with a branch (the latter in or near the axil of a leaf) and, in addition to the normal inflorescence bearing normal flowers, bears at its base usually two flowers in the axils of scales. The pedicels of these flowers nod downwardly and produce seed abundantly by close pollination (presumably). Sometimes these cleistogamous flowers (which never emerge from the water) are produced without an accompanying scape bearing proper flowers. The presence of scale leaves allows no doubt that the spur on which they are borne represents an undeveloped inflorescence. Its position with relation to a leaf and branch are the same as above described for a normal inflorescence.

In this species also air shoots are to be found, usually emerging from the upper surface of the chief axis rather near to an inflorescence. They are absent from others of this group above cited.

A few forms are, with the exception of their inflorescences of course, not only completely submersed, but their chief stolons are buried in in the substrate of sand or mud, and their leafy branches or merely their leaves emerge into the supernatant water. Among these may be counted *U. resupinata* (N. America), *U. biloba* (Australia) and *U. paradoxa* (in Ms.) (Angola).

U. resupinata (23 — 8, 9). — The body of the plant consists of horizontal stolons bearing terete, tapering leaves on the upper surface, with branch stolons emerging laterally, a pair at each node. This is a wide departure from what we have seen above, and foreshadowing what we shall see in the terrestrial forms. The leaves are circinate backwards, that is, away from the apex of the bearing stolon, as first observed by GOEBEL in *U. orbiculata*. The inflorescence arises as a bud in the forward leaf axil, flanked usually by stolon buds. From the base of the scape a number of rhizoids spring out and penetrate the substrate. The method of branching is the same in *U. biloba* and *U. paradoxa* (21 — 22), the differences being in their leaves. In the latter they are much as in *U. vulgaris* but emerge from the substrate and appear as little trees in the water. The traps are borne chiefly on the stolons. In *U. biloba* the leaves are articulated, segment with segment (21 — 21). Sometimes a segment becomes a stolon, illustrating the indeterminate morphological character of these parts often referred to in the literature (GOEBEL). The traps occur on secondary stolons, rarely on the leaves.

Utricularia grows generally, when submersed, in still waters. There are two very striking exceptions to this in *U. neottioides* and *U. rigida*, the former South American, the latter from Africa, both tropical. They grow in running streams, attached to the rocky bottom, recalling the *Podostemonaceae*. Creeping on the rock surface and tightly clinging to it are numerous fleshy, coral-like stolons. From these arise branches which are leafy, bearing traps (LUETZELBURG 1910) and finally flowers. The traps diverge from the *vulgaris* trap in being streamlined — to yield to the vocabulary of the moment — being spindle shaped, the stalk at one end and the mouth at the other. According to O. STAPF (1906), *U. rigida*, which closely resembles *U. neottioides*, has no traps. None of the Kew specimens showed any, and though the herbarium specimens of *U. neottioides* did not show them, LUETZELBURG found them. The material I examined was collected by him, and preserved in GOEBEL's collection.

Terrestrial and epiphytic forms of the vulgaris type. — Of the strictly terrestrial species are, *e.g. U. subulata* L. (W. Africa, America) and *U. Rendlei* Lloyd (Victoria Falls). These grow in a wet substrate of sand or sandy soil, and consist of very delicate thread-like stolons sending up simple spatulate or ligulate leaves of very small size and often difficult to see when collecting, and having delicate scapes with yellow flowers. *U. subulata* shows a cleistogamous condition in Nova Scotia (FERNALD). The method of branching is the same as that in *U. resupinata*. The traps are numerous on the stolons, in lateral rows and one row along the upper surface and along the leaf margins. The leaves face away from the apex of the bearing stolon.

The epiphytic species are usually large and bear showy flowers, and are often grown as greenhouse plants among the orchids with which some of them vie in beauty. Mentioned here may be *U. reniformis*, *U. nelumbifolia*, *U. montana*, *U. Humboldtii*, *U. longifolia*, *U. Endresii* and the small but often large flowered species growing in the soil such as *U. Dusenii* and *U. Campbelliana*, all from Central or South America. Some species grow in the water held by the leaf rosettes of Tillandsias, *e.g. U. nelumbifolia* in the Organ Mts. of Brazil (GARDNER 1846), and *U. Humboldtii*, on the Kaieteur Savannah, British Guiana (IM THURN 1887), both of which grow in the axils of the leaves of bromeliads (*Brocchinia* spp.). These, and especially the forms which grow in wet moss (*U. reniformis*), are conspicuous for their thick, coral-like stolons, the anatomy of which has been described by HOVELACQUE. The method of branching differs with different species.

U. reniformis is on the evidence of its branching related to the terrestrial types, *e.g. U. subulata*. From the 6 mm. thick stolon the leaves arise in a row on the upper surface. These are circinate backward, and have a reniform blade 15 cm. in diameter. The bud of the scape arises in the leaf axil on the proximal side but not always in the middle point indicating a degree of obliquity in the position of the leaf (GOEBEL). The branch stolons arise in single lateral rows (21 — 15). Though the plant is of stately proportions, the traps are small. There are no rhizoids judging from HOEHNE's figure.

U. montana has leaves and branch stolons alternating irregularly in lateral rows, all lying in the horizontal plane of the bearing stolon. Their axillary buds, however, lie obliquely (GOEBEL). Branch stolons may also arise from the upper chief stolon surface. The condition here recalls that of *U. cornuta*, a small terrestrial species.

In *U. longifolia* leaves may occur both laterally and on the upper stolon surface (GOEBEL). *U. Dusenii* Sylv. is a small delicate plant resembling *U. reniformis* in habit and flower structure, and has the same disposition of lateral organs. Instead of a leaf with attendant stolons, the node may bear three leaves. Rhizoids are present.

The traps of all the previously mentioned plants adhere strictly to the kind found in *U. vulgaris*. Some slight differences occur, but these will be better described in a following chapter devoted to the structure of the trap.

2. *The Biovularia type.* — In the only two known species of *Biovularia*, the general morphology aligns itself with that of the *vulgaris* type while that of the trap stands closer to the *U. purpurea* type. The species are *B. olivacea* (Wright) Kam. and *B. minima* (Warm.) Kam.

Utricularia olivacea was described by C. WRIGHT in GRISEBACH's *Plantarum Cubensium* . . . (1866) and was regarded by him as closely related to *U. gibba*, which it is not. KAMIENSKI, who also related it to *U. gibba*, made it the type of a new genus, *Biovularia*, based on the number of ovules present in the ovary, namely, two, arising from the bottom of the ovary and not from an enlarged central placenta, as in *Utricularia*. We call it therefore *Biovularia olivacea*.

The plant consists of extremely delicate axes bearing traps on long stalks in the place of leaves (*23* — 14-18). The latter are absent, but WRIGHT described the plant as having them. To quote him: "utriculis obovoideis ad segmenta folii capillaceo-divisa sparsis." This error seems to have arisen either from admixture with other floating species or from the fact that the long stalks frequently shed the traps at the outer end, and thus appear as leaves. Still they are not divided. When branching occurs one or two branches may arise from a node. In herbarium material (Cotype, Herb. Smithsonian Institution) I could get no evidence bearing on the sequence of development.

The inflorescence arises as a branch near the axil of a trap. This branch assumes considerable thickness, and dominates, in the matter of size (diameter), the mother stolon. From its base arise two branches, with a 120 degree angle of divergence, one somewhat higher up than the other. From the apex of this short thick spur springs a flower pedicel, which is surrounded at its base by an enveloping, involucral scale leaf. Just within this may arise a second pedicel in the axil of a second enveloping scale. In exceptional cases the second pedicel may arise from a point on the first formed pedicel a considerable distance above the base. A third pedicel may arise from the second. We are evidently dealing here with a compound inflorescence in which the chief axis is suppressed.

The ovate sepals continue development during the growth of the capsule, becoming deeply denticulate along their margins, and form a graceful vase-like involucre about the ripened clavate capsule.

Usually only one seed develops. The narrowly ovate embryo (o.28 × 0.15 mm.) conforms to type, there being no organs differentiated. It is invested by a loose and papery covering which probably remains attached to the capsule.

Biovularia minima growing in Lagoa Santa, Brazil was suspected by KAMIENSKI (E. und P. VI, *Lentibulariaceae*) to be specifically identical with *B. olivacea*, both subsumed by him under *Biovularia*. With the courtesy of the Botanical Museum, Copenhagen, I have been able to examine the original WARMING type material, and am now in a position to say that the two plants are specifically distinct on evidence of flower structure.

3. *The purpurea type* (*20 — 3*). — To this type belongs a small group of highly distinctive plants found only in the New World. They are so far as known freely floating plants, and have no terrestrial analogs.

The plant body consists of stolons which send out at the nodes 6 or 7 cylindrical branches forming very regular whorls. The whole displays a minor degree only of dorsiventrality which, however, is more evident at and near the growing apex, where the stolon apex is upwardly strongly circinate, and the branches develop at unequal rates, faster below, slower above. The cylindrical branches in turn can produce branches of the third order, more below near their bases (about 4), fewer above (two), also in whorls, but unevenly spaced. These branches are more definitely and evidently dorsiventral than the chief stolon, and are of limited growth, and each branch is constricted at the end into a slender stalk, bearing a trap. At the base of each branch there is an abscission zone, as there is also at the base of each branch of the third order and at the base of the trap.

BARNHART correctly described this plant as having no leaves, these being represented by verticillate branches. LUETZELBURG, however, regards them as leaves. He studied a species which he called *U. elephas*, which differs from *U. purpurea* in having only two to four branches instead of 6–7. He examined the growing tip and believed that he could see that the pair of lateral "leaves" were united in the early stage of development. GOEBEL accepted LUETZELBURG's interpretation. Had LUETZELBURG examined *U. purpurea* in the same way, the evidence would probably have given him pause, since six or seven "leaves" would have to have been accounted for. I have studied both *U. purpurea* and *U. elephas* in the same way, and can find no evidence that any of the branches are fused at first. This is borne out by the distribution of the vascular strands, which radiate separately out from the central cylinder. Add to this the verticillate arrangement of the branches of the third and fourth order, and it is clear that we have to do not with leaves (even in the restricted sense this term is used when speaking of *Utricularia*) but with branches.

In *U. elephas* as in *U. purpurea* the scape occurs in the axil of a more or less aborted branch arising on the upper surface of the chief stolon. This branch always remains delayed in development. The scape produces no rhizoids, nor any scale except in the inflorescence.

4. *The dichotoma-monanthos type.* — To this type belongs a goodly number of species which are purely Australasian, and so far known only from Tasmania, Australia proper and New Zealand. This type is not present in the recent BRASS collections of New Guinea plants at the Arnold Arboretum of Harvard University. They are at once recognizable by their winged traps.

The series includes one freely floating form, *U. tubulata*, and while the terrestrial forms are readily divided into two groups, those with runner stolons (*U. dichotoma, U. monanthos*, etc.) and those which have only anchoring stolons (*U. Menziesii, U. violacea, U. volubilis, U. Hookeri*), never runners, and which are confined to the extreme S. W. of Western Australia. These have been regarded by GOEBEL as primitive forms, but the only fact to which this view can be tied is the absence of runner stolons. Allied and included with these is the genus *Polypompholyx*, with 2 (or probably 4) species.

Freely floating species. — The only freely floating species of this group known, and that only from herbarium specimens in the Melbourne Herbarium (paratypes at Kew and at the British Museum of Natural History), to which I had access, is *U. tubulata*. It was collected in 1875 by W. E. ARMIT in "mountain swamps near Cashmere, 40–50 mi. west of Rockingham Bay" in Queensland, but never since. In general appearance it resembles *U. purpurea*, but only superficially owing to the whorled position of the leaves (*36* — 10, 11).

The "rather long" stolons bear leaves and traps in whorls, in each whorl four leaves alternating with four traps on long stalks, so orientated that usually two of the leaves lie on one side and two on the other side of the stolon, the traps being then one dorsal, one ventral, and one on each side. Occasional departures from the rule may be observed when two traps may stand side by side, or two leaves. In the mature condition the leaves and traps are joined at their bases to form a complete ring of tissue surrounding the node from which they arise. A dissection of several terminal buds showed clearly that the primordia of the lateral organs are all quite distinct at first, so that the ring supporting them is secondary. The primordia appear at first as low mounds of tissue in transverse series of eight, at first indistinguishable from each other. At about the sixth node the leaves elongate somewhat, overpassing the traps in growth. The apex of the axis is long, naked and slightly circinate. The primordia are not at all crowded. In the axil of a leaf a bud which develops into a branch stolon may arise. Traps with their stalks and leaves attain a length of 2 cm. The leaves are flat, linear and apiculate, the trap stalk foliose (LLOYD 1936c).

According to VON MUELLER, the scape is terminal on a chief shoot and such evidence as I was able to obtain bears out this view. I dissected one terminal bud to find that it was indeed an inflorescence with a lateral vegetative bud. Slender at the base, it swells considerably at or above the middle to form a spar-buoy float. The scales are basifixed. MUELLER's description of the flower does not help us much, but the few specimens I saw in Melbourne indicate clearly that the flower with a widely spreading lower lip conforms to that of *U. dichotoma*. Its color is bluish ("albida-caerulescente").

U. tubulata as a floating plant appears to stand alone in regard to the morphology of the leaves and traps. If the upper and lower traps of a whorl were absent, we would be tempted to homologize the two lateral leaves with the trap between them with the condition found in *U. gibba*, but that would be pressing the matter too far.

U. dichotoma; U. monanthos (*23 — 19, 20*). — These and other related species are characterized by the fact that the stolons display well marked nodes and internodes, the latter usually quite naked, though in some cases (*e.g. U. dichotoma*) traps (facing backward) may arise from the upper surface of the internode. At the node a leaf, its upper surface facing backward, arises from the upper surface and from each side of the stolon near the leaf base a branch stolon and a trap. From the proximal leaf axil two traps and a bud, which becomes a second leaf, usually spring, and from this axil also a scape can arise. Thus these forms align themselves with the terrestrial forms in general, but are striking for the more readily observable emplacement of their parts. The traps are generally long stalked, and in *U. dichotoma* often emerge slightly from the surface of the wet but firm substrate, covered by a water film in normal times. Hundreds of traps could be seen dotting the ground at Narrabeen, N. S. W., using a lens of course. An additional feature of interest in this group is the widely lacunate structure of the stolons and petioles, which consist of scarcely more than the epidermis and the vascular strand with a few collapsed parenchyma cells clinging to it (much as in *Genlisea*). In *U. monanthos*, which grows in shallow water, both stolons and petioles are much puffed up. *U. dichotoma* has very small spatulate leaves and a tall scape; *U. monanthos* relatively large leaves and a short scape. The scapes produce anchoring stolons, leaves and traps on their bases.

Another group of species of the dichotoma type is composed of plants devoid of runner stolons and consisting solely of a corm-like, vertically growing axis springing directly from the seedling (*22 — 25, 26*). The corm is very slender at the bottom where it emerges from the seedling, widening toward the top, having below the structure of a stolon, becoming more and more stem-like as in *Genlisea* (WARMING). This puts out anchoring stolons, traps and leaves, and terminates in an inflorescence. They are either annuals of small, very delicate structure (*e.g. U. capilliflora, U. Dunstani, U. albiflora*) which grow in wet places during the rainy season, chiefly in N. W. Australia; or much more sturdy plants, but of the same plan of structure, all but one (*Polypompholyx tenella*) of S. W. Australia. These latter may be annuals found in wet sandy soil (*P. latifolia, P. tenella*) or in very shallow water (*U. violacea, U. Hookeri*); or perennials in wet clay-sandy soil (*U. Menziesii*) or in water (*U. volubilis*). All these with the exception of *U. volubilis* and *U. Menziesii* conform in morphological features to *Polypompholyx*, and are sufficiently indicated in the figure of this genus (*22 — 25, 26*). General descriptions have been given by GOEBEL in his *Organographie*. The perennial species *U. Menziesii* and *U. volubilis* require some further description.

U. Menziesii (*20* — 8, 9; *23* — 23, 24) was seen growing near Perth, W. A. The plant body consists of a minute corm which grows upwards, dying off below. From it spring hundreds of minute long stalked traps penetrating the soil in all directions, those growing upward coming close to the surface. The latter are covered by a rosette of long petioled spatulate leaves, from the middle of which emerges early in the wet season the scape (one or two) with unique, conspicuously brilliant red, large-spurred flowers. My material allows the inference that the plant begins its course by forming from the seedling primary stolon an oval tuber penetrating deeper into the substrate. From a lateral bud on this a small corm is formed, which again produces penetrating tubers. At length a substantial corm is formed which produces near the apex only laterally borne tubers, two to four in number, regarded by GOEBEL as water storage organs, tiding the plants over the dry season, which they undoubtedly do. They contain some starch. The scape is always borne laterally, and is not, as in the annual species, a finial of the corm.

U. volubilis (*23* — 25). — I found this growing near Albany, W. A. among the fibrous matting of a wet swamp. The young stages are not known. The plant body is a stout upright corm, which grows at the top and dies behind. It bears numerous filiform leaves about 3 cm. long and numerous long stalked traps, often with leaf-like stalks. The scape is terminal, but the corm is continued by a large lateral bud at the base of the scape. There are also produced long anchoring stolons of strong texture, bearing traps in groups of three. The scapes are very long, and twine about supporting reeds.

In the foregoing pages an account of the general structure of the plant body has been presented, which practically covers all the major varieties of habit. It is still insufficient for our present purpose in not embracing all the types of *Utricularia* as indicated by their kinds of traps. Those still to be mentioned include the species *U. cornuta, caerulea, capensis, orbiculata, longiciliata*, and *simplex*, taken as typifying large or small groups of species having traps of peculiar structure, to be mentioned beyond. While some of these grow in shallow water, most of them grow in wet sandy soil, and all have in common the general structure above indicated for *U. subulata*, with some slight exceptions, most of which need not here be amplified upon.

U. cornuta is an American plant and was described by SCHIMPER. Its leaves and branch stolons are borne laterally on the runner stolons, with no very regular alternation.

U. caerulea represents a large number of Asiatic and African species with leaves bearing numbers of traps and branch stolons. GOEBEL (1891) has studied this type. I refer to the plant studied by GOEBEL. There is doubt about its proper specific name (BARNHART), but as I had access to the same material as used by GOEBEL, I continue to use the name he used.

U. capensis is a good representative of a number of African and Asiatic species, the latter including *U. rosea* and *U. Warburgii*, both studied by GOEBEL. This group is represented in the New World by *U. peltata* which, like some cognate species in Africa, has peltate leaves, their petioles bearing traps.

U. orbiculata, *U. striatula*, *U. brachiata*, *U. multicaulis* and possibly some others are minute Asiatic and African species, most epiphytic in wet moss on leaves, tree-trunks or on rocks. It was on *U. orbiculata* that GOEBEL first noted the peculiar back-facing position of the stolon leaves and the coordinate position of the axillary buds (GOEBEL, 1891). This species produces a number of minute spherical pearl-like tubers strung along its stolons, probably for water storage (GOEBEL). *U. longiciliata* (America) is unique so far as the structure of the trap is concerned. It is a typical small terrestrial species similar in habit to *U. subulata*.

U. simplex (S. W. Australia) exhibits a rare peculiarity of producing its scape directly from the margin of a leaf, a habit which it may have in common with its relatives *U. lateriflora* (S. E. Australia) and *U. calliphysa* (Borneo) (STAPF 1914), another species still undescribed from India, and one from Ceylon. Of over a hundred complete plants of *U. simplex* (23 — 7) exhumed from a sandy substrate not far from Albany, W. A. not one showed a different origin of the scape, though specimens of *U. lateriflora*, from near Sydney, N. S. W., showed the primary origin to be from the seedling in the usual way, as in *U. Barnesii* mihi in ms. (22 — 27). Their traps are minute, of similar structure, but display specific differences.

U. globulariaefolia and a few similar species are American. They are terrestrial, rather large and become perennial by their stout, tough stolons. Aside from their considerable stature, growing as they do among the grasses and reeds of such habitats as the Aripo Savannah of Trinidad, they display no striking peculiarities beyond the possession of distinctive traps.

U. Kirkii is an African species with apparently few associates, if any, and has a distinct form of trap. It is of the usual terrestrial habit.

U. nana and *U. Lloydii*, small terrestrial species, are unique as regards the character of the traps. Both S. American, each appears to share its peculiarities with no other species yet known.

It will be the purpose of a succeeding chapter to consider the mechanism of the trap and the various peculiarities of the various kinds of traps characteristic of the above mentioned types.

— (*References on p. 267*) —

Chapter XIV

THE UTRICULARIA TRAP

General description of the trap; terminology. — Historical account. — Anatomy and physiology of the trap. — Two mechanical types of trap as regards the posture of the door (the vulgaris-biovularia-purpurea type. The capensis-caerulea-cornuta type. The monanthosdichotoma-Polypompholyx type). — The variety of traps. — Digestion; the fate of prey.

In the account of the character of the various sorts of *Utricularia* already given, their arrangement in groups or types was based on the character of the traps. In order to explain the workings of all of them we shall begin by a detailed examination of the longest studied and best known, that of *Utricularia vulgaris* and its close relatives. What we learn of this we may then use as a basis for comparison with other types.

The traps have been called urceoli, ampullae, vesiculae, utriculae, pitchers, bladders, or traps. The most widely accepted term, bladder or vesicle, or the Latin, *vesicula*, is not so bad as it seems, since a bladder has an opening guarded by a valve in the form of a sphincter muscle which keeps it closed except under certain physiological conditions when the muscle is temporarily relaxed. It was called a pitcher by analogy with other carnivorous plants (STAPF), but this suggests a passive trap, and it is anything but that. Utricle (*utriculus*), a small bottle with yielding sides (of skin or leather), presumes a stopper. "Trap", used in this work, precisely fits, because the mechanism is that of an elaborate trap which is set automatically and, after capturing prey, resets itself repeatedly, by observation as many as fourteen times, and this is certainly not the limit.

A description, in general terms, of the trap. Terminology. — The vulgaris type of trap is a small flattened pear-shaped hollow body attached to the plant by means of a stalk placed laterally, and truncated obliquely across the narrow end, where occurs the mouth of entrance. The stalk side is ventral; the opposite dorsal. The edge of the mouth carries in most cases a pair of branched antennae, and the sides some slender elongated bristles ($27 - 7$). These form a sort of funnel leading to the entrance, acting as guides for prey. In some species these appendages are absent or much reduced in size (*U. oligosperma*). Because of the flattened shape we may speak of the sides and the edge of the trap. The sides may be convex or concave, as first clearly recorded by BROCHER, according to physiological circumstances. When the trap is set, they are concave; after action, they are less so, and the trap has now a more rounded form. Scattered over the outer surface there are numerous small spherical glands, devoid of cuticle, which give off mucilage. These glands are common to the whole plant surface.

The entrance ($26 - 1$, 2) is guarded by two valves, a larger, the door, and a smaller membranous one, the velum (LLOYD 1929). The door is attached to the trap along a semicircular line on the dorsal part of the entrance, its free edge hanging and in contact with a firm, semicircular collar or threshold, against which the door edge rests. The convex outer surface of the door bears a lot of longer or shorter stalked mucilage glands, throwing off mucilage and sugar (LUETZELBURG), which have been said to be attractive to small animals (Cyprids, *Daphneae*, etc.) and so to act as a lure. In addition it bears four stiff, tapering bristles, based near the free, lower door edge. These are the tripping mechanism. The surface of the threshold, against which the door edge rests, is covered with a "pavement epithelium" of glandular sessile cells secreting mucilage. Along the outer edge of this pavement there is attached a thin but firm transparent membrane, the velum, which lies against the lower edge of the door, filling in the chink between this and the threshold.

The internal surface of the trap carries many glandular hairs ($26 — 9$-13), with two or four projections, the former on the inside of the threshold, the latter everywhere else ($26 — 2$). DARWIN called them bifids and quadrifids. The capital cells are devoid of cuticle. The rest of the surfaces except at these points is cuticularized.

In size the traps, at their largest, are usually not more than 5 mm. long; in the majority of species, 3 mm. long and less. Their small size has militated against readily understanding them.

An ample, partly incorrect description of the trap was furnished by BENJAMIN in 1848. He recalled the more important earlier observations: MEYEN had thought the traps open in the mature plant, SCHLEIDEN thought the entrance was merely guarded by hairs. TREVIRANUS realized that the tightly closed door prevents the escape of air when inclosed within the trap. DE CLAIRVILLE said that the door opens outwardly, but, as BENJAMIN pointed out, he failed to see that, if this were the case, air could escape, but nothing could enter. BENJAMIN himself clearly demonstrated that the door opens inwardly — he could push it in with a needle — but not outwardly — for if you push a needle against it in this direction it is torn. The function of the traps — he called them bladders — he thought to be connected with the supply of air to the plant. They were to him air reservoirs, getting it from the water through the four-armed hairs. DE CANDOLLE (1832) and VAN TIEGHEM (1868) believed that they had to do with the floating and sinking of the plant in spring and autumn. As pointed out by GOEBEL, the plants float just as surely after the bladders are removed. What had not then been observed is that normally the traps hold no air, but that this enters when the plant is raised out of the water. As COHN remarked, the failure to understand the traps arose out of a wrong point of view. He and DARWIN adopted another only in turn to prove wrong. COHN recorded finding various forms of *Daphnia* and *Cyclops* in the traps of a herbarium specimen. He then put a living sprig in an aquarium where it grew rather feebly for some time. There was no prey in the traps — none in the water. He then added some Ostracods from a culture, and next morning many of them had been caught in the traps. But COHN's observations did not stand alone; the brothers CROUAN (1858) had recorded the presence of small beasts in the traps. In America, in 1873 Mrs. MARY TREAT and a coworker found entomostraca in the traps of *U. cleistogama*. Prompted by this she made a careful examination to see if she could observe the method of capture. She thought in 1875 that the animals "open the door and walk in", agreeing with DARWIN and with COHN that prey push in the door, which then closes and prevents escape. In her 1876 account she revised her conclusions, for she then found, in *U. purpurea*, that prey is suddenly engulfed, as if drawn into a "partial vacuum". Not seeing that the trap walls change their posture, she was ignorant as to how the vacuum could be achieved; yet her idea foreshadowed the discovery to be made in 1911 by BROCHER. Mrs. TREAT learned through Dr. ASA GRAY, in correspondence with CHARLES DARWIN, that the latter was making similar studies; so that it is of interest to see that COHN, DARWIN and Mrs. TREAT, whom DARWIN later quoted, were arriving at similar conclusions at the same time independently. She further saw evidence that larvae were digested in the course of 48 hours. "I was forced to the conclusion that these little bladders are in truth like so many stomachs, digesting and assimilating animal food", she remarked.

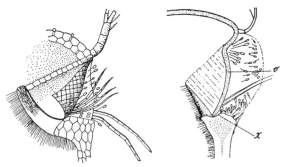

FIG. 7. — Copies of the original drawings of COHN (left) and of BROCHER, of the entrance of the trap of *Utricularia vulgaris*.

COHN'S and DARWIN'S conceptions of how the trap works were identical as is shown by their descriptions. COHN said that "the valve is held against the threshold by a pressure of water within the trap, but that it is easy to open by pushing it inwards. This arrangement makes it understandable that living water animals, entering the peristome, lift the valve and without difficulty enter into the hollow cavity of the bladder, whence they cannot escape since the valve opens only inwardly, not outwardly." And DARWIN spoke in the same manner, saying that "animals enter merely by forcing their way through the slit-like orifice; their heads serving as a wedge." GOEBEL accepted this explanation, as did MEIERHOFER and LUET-ZELBURG. An impressive drawing by GOEBEL as well as that by COHN (TEXT FIG. 7), though incorrect, are still used as illustrations. It is clear that up to this time the trap was regarded as a passive mechanism, the animal caught having to do the work of forcing entrance. We must add however that it was thought that the door was either forced against the threshold by a *"vis a tergo"*, the water pressure (COHN), or by its own property of elasticity, the latter implicit in all DARWIN's statements. It remained thus till 1911 when a Swiss entomologist, BROCHER, became interested in *Utricularia*. Pointing out that the view just above expressed is but an hypothesis, since no one had actually observed what happened, BROCHER tried to do this.

In a series of experiments (CZAJA does him the injustice of saying he did none) BROCHER established the following points, to his own satisfaction. When an animal is caught it always disappears very suddenly. DARWIN and BÜSGEN (1888) had all seen this and recorded their observations, but had drawn no correct inference therefrom. Further that, at the moment of this disappearance, the trap gives a spasmodic jump, and widens a little, from which BROCHER concluded that the trap sucks in the prey (*37* — 4, 6, 9). This observation was of fundamental importance. He was able then to explain why, when a leaf is raised out of the water, the traps are often found to contain air bubbles, whereas before they were absent. On lifting a plant from the water he could hear a *"crépidulation"* (an observation made independently by others) explained by the swallowing of air by reacting traps. He saw that in traps which had not reacted, the sides were concave, but after reaction were flattened or slightly convex. Finally he found that he could cause a trap to react by "titillating" the door bristles with a needle point, and that when this was accomplished there was each time a spasm of movement, and a change in profile. These observations by BROCHER, made with exactitude, furnished a point of view which finally led to the correct explanation of the workings of the trap.

Passing on to hypothesis, he supposed that the collapsed form of the trap is explained by the principle that the rate of development of the tissues, being *quasi* superficial, is greater than the rate of expansion of the volume. To the extent that the walls are depressed, the tensions of their tissues are augmented and thus they try the more to take a normal position, that is, to obliterate their re-entrant curvatures. The walls are therefore in a position of unstable equilibrium, during which the interior is in a state of "negative", that is, reduced pressure. The proof of this is the fact that, when punctured, the walls take up the normal position, dilating to a maximum. This could not be possible if the structure of the trap is as represented in the textbooks, he remarked at this point, since a simple check valve could not preserve the reduced pressure. He further supposed that the door is strongly curved, especially transversely, and that, because of the curvatures of the wall, it is held firmly against the lip, and, with the addition of mucilage, is thus rendered a watertight valve (TEXT FIG. 7). In order that the equilibrium thus preserved may be upset, BROCHER assumed that the door is endowed with a certain "sensibility" and "contractility", so that, on touching the bristles, it can shrink a little, and thus allow the water pressure to exert its force. An animal doing this would be swallowed with the inrushing water. That minute fish are sometimes caught by the tail shows that it is not because they try to get in, but that merely by the flick of the tail, they have stimulated the trap. The action of the door or "operculum" is so rapid, BROCHER observed, that it closes before the walls can more than partly expand, so that the trap may act again, but this remained questionable. It was admitted that the contents of the vesicle might be absorbed by the "rhizoids" (quadrifid hairs), in which case the walls would again be drawn in, and the trap re-sensitized. But BROCHER, not being a botanist, was too modest to undertake to solve this part of the problem.

EKAMBARAM (1916, 1918, 1926) in India made observations on the traps of *U. flexuosa* (similar to *U. vulgaris*), which substantiated those of BROCHER above mentioned, though apparently in ignorance of this author's work. That is, EKAMBARAM recognized the two states of the trap, one with concave and one with convex sides, and that in the latter, when the "irritable" hairs are touched by a prowling animalcule, it is sucked into the trap with the inflowing water. It had been noticed by him also that when the whole plant is lifted from the water there can be heard "light crackling sounds like the ticking of a watch" and this was referred to the action of the traps when released, presumably by water films. When pushed in by the water, the door becomes inverted and boat shaped, with the "irrita-ble" hairs folded up into the groove (*26 — 7*). The movement of the door he considered to be due to the momentary loss of turgidity, as quickly regained leading to closure, but he does not offer any evidence for this. The irritable hairs he mistakenly thought to have the same structure as those of *Aldrovanda*.

EKAMBARAM was able to reset the trap by carefully pressing out the water by compressing its sides, but it does not appear that he understood that the trap can automatically reset itself. The escape from the walls of intercellular air during this operation must have been accident, and can have no bearing on the matter. MERL found the contrary.

At about the same time WITHYCOMBE, a British student, announced, in 1916, "that the bladders of *Utricularia* . . . are not passive traps, but that they capture prey by active movement in response to stim-ulation. A bladder becomes sensitive to contact after its walls be-come concave on each side. Then, on touching certain short hairs at the mouth of the bladder, the lateral walls spring outwards, be-coming somewhat convex, and so drawing a current of water into the bladder which swept with it, of course, any body sufficiently light to be sucked in." Again, this observation was made quite independently, as WITHYCOMBE learned of BROCHER'S work only ca. 1922 through MERL. Nor did he yet know of EKAMBARAM'S observations. In his paper of 1924 WITHYCOMBE, thinking BROCHER'S explanation of the working of the trap valve inadequate, agreeing, however, about the matter of "negative" pressure and its results, advanced the idea that the edge of the valve or door, instead of being merely pressed against the collar or threshold (BROCHER), is caught in a groove from which it can be released only by an upward movement. This groove stands in front of the zone of specialized cells (see beyond) and is as deep as these. "A certain amount of mucilage is secreted apparently by the middle layer, and this makes a complete watertight fitting of the valve." Here is a specific attempt to account for the hermetical sealing of the door mechanism, and though as it will appear a mistaken one, the idea was correct. The internal water is absorbed by the quad-rifid hairs, so that the trap can be reset by setting up anew the strains expressed in the convexity of the side walls. In his experience this required about 30 minutes. The action of the door is due, he says, to its irritability, and the slender four hairs inserted in the door are the only organs which can be stimulated. Irritability, however, was not proven to exist.

MERL's work, above mentioned, appeared two years before WITHYCOMBE's second paper. He set out from BROCHER's important observation that on stimulation the walls of the trap expand, drawing in water in the capture of prey, but further showed that the operation can be repeated again and again. During three days he observed the trap to act thirteen times. MERL correctly determined also that traps which contain some air can react, contrary to BROCHER's view (but this could happen only if the bubble of air in the trap is not too large!). It is only if, owing to the shape of the trap, the bubble can be moved or distorted, that this can happen. The time required for resetting in *U. flexuosa* was found to be a minimum of 15 minutes, but full resetting requires about 30 minutes. In *U. purpurea* (37 —1) it takes upwards of two hours (LLOYD 1933*a*). It was shown by MERL that the full expansion of the trap sides takes place when the door is forced open or when the wall is punctured. The reverse of this, the sucking in of the side walls, is more pronounced the longer a period of non-stimulation, until of course the cohesion of the internal water sets a limit. Apropos of BROCHER's note to the effect that on removal of a plant out of the water a clicking sound was noticed due to the swallowing of air by the traps, MERL was able to do this without setting off all the traps. Some of them did not react and remained unaffected under a bell glass. He was then able to procure the re-action by touching the bristles. Aside from furnishing him an argu-ment against BROCHER's theory that the compression of the trap walls is due to "atmospheric and hydraulic" pressure (MERL's statement concerning this view seems incorrect) the experiment shows that it is on general grounds not surprising that some species are not submersed, species the traps of which normally exist and act in moist air, sur-rounded by wet moss, detritus or sandy soil. The action of the traps on lifting from water is therefore due, it is suggested by MERL, to the action of water films on the bristles of the door and not to the mere re-lease from water pressure.

MERL then tried to determine whether the reaction of the trap, or specifically of the door, is an irritable response. He could not procure reaction by wounding or by electrical stimulation. As to the temperature relations he found that the traps reacted as long as they remained alive, and that by chemical means no condition of rever-sible inactivity (rigor) could be induced. Incidentally he found that the trap is so completely sealed by the door that there is no entrance even for dyes, such as eosin and methylene blue, so long as the dyes do not induce death of the trap. Nevertheless MERL could not quite rid himself of the feeling that the mechanism is irritable, and would have adopted this view if so much evidence "had not spoken against it." Among this evidence, he found that during action there was no disturbance of the air in the intercellular spaces, which would occur if there was an extrusion of water into them such as occurs in irritable tissues. In spite of inimical evidence, however, MERL inclined to think that the bristles are irritable hairs analogous to those of *Dionaea* and *Aldrovanda* (as had EKAMBARAM and BROCHER). He proposed, however, the only alternative theory, a purely mechanical one. The four-armed hairs withdraw the water from the interior of the trap, thereby setting up a tension, the walls responding to the draft by cohesion of the water. The highly elastic door, the free edge of which rests firmly against the threshold, opposes this draft and comes into a position of labile equilibrium, which must be disturbed "by the slightest movement or by shrinkage" of the (door) cells, to allow the walls to retract into their relaxed position. Even now he could not quite exclude a certain irritability as a capstone of the bridge. This view was to be championed later by KRUCK.

Working at the same time, independently of MERL, CZAJA examined the problem of the *Utricularia* trap. His publication was but a trifle later than MERL'S. Proceeding from the same point of attack, CZAJA agreed with MERL that the trap could repeat its action, and could reset itself in a short period of 15 to 30 minutes and that the reaction (on suitable stimulation) takes place very suddenly. The concave sides then became much less so. The door in this reaction opens to a narrow slit, and closes as suddenly as it opens (neither of which, however, is quite true) allowing the entrance of a stream of water. The process is released by touching the bristles. By chemical means CZAJA could not decide definitely on the nature of the mechanism, and this left him for the moment at the same point as it did MERL. With respect to the anatomy of the trap, he examined first the closure of the trap by the door, in order to settle the question of the path of the internal water when the trap is exhausted as it must be when the walls pass from the less to the more concave posture. He determined that the entrance is hermetically sealed. The proof consisted in inserting a fine hair beneath the door edge, when the trap could not again set itself. When the hair was withdrawn, again the trap became effective. Further proof was supplied by the fact that congo red and methylene blue never entered healthy, but only damaged, traps. All this he believed points to the membrane, or rather the wall of the trap, as important.

As had been demonstrated by COHN in 1875, the walls of the trap, if set free to act by removing inhibiting structures (the threshold and contiguous walls), will expand. Because of their structure and the turgidity of their cells they always strive to take an outwardly convex form. Substances which can reduce their turgor (5% KNO_3) put the trap out of commission. On the other hand substances which cannot penetrate but which withdraw the water from the trap (glycerine, cane sugar) can up to a certain limit of concentration reset the trap but if in too great concentrations, cause its total collapse. The resetting of the trap is therefore the result of withdrawing water from its lumen, and not of direct participation of the walls which would involve turgor changes.

This is made possible by the tight application of the door edge to the threshold (specifically, to the layer of epithelium on the top of the threshold) enhanced by the mucilage which has an added sealing effect. Since the cells of the wall are not plasmolysed by glycerin etc., water is not withdrawn from these cells but only from the lumen without changes in turgor. This is what happens in nature. The setting of the trap results from the withdrawal of water from the lumen. The only agent for this is the action of the four-armed hairs. It is allowed that some water may penetrate through the walls inwardly but at a slower rate than that at which it is thrown off, for otherwise it would lead to overtension, and this, he held, would bring the trap into a condition unfavorable for prompt action.

CzAJA holds that the withdrawal of water results not only in the change in position of the walls, but that this results in turn in a cramping effect on the door, forcing it against the threshold more tightly and so effectively increasing its watertightness, an idea held by BROCHER, but which is untenable in the light of the structure of the walls, which are thin, acting as hinges near the threshold (26 — 3). When the trap is in the set posture, the walls concave, and the door tightly in contact with the threshold, the bristles stick out at an angle in such position that on touching them the edge of the door is disturbed and a narrow opening is formed between the door edge and the threshold, through which water is drawn in by the expanding walls. The action is mechanical. In support of this CzAJA records that it is easier to fire the trap if the bristles are swept from above downwards than transversely to this direction. This can mean only that the leverage is more effective in disturbing the door edge when the levers are moved in one direction than another and rules out mere irritability. Firing the trap is due to the deformation of the door edge and the consequent lifting of it from the threshold allowing water pressure to act. For the rest, CzAJA did much experimentation showing that the trap is surrounded by a selectively permeable membrane but PRÁT (1923) found that the entire plant is protected by this membrane.

CzAJA was the first to take a definite stand that the trap action is mechanical, aside of course from the water-extruding power of the walls, and the general condition of turgidity. That is, the springing of the trap is purely mechanical. This was opposed to the views of BROCHER, EKAMBARAM and WITHYCOMBE, and to MERL insofar as he allowed the question to hang in the balance. HEGNER (1926) (not knowing of the work of BROCHER, MERL or CzAJA) made independently the observations as to the method of catching prey recorded by BROCHER, noting its rapidity, but did not venture into the question of the method of function of the bristles. Thus CzAJA was left the sole champion of the view that the whole capturing action of the trap is mechanical, but he was not to go unchallenged; for Miss M. KRUCK in 1931 undertook to prove the contrary, but, to state it abruptly, she quite failed (LLOYD 1932b). In the first place her presentation of the structure of the trap was askew and it was patent from her figures that she did not grasp the anatomical facts. The drawings showed initial and final positions of the door, after stimulation and reaction, which simply do not occur. The physiological evidence consisted in the observation of the extent and position of intercellular spaces in the tissue of the door before and after response. To meet this I reproduced photographic evidence which showed clearly that such changes do not occur, though it is evident that changes in the mere distribution of air might occur without vitiating my evidence. Again KRUCK stated that the cells of the door change their shape, but this was found equally illusory. In the course of response she stated that the bristles lose water, supplying a stimulus to the neighboring cells of the door which respond in like manner, with the result that the shape of the cells of the door changes through loss of turgor, but evidence for this was quite absent. She further allows 15 minutes for the restitution of irritability, in this agreeing with CZAJA and MERL, both of whom allowed this as the time necessary for the withdrawal of sufficient water to set the mechanism. If KRUCK was right, it is not clear why the restoration of irritability should not proceed when a trap is punctured, but this never occurs. Most impressive is the fact shown first by EKAMBARAM, repeated by myself, that by careful expulsion of the water from a trap, it may be reset repeatedly without allowing time for the restoration of irritability, unless, to be sure, an immediate restoration is predicated. The claim that the bristles are irritable was shown to be not true by first killing them with iodine, after which they could procure response on touching (LLOYD 1932b). It should here be recalled that WITHYCOMBE observed that this response could take place even in traps which had lain for a half-hour in Bouin's picro-formal solution. It seems clear that KRUCK failed in supporting her contention. The evidence points to the contrary, that the action of the door is purely mechanical, always granting the turgidity of the component cells, devoid of which they could not give to the door the necessary properties.

The walls, because of their activity in excreting water from the trap lumen, are an important part of the mechanism. The total amount which a trap throws out amounts to 88% according to HEGNER (1926), much less according to NOLD. Such figures are in any event not important since the total amount excreted depends on the type of trap. In *U. purpurea* it must be much more than in *U. vulgaris*. That they do excrete water is all we need to know to explain the action of the trap, and this was first demonstrated by BROCHER, later independently by others, EKAMBARAM, WITHYCOMBE, HEGNER, and possibly HADA (but who had seen HEGNER's paper). It may be emphasized, however, that this action can go on when, as a result of the introduction of much food material, including salts, in the form of the bodies of water animalcules, the osmotic pressure of the internal fluid reaches a considerable but never measured figure. This cannot be overdone, however, for if glycerine be introduced (MERL) water is then drawn into the lumen. Experiments show that the trap works within wide limits in nature. Nevertheless the physiological properties of the walls remained a subject of inquiry, and this has been pursued by CZAJA and by NOLD. CZAJA's conclusion was that the trap is surrounded by a selectively-permeable membrane, the cuticle, which excludes solutes. The four-armed hairs of the internal surface absorb water more rapidly than it can find its way in. NOLD (1934) had advanced the theory that the potential difference existing between the outer and inner surfaces of the traps accounts for the movement of water outwardly. He localized this difference in the only parts of the walls free of cuticle, namely the outer spherical and the inner four-armed glandular cells, the only ones through the walls of which the water can pass. That this shall pass outwardly, he believed, is assured by the difference in pH at these places. At the inner surface this is 6.2 and for the outer 6.6, determined by the Folin colorimeter; or 7.5 and 8.2 with the quinhydrone electrode, differences which seem non-significant for water movement. NOLD seems to have shown, however, that the loss of water from the trap increases inversely with the pH of the outer medium, the normal behavior taking place at pH 5–7. The traps are damaged at lower and higher pH values. Yet it has been shown that *Utricularia* can prosper in water of pH 4 (EMIL WEHRLE, 1927) and *U. minor* in "weakly alkaline water" (NOLD). In any event, since a difference of potential between inner and outer surfaces is known to cause a water loss, but since also organs are known which show such differences without water movements, it is scarcely possible to regard NOLD's hypothesis as proven. This judgment is not weakened by inspection of the evidence advanced.

There is a further point in the mechanism of the trap about which opinions had been expressed previous to 1929, without the provision of proof. I refer to the method by which the watertightness of the door is procured. That watertightness is a necessary condition for the successful action of the trap was first recognized by BROCHER, and by his successors in investigation, all of whom placed faith in the contention that it is due to the tight application of the door selvage to the threshold, aided by the mucilage present. WITHYCOMBE realized the inadequacy of this explanation, and supplemented it by arguing that the door edge rests against the outer edge of the "middle layer," the pavement, seeing in this a valvular seat. An examination of the action of the trap and certain details of the emplacement of the door led me to suspect that the explanation was a lame one. This led to the discovery that the entrance of the trap is guarded, not merely by one valve, the door, *but by two*, the door and a second valve, the velum, attached to the threshold and finding its seat against the door selvage, thus blocking the chink. This second valve has been seen in some 75 species, in slightly various form to be sure, but always present (*24, 25*). This discovery led to a minute examination of the structure of the trap in all material available from various parts of the world. The results of this survey, made on many living species and on still more preserved ones, lie in the field of anatomy, which in the presentation thus far has received only minor mention. This is now to be taken up in the following, in which it will emerge that WITHYCOMBE was quite right in principle if wrong in his understanding of the mechanism. I myself erred similarly in 1929.

The physiological anatomy and histology of the trap of *Utricularia vulgaris* and closely related forms will now be considered. Within the limits here imposed it will be practically impossible to show in detail the contributions of the several investigators to our knowledge in this field, and it must suffice to indicate critical observations. It may as well be said that the study of the anatomy of the trap is by no means easy, if we desire to have exact knowledge of the emplacement of the various parts. This is because on cutting the trap, the tissue tensions are disturbed and the parts (especially the door) disarranged; and it is necessary to know the exact relation between the valves (door and velum) and the threshold. This cannot be finally determined by the study of the traps which have been cut, though useful evidence can be got this way, but only by the examination of the entire, healthy organ. An accurate description must be based on living turgid material, and errors have been made by placing faith on paraffin sections. Again, the presence of mucilage makes the trap slippery, and the knife, which must be very keen, readily slips, so that to make a true sagittal section is difficult and this has led to mistakes. The much used figure first published by GOEBEL in his 1891 paper is wrong for this reason, and the figure used in a recent (German) edition of the Bonn textbook is equally wrong.

Accounts dealing with our knowledge of the anatomy of the trap (*U. vulgaris* and closely allied forms) are those of BENJAMIN (1848), COHN (1875), DARWIN (1875), HOVELACQUE (1888), DEAN (1890), GOEBEL (1891), MEIERHOFER (1902), LUETZELBURG (1910), EKAMBARAM (1916), FRANÇA (1922), MERL (1922), CZAJA (1922), WITHYCOMBE (1924), LLOYD (1929), KRUCK (1931) and NOLD (1934). During the prevalence of the earlier view that the role of the trap was wholly passive, the results of investigation fell far short of adequacy in the presentation of details of structure later found to be important. This period ended with LUETZELBURG in 1910. With BROCHER's discovery in 1911 attention was concerned more and more with these details, though not always with sufficiently critical observation, and sometimes with the entire lack of it. This applies particularly to the entrance structures, more so to the door, of which the special features began to be appreciated only with WITHYCOMBE and MERL.

The general features of the trap have already been described. Broadly speaking two regions are to be considered alone and in relation with each other, the walls and the entrance mechanism. The appendages (antennae etc.) are of less importance and will be described in a comparative study of the various types of traps.

The walls. — In the species before us the walls are composed of two courses of cells, the outer and inner, both clothed with a thin cuticle on their exposed surfaces. In general the outer course cells are smaller in surface extent than the inner, in the ratio of about three to two, linear dimensions. The relative thickness of the two courses varies. Along the profile of the trap, the inner cells are the deeper, but this relation is reversed on the sides of the trap, where the outer cells are deeper. This is connected with the movement of the walls from convex to concave, the outer cells suffering increasing compression during the excretion of water. Nor is the total thickness of the wall the same everywhere. Under the entrance the threshold, a part of the wall, has a thickness at the top of four or five parenchyma cells plus the epidermis on either side. The threshold extends upward on both sides to form the "collar"-like thickening which stands out from the wall in shelf-like fashion. Beneath this shelf the side wall is attached to the threshold, and is here quite thin, so that the wall swings here as on a hinge, thus not bringing any torsion on the threshold and door. This structure excludes the theory advanced by BROCHER, that the walls help to cramp the door in position (*26* — 3).

Chlorophyll bodies occur in both courses, perhaps somewhat fewer in the inner, but not absent, as NOLD has said. Anthocyanin often occurs in the inner course cells, but is absent from young traps and increases with age after once appearing. Interspersed with the larger epidermal cells are smaller ones, more numerous in the inner epidermis, the basal cells. These bear each a short cutinized cell, the "middle" cell, bearing two to four glandular, non-cutinized cells to form a capital. In the outer course, the gland is spherical, of two cells. On the inside each middle cell bears two or four elongated cells. DARWIN called these hairs the bifids and quadrifids. The former are to be found only on the inner face of the threshold; the quadrifids elsewhere all over the inner surface. In *U. vulgaris* two of the arms are reflexed, and the whole is tilted towards the entrance to induce inward movement of prey, it may be argued. In *U. gibba* and allies all four arms extend radially, but two are shorter (those toward the entrance), and with more spread. These quadrifids are also tilted toward the entrance. The bifid hairs, forming a *chevaux de frise* on the inner face of the threshold, appear to be there to discourage prey from working its way toward the door. In these hairs each arm is a cell terminating proximally in a slender stalk. The two or four stalks are united to form a single short round stalk basing on the middle cell (*26* — 9-13). The arms are not cuticularized, and absorb dyes very readily. They are generally regarded as the organs of absorption which take up digested food materials, and at the same time secrete ferments and acid to accomplish digestion. The function of the spherical glands of the outer surface is more in question. These hairs may belong to the category of hydropotes (proposed by MAYR 1915), the function of which is to absorb water in submersed plants, the general epidermis being cuticularized. In the case of the *Utricularia* trap the function of water excretion seems likely a reversal of function which may be determined by the greater activity of the quadrifids in absorption, these presenting much more surface to the surrounding medium. That the function of hydropotes may be the excretion of water has had some support, cited by MEYER (1935). In one form or another both these kinds of hairs are common to all species of *Utricularia*. In 1931 KRUCK questioned CZAJA's contention that the water, when being excreted by the trap, escapes through the cuticle and therefore the whole significance of his results from examining the permeability relations of this membrane. On her part she held that the internal water is absorbed by the quadrifids, and excreted by the spherical glands of the outer surface. In proof of this, which she contends is convincing, she claims to have followed the path of dyes from the inside of the trap, which she saw to enter through the quadrifids and escape from the outer surface glands, and made the observation, in agreement with this view, that the quadrifids take up the dyes more readily than the outer glands. Her method of experimentation was (a) to lay the traps in the solution, and (b) to fill the traps with the solution. As however she does not tell us in detail how the latter was managed, one hesitates to accept her observation without reserve.

That the quadrifids are active during digestion was observed by DARWIN and by GOEBEL. DARWIN's experiments showed that substances in solution (urea, ammonium carbonate, infusions of raw meat) are absorbed by the quadrifids, but not by these alone as he found the spherical hairs of the outside surface to do the same, as also the mucilage glands about the entrance. He realized and admitted that his experiments were not critical, but they indicated the importance of the problem. GOEBEL detected the presence of fat droplets after feeding, and SCHIMPER noted, in *U. cornuta*, appearances in the absorbant hairs (here bifid) which had been absorbing food different from those in traps which had not been fed. The protoplast showed activity which he compared with DARWIN's aggregation, saying that the protoplasm swells and the vacuole is broken up more or less, as he observed also in *Drosera* and *Sarracenia*. Less constant in occurrence were yellow granules or droplets.

Later KRUCK, in the paper already cited, presented her results of study of the cytological changes which are to be seen in the glands in various conditions of rest and feeding. Her observations lie in the field of cytology and are open to various interpretations. At any rate they need not concern us here.

The trap wall is traversed by vascular bundles which branch from a single strand which enters by the stalk. On reaching the trap it divides into two branches, one of which goes forward around the longer edge to the entrance where it ends abruptly. The other branch moves toward the threshold, on reaching which it branches, each arm following beneath the threshold and ending at one extremity. Xylem is present but is very meagre.

Far more complicated in structure is the trap about the entrance. The opening arises in the very young trap as a slit caused by the invagination of the rounded primordium. The lips of the slit turn inwards, the upper becoming the door and the lower the threshold (MEIERHOFER). Two conditions are found. In one (as in *U. vulgaris*) the wall of the trap bends abruptly in to continue as the door (*26 — 6*). In the other (*e.g. U. gibba, minor*) the wall extends forward to form an overhang, the door springing away from its inner under surface (*26 — 2*). In any case, from the edge of the fold arise the antennae, stout branching emergencies springing from the upper limb of the opening, right and left (*27 — 8*). The arrangement of these together with their curvature produces a pair of drift fences funnelling toward the entrance, thus serving to guide prey to their doom. This condition is found in *U. gibba* and a good many other species, in all of which the antennae are curved forward and downward in front of the entrance and are strong prominent appendages. The branches of the main

trunk of the appendage are long uniseriate hairs.   In other species
(*U. vulgaris americana, U. oligosperma*) the antennae are much smaller
and curve upward, away from the entrance.   There are often no
antennae in these species, and there are others from which they are
always absent (*U. nana*) (*28* — 5).   In still other species, as will be
seen later, quite other arrangements are met with.   In the water-
dwelling species, while they can evidently be regarded as elaboration
of the trapping mechanism, it must be said that their absence does not
seem to make any practical difference in the number of prey captured.   In the mud dwelling species, they may serve to keep the
entrance free from detritus, and so help in preserving the effectiveness
of the trap.   In the wet sandy soils and in wet moss, where the water-
is not continuous, such arrangements may be important in keeping
capillary water, in which prey may move, in contact with the entrance,
so that when the trap acts it does not draw in air.   The capillary
action in such cases is helped by the mucilage secreted by glandular
hairs in large numbers attached to the door itself, and to the sides of
the entrance.

After the two lips are laid down during the development of the
trap, the sides of the entrance extend, moving the lips apart so as to
produce a funnel-shaped approach.   These sides, called by COHN the
cheeks, are continuous with the overhang, when this is present, to
form a sort of hood or "vestibule" around the opening (*27* — 9).

From each cheek, and from the edge of the overhang, springs an
oblique row of long uniseriate hairs, about four on each cheek, and two
or three from the overhang (*27* — 7).

It is only in the front of the opening that the lips are drawn apart.
At their free edges they remain close, and in the final stages of development are in mutual contact.   At their lateral extremities they are
continuous, though their anatomical character changes.   Another
important feature is alteration in the form of the lower lip.   Though
transverse at first, it becomes finally semicircular in shape and thickened by the growth of additional layers of wall cells beneath it to form
a massive thickening and strengthening of the wall in this zone.   This
structure so produced was called the collar by DARWIN, and the abut-
ment by GOEBEL.   In this account it is called the threshold.   By its
form and strength it preserves the shape of the opening, and resists any
cramping effect (said to occur by BROCHER and CZAJA) of the distortion of the walls when the maximum of internal water has been
withdrawn.   Measurements made by myself did not reveal any difference in form in the set and the extremely relaxed condition of the trap
after puncture.   In fact, the walls where they articulate with the
threshold are thinner than elsewhere, so that they can bend without
exerting distortion on it (*26* — 3), besides which is the fact that the
inner part of the threshold is supported free of the wall, so that this
cannot press upon it.

The structure of the threshold in detail is best understood first by
an examination of a transverse section through its middle point (*25* —
1, 2, 5; *29* — 4) and then by viewing it from a point of view which
embraces the whole inner surface, flattened out for convenience of
study (*25* — 9).   In the transverse section the threshold is roughly

triangular, the base forming the free surface, the apex continuous with the wall. The free surface is slightly convex, with broken curves indicating three regions, an outer, continuous with the cheeks, carrying scattered stalked glandular hairs; a middle, clothed with a layer of densely crowded glands, called the pavement epithelium by GOEBEL, and an inner of epidermal cells, forming a shelf projecting into the interior of the trap.

The outer region is part of the vestibule, and we may think of it as a doorstep. The inner region is merely a part of the inner wall surface, but re-entrant. The middle region is of critical importance. We shall use GOEBEL'S name for it, recognizing however that the surface is not epithelial but consists of closely set glandular cells which arise from the epithelium below. It is a pavement of packed tiles, each tile being the capital of a glandular hair. We pause here to recall the structure of the glandular hairs in *Utricularia*. Arising from a basal epidermal cell, each consists of a middle cell (GOEBEL), strongly cuticularized, short and discoid in shape, supporting a glandular capital of one, but more usually two cells, sometimes four (quadrifids), uncuticularized (BÜSGEN 1888). The middle cells may be supported on a shorter or longer tubular extension of the epidermis cell wall, as is the case of the hairs surrounding the entrance. Those of the pavement are similar to the glandular hairs of the general outer plant surface, but differ in having capitals elongated, at right angles to the axis of the entrance, so that, on looking down on the threshold, the pavement appears to be made of closely packed sausages. The capitals may be one or two celled. Each gland arises from a laterally compressed epidermal cell, so narrow that the middle cell lies tightly against the neighboring ones. The terminal cells are similarly tightly packed, forming the visible pavement (GISLEN 1917) (*Cf.* various figures on 25 to 29).

Like the glandular hairs in general, the pavement glands loosen and shed their cuticles, but most curiously in a single piece, except in the inner zone (29 — 4). To describe this behavior we have to recognize three zones of the pavement epithelium, outer, middle and inner. In the outer zone, the cuticles of its glands enlarge into balloons, but remain attached mutually and to the glands which bear them. In the middle zone, broadest at the ends, the cuticles remain mutually attached, but are freed from the capitals which produced them, and from the inner zone glands, but remain attached to the ballooned cuticles of the outer zone. The glands of the inner zone behave individually, their cuticles enlarging and bursting. There is formed in this way a membrane, which I call the velum, consisting of two parts, a cushion of cuticular balloons running from one end of the pavement to the other on the outer zone, and attached to it a thin membrane, bearing the markings of the capitals which produced it, the two together forming a valve which, stretching from one side of the pavement to the other, overlies the door edge (25 — 4-8). The inner zone is lenticular, broadest at the middle, and scarcely reaching the outer ends of the pavement. Its glands are larger and not very tightly packed. The middle zone, entirely free of cuticles, presents a soft yielding surface into which the door edge can sink somewhat under pressure.

We consider now the door or valve. This is a flap, two cell courses in thickness, forming the upper free edge of the entrance opening, and, in nature, bulges outwardly (25 — 2, 5). If it is removed by cutting along its line of attachment to the trap wall and is allowed to lie in water, it retains the shape it has *in situ* as BÜSGEN observed (1888). It is, if we disregard minor curvatures, roughly semicircular, the shorter side being the free edge. For the sake of description we may flatten the door and then map out certain regions, shown in the diagram (29 — 13). A wide zone around the edge of attachment is the hinge region, where strong reverse flexures occur when the door is opened. The middle region of this zone is the upper hinge, the two lateral the lateral hinges. The upper hinge is characterised by marked flexures when the door is at rest. The hinge area surrounds a lenticular middle area, which may be called simply the middle area. At the lower part of this a small circular patch of the door is quite thin, and this is the central hinge. Out from just below this project four to six stout, curved, tapering bristles. That part of the door below the central hinge is thick and strong. This is the middle piece. Towards the flanks, the door selvage becomes thinner. With this terminology (26 — 1) we can more easily describe the histology.

As above said, the door consists of two cell layers (25 — 2, 5; 29 — 1, 2), an outer, and an inner. The two are very different in structure, the general relation between them being that existing in a bimetallic strip, one of the metals having a greater index of expansion than the other; the former under changes of temperature is active, the latter relatively passive. The cells of both layers are equally turgid, but the inner is capable of ready expansion and contraction of its inner surface, the outer not. This is ascribable to the differences of structure. The door has been described as highly flexible and elastic, as for example by DARWIN. Highly flexible it is, but if by elasticity we mean extensibility, this adjective does not apply. The tissue has a sort of cartilaginous quality, bending without breaking in any direction. If the door is freed in part by cutting a median strip, releasing this from the pull of the sides, it will spring outwardly and only on plasmolysis can it be brought back. This shows that the door as a whole is always normally insistent in pushing outward, and is held in its proper position only by virtue of its semicircular attachment to the trap wall. As BENJAMIN showed, it can be pushed in- but not outwardly. When fully inwardly inflexed, it is folded along its middle line, becomes somewhat concave, and the tripping bristles then lie in the groove of the fold (26 — 7), as EKAMBARAM described it.

The inner reaches of this attachment, that is, the lateral hinges, coincide with the inner ends of the threshold, the extreme end of the free door edge coinciding with the inner angle of the threshold. The outer surface of the lateral hinge therefore lies against the outer reach of the threshold. But the free edge of the door, starting from the inner angle of the threshold, passes obliquely across it, the angle between the face of the door gradually changing till, in the middle reach, it stands obliquely on edge (26 — 2). Only the middle reach of the door selvage is thickened and stiff; the outer reaches are thin.

The rest of the attachment extends along the wall of the trap, curving around from one end of the threshold to the other in a semicircular sweep. Here the door curves inwardly at first, to form the upper hinge, below this outwardly to form the bulging middle area. The curves of the upper hinge are most pronounced in front, and are reduced at the sides. The outward spring of the door depends on the physical properties of the upper hinge chiefly. The lateral hinges resist this pull, but can bend passively.

If now we examine the histology of the door we find ($29 — 1, 2$), on inspecting a section in any direction, that in general the outer course of cells is thin, the inner thick, in the ratio of about one to three, differing from place to place. In the central hinge they are of nearly equal thickness, as also in the middle piece. The cells of the outer course are all flat, their anticlinal walls zigzag (Büsgen) and these walls are strongly supported by buttresses at their angles. These prevent their collapse under bending. This layer must put up with as much bending as the outer, but passively. Many of these cells bear glandular hairs ($24 — 1$; $26 — 2$), some with pyriform, some with spherical capitals. Those with pyriform capitals are scattered over the upper part of the door surface, and are shorter stalked as one approaches the middle point of the door. Near the door edge, arranged in a crescent parallel with it, is a row of glands with short stalks and globose capitals, a quite large one at the middle point. Just above the level at which this stands are hairs of different structure. These are stiff, tapering, sharply pointed bristles, four in number, standing at the angles of a trapezoid, in an oblique posture, extending upward, then curving delicately ($25 — 3, 5$). Each is composed of three to five cells, the basal the shortest, the terminal the longest. Ekambaram described short hinge cells, like those in the sensitive hairs of *Aldrovanda*, but this is a mistake. They anchor in the outer cell layer, by a broad base, as correctly shown by Meierhofer, without any bulbous insertion as Merl showed ($26 — 4$). These four (or in *U. flexuosa* six, Ekambaram) hairs constitute the tripping mechanism of the trap. A touch of these in any direction but, according to Czaja, best from above down, causes some distortion of the middle piece of the door selvage. This distorts the door edge from its equal seat, upsetting the delicate equilibrium, and permitting the water pressing against the door to push it in, assuming the trap to be properly set. As we shall see, the tripping mechanism shows a wide variety of form in the genus. That just described is found only in the *vulgaris* type and in *Biovularia*, though in the latter the door has a different plan of structure.

When facing the door, the outer course of cells presents a plan as follows. In the region of the upper hinge, the cells are isodiametric, very wavy walled, with strong buttresses (Cohn 1875). Their walls lie athwart those of the inner course cells. The same is true of the middle area. In the central hinge they are very small, corresponding in size to the cells of the inner course. The same is true of the middle piece, where the cells are very small and their walls are strongly fortified with broad and thick buttresses. These cells, however, while small when seen *en face*, are deep, and equally deep with those of the inner course. Along the selvage to the outer limits of the lateral

hinge, the cells are elongate, and have numerous very small buttresses, difficultly seen. That is to say, the cells in the regions of
maximum bending have zigzag walls with many buttresses. Where
the door is stiffest, *i.e.*, in the middle piece, the buttresses are at a
maximum in numbers and size. In these cells also the walls are thick,
especially the outer.

Looking at the inner face of the door, we note a different pattern.
With the central hinge as a center, the inner course consists of elongated cells radiating from this center to this circumference (*24 — 9*).
The closer to the center the shorter the cells become, so that at the
center they are isodiametric and thickly studded with buttresses.
Below the center, the cells of the inner course of the middle piece
are also isodiametric and match the outer course of cells in the degree
of buttressing. From here, tending toward each side of the door, the
cells become longer and run along the selvage parallel to it. This
seems at first glance simple enough, and it seems surprising that the
cells of the whole inner course should have been more than once
described as isodiametric. The mistake is easily explained, for when
the inner surface of the door is examined without flattening it out,
to do which it must be fully plasmolysed, a series of concentric lines
can be seen (*24 — 9*; *29 — 3*). DARWIN saw them. They were correctly understood first by MEIERHOFER. They are nothing more than
an optical effect arising from the fact that the inner cells are constricted
at regular intervals (*29 — 1-3*). Wherever the constrictions meet the
side walls of the cells, these are here buttressed by props. In sections
the spaces between the constrictions are usually taken for single cells,
a mistake which I made myself at first. Within the central area
these lines, indicating the constrictions, run with great regularity from
cell to cell. In the region of the outer and lateral hinges they are
equally present, but are less regular. In the central hinge and in the
middle piece they are also present, but are here quite irregular and
numerous and are only with difficulty observable.

The effect of these constrictions is to render the outer wall of the
inner course of cells readily compressible, like a bellows, without injury
to the cells. Without them it is hard to see how so great flexibility of
the door tissues combined with firmness and quick reaction could be
attained. It is indeed, as MEIERHOFER exclaimed, a "most wonderful" arrangement. In the upper hinge the constrictions are not so
deep as in the middle area but are more numerous, which may be a
better arrangement for the maximum bending which this has to en-
dure.

It may be pointed out that these cells have been represented (by
EKAMBARAM and MEIERHOFER) as having their anticlinal walls constricted like the periclinal. This is not the case. It is true that if a
door is torn from its moorings and laid in water for examination the
injured cells along the torn edge will collapse and their uninjured
neighbors will swell and present the picture recorded by these authors
(*24 — 9*). But this cannot occur when the door is *in situ* and uninjured.

We now consider (*a*) the way in which the door edge lies in contact with the threshold, so that it can maintain its posture in spite of

the water pressure it must sustain when the trap is set, and (b) how the water is prevented from leaking under the door edge. Recalling the structure of the threshold and especially that of the pavement, it is necessary to point out that the latter along its middle reach is curved in such a manner that it slopes somewhat, so as to face the interior of the trap. At the bottom of the slope, where the inner zone begins, there is an abrupt change in the direction of the slope so that a slight depression is produced (29 — 4). Here the pavement is most closely packed. The middle reach of the door edge is, as we have seen, strengthened so as to make a firm edge, which rests against the pavement just in or beyond the depression, its outer selvage surface resting more or less against the pavement, according to the amount of strain produced by water pressure. When the water pressure is greatest, that is, when the trap is fully set, the position of the door edge is more nearly normal to the pavement than when the trap has just been released. This can be inferred from the measurements of photographs of traps before and just after "firing" (LLOYD 1932b) (29 — 11). It is indicated also by the position of the bristles, which are more erect when the trap is in the set condition. It may be added here that the whole shape of the trap is altered a little by the change in postures of the side walls. Since the ends of the door edge coincide with the inner angles of the threshold, it follows that its lateral reaches cannot follow the pavement parallel to its midline. It is only its middle reach (the middle piece) which impinges edgewise on the pavement. The lateral reaches merely lie with the outer surface of the selvage flat against the pavement, thus forming a re-entrant slit through which the water must leak under pressure unless this contingency were provided against, which is the case. The cuticular membrane, the velum, attached to the outer zone of the pavement, is slung completely across from end to end of the threshold (25 — 5-8). When the door swings outwardly after springing the trap, it pushes against the velum which folds against the door (25 — 4), covering the re-entrant slits on the sides and blocking the door edge in the middle. When the door is in position, the velum reaches in front up to the short spherical hairs which stand in a curved row just below the level of the tripping hairs (24 — 1; 25 — 3-5). Experimental proof that the velum thus blocks the entrance by its valvular action, consisted in cutting the side reach. This was accomplished with a very small knife several times and the parts carefully examined afterwards for assurance that no other damage had been done (LLOYD 1932b). In no case after the velum was cut did the trap reset itself. In CZAJA'S experiment in which he thrust a hair beneath the door edge, this not only held up the door edge but depressed the velum also, but this escaped his attention.

As CZAJA found, the distortion of the door edge (and that of the velum at the same time) when it rests on a hair, prevents the traps from working. This does not seem to be the case if the entrance is filled with the soft body of a large capture, sufficient to plug it (20 — 11). MATHESON (1930) states that such prey may eventually be ingested, indicating that the trap, plugged by the animal's body, still evacuates its water. In the meantime the prey may be softened and respond to the sucking action when re-established, and thus eventually be drawn in. Mr. J. H. Buzacott writes me that this has been observed at Meringa, Queensland, (20 — 11) where tadpoles of *Bufo marinus*, imported to control insect pests in sugar cane, have been destroyed in numbers.

On the sucking-in of prey: — The fact that large prey (young tadpoles and fish fry, worms etc.) can be caught by some part of the body, usually the tail, has long been known. After a tadpolette has been trapped but not completely engulfed, it has been stated that the body is later sucked in. This would obviously be limited by the volume of the trap. The question has been raised by me, does this sucking-in actually occur and if so what is the mechanical procedure? I have recently taken pains to get evidence on this point. I employed *Utricularia* aff. *gibba*, sent me from Pasadena, Calif., by Dr. F. Went.

In a series of experiments young mosquito larvae about 2 mm. long were used. By manipulation it was possible to get one caught by the tail, the head being too big to enter the trap. When this occurred, one half of the body was instantaneously engulfed, leaving four or five joints behind the thorax projecting beyond the mouth of the trap. The joints served as clear-cut measures. Several cases were observed, and all followed the same pattern. One example will suffice. The larva was caught by the tail, the door clamping down between the sixth and seventh joints, while six remained protruding (11:30 hrs.). At 18 hrs. only the thorax and head remained protruding. Next morning, the thorax had also been engulfed, the head only, too big to enter, being left outside. (Text fig. 8, A, B). Since the body of the larva prevents the door from assuming its normal set posture, and though the trap walls did not become concave, as observed from time to time, it must be inferred that nevertheless the entrance was sufficiently occluded by the door and larva so that the exhaustion of the water from the inside of the trap could proceed, creating a suction on the prey from time to time, and drawing it gradually in. As I did not see this happening during a prolonged period of observation, I cast about for more suitable experimental material. This I found in fine shreds of albumin, made by stirring egg-white in boiling water. These were soft and of fairly even caliber. Of a goodly number of experiments I choose the following. Case 1 (Text fig. 8 C, D). A shred about two millimeters long was presented to the trap by touching the tripping bristles with its end. One half of the shred was swallowed; the rest remained protruding. On this some bits of rust, detached from the needle point, adhered, serving as marks. When examined 18 minutes later, the entire shred had been taken in. In the meantime the experiment was repeated (Case 2) (Text fig. 8 E–H) and kept under close and continuous observation. Immediately after the door had clamped down on the partially engulfed shred, the latter was seen to slide slowly in for two minutes, when it stopped (F). This movement was the result of residual wall action. Nothing further happened for about ten minutes (during which time a partial reduction of pressure within the trap took place) when the door opened and closed rather slowly (the movement was quite visible to the eye) and another portion of the shred entered (11:43 hrs.). By 16:00 hrs. the shred had been entiredly swallowed (H). The walls were now concave, and the trap, completely reset, reacted to touch on the tripping bristles. In still another case, a very slender bit of a swallowed shred remained protruding, and the walls of the trap had become concave. The delicacy of this protruding shred had permitted the door to take the set posture, allowing full exhaustion of the internal water. On stimulating the tripping hairs, this shred was swallowed.

It is evident from these experiments that: 1. When the prey is soft and yielding, but, caught part way in, is large enough to prevent the door from taking the set posture, this still may clamp down enough to enable the trap walls to bring about a sufficiently low pressure to exert suction and thus draw in the body of the prey and, by repetition, finally engulf it, if small enough.

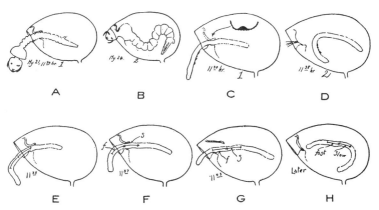

Fig. 8. — The sucking in of prey by the trap of *Utricularia gibba* or a related species; A, an injured mosquito larva was presented and suddenly but only partly swallowed, May 21, 1941; B, the same three days later; C, a shred of albumen presented and partly swallowed at 11:20; D, at 11:38, the shred entirely swallowed (the insert figure indicates the edge of the door looped over the soft and yielding prey, the surface of the threshold indicated by the broken line); E, a shred of albumen presented at 11:35, and the trap observed continually; F, at 11:37, part of the shred indicated by a double arrow had been slowly sucked in; G, at 11:43, the door quickly (but not very suddenly) opened and another portion of the shred (*f*) swallowed; later (H) the remainder was engulfed.

2. If the prey is slender and yielding enough, the door may assume a sufficiently exact set posture to insure the full setting of the trap, when it will react normally but, of course, only in response to movement of the tripping bristles. When the prey, still not engulfed, dies, it may not be swallowed unless the tripping bristles are touched by some other agent. If a stiff, unyielding object such as a hair is used (as did Czaja), this cannot happen because of inleakage of water at the side of the hair.

Traps which have captured mosquito larvae (the head remaining protruding) do not survive, dying in 10 days or so, evidently from overfeeding.

We now resume our discussion of the structure of the trap. In addition to the front view of the velum, which can be seen in the living trap, a side view can be had under favorable conditions, when it is seen that the velum forms a bolster in front of the door edge $(25 — 3, 4)$.

It is of interest and mere justice to record that the velum had been seen previously by two observers, both in 1891. GIESENHAGEN, I believe it was, made a drawing for GOEBEL'S paper of 1891 of a transverse section of the threshold of *U. flexuosa*. In this drawing the velum was shown in the clearest manner, but no mention of it was made in the text. And in 1891, at Cambridge (England) R. E. FRY, a student who was later to become an eminent art critic and Professor of Art in that university, and who is better and more widely known as "ROGER FRY," prepared a Ms. which was never published, but to which I fortunately had my attention drawn when attending the International Botanical Congress in 1930. It was lying on the shelves of a bookshop. ROGER FRY was evidently a close observer, for in one of his drawings, meticulously executed in fine pencil and color, he showed the velum, and in his description he described the pavement epithelium (he used GOEBEL'S 1891 term), saying that "the whole of this secretes mucilage, the cuticles of the hairs being raised in a mass;" but he did not examine further into the matter. One cannot help wondering why others, who saw other minute details, failed to see the velum. ROGER FRY'S Ms. has now been deposited by me in the Library of the School of Botany, Cambridge University.

Two mechanical types of trap. — Having described in some detail the structure of the trap of *Utricularia vulgaris*, it must now be pointed out that, though working according to the same mechanical principles and being of the same morphological type, there are two distinct kinds of traps (LLOYD 1936a). They can be distinguished readily by the posture of the door in its relation to the threshold (TEXT FIG. 9). If we consider the entrance as tubular, in one kind the tube is short, in the other long. *U. vulgaris* has a trap with a short tube entrance. In it the door stands approximately at right angles to the axis of the tube, or at any rate forming a wide angle with it. In the other kind, of which *U. capensis* is a good example, the entrance is tubular (STEPHENS 1923), and the door stands obliquely, forming a narrow angle with the axis. Considered as a valve, this is the less efficient, *ceteris paribus*, but its inferiority is compensated for in various ways, to be noted. Of the latter kind there are two variants represented by such species as *U. monanthos*, and *U. dichotoma*, on the one hand and *Polypompholyx* on the other, all purely Australasian types, with differences demanding separate description.

The description of *U. vulgaris* above given will serve as a standard of comparison. Correlated with its position in the short tubular entrance, the shape of the door is such that its sagittal measurement is less than its transverse. The top of the threshold is narrow. In *U. capensis*, with a long tubular entrance, the door has reversed measurements: it is longer than broad, and the threshold is broad (*29 — 12, 13*). The door stands obliquely. A glance at the diagram (TEXT FIG. 9) will reveal these differences. It is seen that, considered as a check valve, the long door, presenting a re-entrant angle with the threshold, and with no opposing seat, is, with respect to the direction of the water pressure, at a disadvantage. In our blood vessels the valves, which are also obliquely set flaps, are in the reverse position. But from the point of view of the efficacy of the trap, the door would be useless if it were set in this way. In the trap it must be able to resist the water pressure to which it is normally subjected, until a trigger action is applied, when it must then be weak enough to fold up, allowing the entrance of a water column. And it must of course not allow the leaking in of water when the trap is set. How these demands are met may be understood by examining the structures involved. For models of the *U. vulgaris* trap, see p. 266.

The door is divided into a relatively thin anterior half, and a thick posterior half (*31 — 3 etc.*). The former includes the areas of the upper hinge and the middle area. The two cell courses of the upper hinge have the structure seen before, with deeply constricted walls in the inner course (*31 — 9*). Those of the middle area, not a region of sharp bending, have about equal thickness, with no constrictions. There is no central hinge and below the mid-point of the

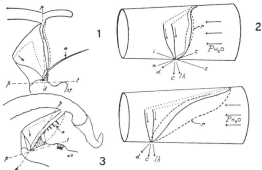

FIG. 9. — Diagrams of the entrances of *Utricularia vulgaris* (1, 2) and *U. capensis* (3 *right*) or *caerulea* (3 *left*) embodying the different mechanical conditions in these two types of trap; *pd*, general direction of thrust of the door, and, *pt*, of the threshold; *r*, relaxed position of the door; *a*, point of impact of prey; *P*H₂O, pressure of water against the door; *iz*, slope of inner zone of the pavement epithelium; *mz*, slope of middle zone of same; *d*, thrust of the door; *lh*, thrust of the lateral hinge; *c*, composition of these thrusts.

door lie the middle piece and the lateral hinges. Their total thickness is usually greater than elsewhere, and in the lateral hinges the outer course cells are thin and the inner thick and are constricted with many constrictions (*30 — 6-8*). As these merge into the middle piece the two cell courses become nearly equal in thickness and the walls are thick. The threshold is broad and semicylindrical in form (*30 — 5-8*). The outer third as seen in sagittal section (the "doorstep") bears glandular hairs, the middle third of pavement cells supplying a voluminous velum of balloon cells, and the inner third being dense pavement (*25 — 2*). The whole is surrounded by the massive trap walls, giving firm support. The lower part of the door, when closed, rests cramped into the relatively narrow arc of the threshold, exerting a firm pressure by its middle piece (*30 — 8*). In the set posture the upper part of the door assumes a convex form, thereby increasing the pressure of the door selvage on the pavement, widening the angle between the two (*30 — 3*). Just after release, the door, now in the relaxed posture, has its upper part convex. It is watertight in this condition. As water is withdrawn the upper half of the door becomes more and more concave till the set posture is reached. This account has been substantiated by a photographic record of silhouette of living traps in the set and relaxed condition of two related species. Seeds of *U. Welwitschii* collected by YOUNG in Angola were grown for me at the Edinburgh Royal Botanical Garden in 1934 and the traps studied there. *U. capensis* was studied alive at Capetown later, and the results were published in 1936 (*24 — 5*) (LLOYD 1936*b*).

Another, an Australian species, *U. lateriflora*, typical of a small group of species distributed in S. E. Asia, and Australia, having very small traps less than 1 mm. long, yielded to experimental methods (1936*c*) and the results are shown in *33 — 9*, demonstrating that the behavior is quite like that in *U. capensis* and *U. Welwitschii*. The living material was available at Sydney, N. S. W.

The same behavior is displayed by *U. caerulea* (Asia) (*24 — 2*) and by *U. cornuta* (N. Amer.) (*30 — 3*) in both of which the living trap was studied.

In all these, when the trap is in the set condition the outer selvage of the door rests on the pavement, held there firmly by the thrust of the lateral hinges. The wide angle between door and threshold is filled by the massive velum, preventing inleakage of water. A thrust on the tripping mechanism, the kriss hair (p. 259) in *U. capensis* and *U. Welwitschii*, a group of sessile glands in *U. caerulea* and *U. cornuta*, disturbs a delicate balance of forces in unstable equilibrium, and the trap is "fired."

Both *U. monanthos* (*24 — 3*) and *Polypompholyx* (*24 — 8*) act in the same way, and they also have been studied in the living condition. *U. monanthos* was grown for me in Edinburgh in 1934 (1936*a*) and *Polypompholyx* could be examined in 1936 at the University of Western Australia at Perth near which it grows. The structures involved are, however, to be considered separately.

U. monanthos (*34 — 1-5*). — In this and allied species, the threshold is very broad, front to back, and near its inner limit is bent, curving downwards. Beyond the bend lies the dense pavement which receives the middle piece, which is therefore applied on the inside of the bend. This looks like a pretty poor arrangement, yet it works. The major zone in front of the bend is occupied by an ample velum which arises also from the walls projecting in front of the door. Here is formed a complete massive ring resting against the bulge of the upper part of the door when in the relaxed posture. When in the set posture, the inner portion of the velum arising from the pavement alone continues to block the entrance of water. The door is still longer than in *U. capensis* etc., but the middle piece is relatively smaller, and the middle area is correspondingly large, occupying about four-fifths of the door length. When in the set posture, the whole of this large area is concave, so that the sagittal curve is now continuous with that of the middle piece, which by virtue of the thrust of the lateral hinges is impressed against the dense pavement just inside the bend of the threshold. The trigger consists of a group of sessile hairs just above the bend of the door. The action when the trap is fired is like that in *U. capensis*. It must be confessed at this point that my earlier account of door action (1932*a*) based on preserved material of

U. Hookeri was wrong. This species conforms in every way to *U. monanthos*. Living material was examined in Sydney, N. S. W.

In *Polypompholyx* the case is again quite special, for here the door is as broad as long, but works as in *U. monanthos*. The whole trap to be described (p. 262) is extremely curious. Because of the thickness of the walls and other parts and the masses of glandular hairs on the door and on the floor of the antechamber, it was difficult to study the trap in action, and especially to photograph it. Nevertheless the attempt succeeded (*24 — 8*). When the trap is set, the door shows a simple curve, along the sagittal line from the upper hinge, which is very thick and does little bending, to the edge which lies just within the ridge of the pavement. When relaxed, just after discharge, the lower two-thirds of the door is convex, the upper hinge showing little movement — a slight bending in its distal zone only. It is evident that the very deep cells of the outer course of this tissue exert a strong tangential pressure on the lower parts of the door, ensuring a tight application of the selvage to the pavement when the door is relaxed and a still tighter application when the trap is set.

The variety of traps. — The following account, necessarily brief, will give some idea of the diversity of structure and form displayed by the traps of *Utricularia*, *Biovularia* and *Polypompholyx*. We may conveniently follow the grouping into those having short and long tubular entrances.

Traps with a short tubular entrance. — These are found in the *U. vulgaris* type, in *U. Lloydii* Merl and *U. nana* St. Hil., in a group of few species represented by *U. globulariaefolia*, in *Biovularia* and in *U. purpurea* and associates.

The trap of *U. vulgaris* has been sufficiently described already. Those of such species as *U. gibba*, and of the terrestrial *U. subulata*, *U. biloba* (*27 — 1*) and a number of others, all small plants, show only slight differences. In *U. neottioides* (*27 — 9*), growing in running water, the traps present a streamline contour and a deep overhang. In those species, such as *U. reniformis*, which live more or less epiphytically in wet moss, etc., the antennae are broad at the base, unbranched, and appear to be adapted to holding water in the entrance by offering support for surface films. Sometimes the entrance is tilted forward (*U. longifolia*) involving the threshold (*26 — 4*), so that the pavement also faces forward. There are two apparently unique S. American species, both small and terrestrial, *U. Lloydii* Merl and *U. nana* St. Hil. The former, *U. Lloydii*, has two forms of trap, one on the leaves, the other on the stolons (*28 — 1-4*). They differ in the character of the hairs, and notably in the presence on the door of a single tripping hair, with a saddle shaped cell next its base apparently to facilitate hinge movement, on the leaf trap, which has also slender backwardly curved antennae, while the stolon trap has short forwardly directed antennae with long hairs, but no tripping bristle on the door. Such differences are difficult to explain. In *U. nana* the trap is quite devoid of appendages, but is otherwise much like that of *U. Lloydii* except that the tripping mechanism consists of two bristles set transversely (*28 — 5, 6*) (LLOYD 1932*a*).

U. globulariaefolia and *U. amethystina* represent a group of Central

and South American species which are terrestrial. Their traps (*28 —*
7–9) are superficially much different from the *vulgaris* type, yet conform in having a short tube entrance, though this has a long funnel-
shaped approach, lined with numerous long-stalked glandular hairs.
The door, while lacking in well demarked mechanical areas, is extremely flexible because of very numerous constrictions in the inner
course cells (LLOYD 1931).

Biovularia has a door in which the middle piece is half its depth
(*27 — 5, 6*). At the upper edge of this there are always six tripping
bristles arranged transversely and radiating outwardly (LLOYD 1935*a*).
In *U. purpurea* and its allies (*27 — 2-4*) the tripping hairs arise in a
radiating manner from a tubercle centrally placed on the door which
is naked of other glands. Either the entrance is quite simple and
unadorned (*U. purpurea*) or the lower lip may be extended into a long
upturned rostrum carrying a few unicellular hairs, with a tuft of these
on each side of, but somewhat above, the middle of the entrance
(*U. elephas* Luetz.). The tripping hair consists of a long stalk (*29 —
7*), an elongation of an epidermal cell which is part of the tubercle,
expanded at the top, bearing a short basal cell, and a large mucilage
cell with expanded cuticle. The edge of the door is thickened by a
beading which rests in a slight depression of the narrow pavement
(LLOYD 1933*a*, 1935*a*; LUETZELBURG). The outer surface hairs are
sickle-shaped mucilage cells and sessile, oil-bearing ones (*29 — 6*).

The mechanical response following a contact of prey against the
tripping hairs cannot of course be seen, but may be fairly guessed at.
Movement of the hairs causes slight rotation of the knob to which they
are attached. This results in slight displacement of the door middle
piece, disturbing the even contact of its edge on the threshold, thus
allowing the pressure of water to push it in. In a diagram (*26 — 8*)
I have shown the action (much exaggerated) as in the up and down
plane. The thinness of the door about the knob allows its rotation
(LLOYD 1933*a*).

Traps with a long tubular entrance. — The species belonging to this
group present a by no means homogeneous picture, and in some cases
are obviously less closely related to each other than those in the
short-tube entrance group. With regard to the mechanism of the
entrance they fall into two sub-groups: (*1*) That in which the door
when in relaxed posture presents along the sagittal axis a single continuous curve; and (*2*) that in which the door shows two curves, a
strong one in the upper hinge region, and a lesser one in the middle
piece. To the former belong *U. cornuta* (N. America) and *caerulea*
(Old World), the latter representing a large number of allied species.

U. cornuta will serve as an example (*30 — 1-8*). The trap is
wholly devoid of appendages. Just below the entrance there is a
rounded group of sessile glands (SCHIMPER) which may be regarded
as a lure for prey. The tripping mechanism consists of a scattered
group of sausage-shaped glands on the lower half of the upper hinge.
They can be seen when one looks straight into the entrance. The posture of the door in the living trap in set and relaxed condition was
studied, and recorded photographically. In the set posture, the outer
selvage of the middle piece rests on the middle zone of the pavement.

From that point as seen along the sagittal line, the door is gently concave throughout its whole length. The whole extent of the middle piece is covered by the velum ($24 - 6$), leaving the upper region with the tripping hairs exposed. A touch on this surface discharges the mechanism, and the door immediately returns to the closed but now relaxed posture in which the whole door is convex outwardly. In the set posture, while concave along its middle axial line, it is slightly convex transversely, that is, it is saddle-shaped. It was possible to make transverse sections of the living trap, and these disclosed the door posture in the middle piece region, from which it was clearly seen that the close application of its selvage to the pavement is procured by the thrust of the thick lateral hinges. The release from this position results only from the longitudinal extension of the shallow fold already present in the set posture of the door.

SCHIMPER (1882) was the only previous student of this plant. Since he accepted the COHN and DARWIN view, he was not aware of any special significance to be attached to the structures of the entrance mechanism.

U. caerulea ($31 - 1$), U. ogmosperma, U. equiseticaulis, U. bifida (Asia), U. cyanea (Australia) and a lot more species, with the general features of the trap very similar, conform to U. cornuta, except in relatively unimportant details. They are usually provided with two simple antennae and a small overhang, and the tripping mechanism consists of a group of short-stalked glandular hairs, the longer nearer the top of the door, and the shorter as the middle piece is approached. GOEBEL's very brief account of the trap of caerulea shows the general position of the door correctly though sketchily. U. bifida is evidently of this group (GOEBEL) as I have myself determined, confirming GOEBEL's drawing as correct. Only bifid hairs are present in the interior of the trap, as DARWIN observed. In such species, however, the glands below and at the edge of the threshold have a single capital.

As a type of the second sub-group, we choose U. capensis, and U. Welwitschii. A number of other species peculiar to S. America, Central and South Africa, all small plants, fully conform to this type. A description of the form of the door and of its manner of operating has already been given above (p. 255). The tripping mechanism ($31 - 8, 9$) consists of a curiously formed large trichome, the capital cell of which resembles in shape a Malay kriss, called therefore the kriss trichome (LLOYD 1931), supplemented by a group of curved glandular hairs on the upper part of the door. In some species the kriss trichome is not present, its place taken by large globular sessile glandular cells (U. peltata, U. Deightonii Ms.) ($31 - 6, 7$). A conspicuous feature of this group of plants is the development of a funnel shaped approach to the entrance by spreading of the cheeks, and the lining of this funnel with about ten rows of stout glandular hairs radiating towards the entrance. In U. Welwitschii these are reduced to mere sessile glands but a rostrum bears a radiating row of longer glandular hairs ($31 - 4$). The S. American U. peltata, so like U. capensis except for the globular tripping hairs, has in common with some African species (U. Deightonii in Ms.) minute peltate leaves very thickly covered with stiff mucilage ($29 - 9, 10$), a significant fact of geographical distribution. Some Asian species (*U. rosea, U. Warburgii*) (*31* — 10, 11) studied by GOEBEL have an extension of the funnel to form a long projecting beak of the shape of a knife blade, armed with gland hairs. Apparently some degree of trap dimorphism occurs in *U. rosea*, affecting the size of the trap and the form of the beak (LLOYD 1932*a*). Species showing these peculiarities are found also in Australia and New Guinea.

    U. Kirkii, occurring in central Africa, is apparently unique (*33* — 1, 2). Of the same general form and appearance of *U. capensis*, the threshold retreats into the interior, and has no step leading to the pavement. The tripping mechanism consists of two long upwardly curved bristles based at the juncture of the hinge and the blunt edged middle piece. The latter is fortified by two large tubercles developed from inner course cells, each semi-pyriform, with a thin line of tissue between, along which the middle piece can fold during opening.

    U. orbiculata (*32* — 1–4). — This, representing a group of species in Asia and Africa, was examined by GOEBEL, who did not observe more than the stubby, branched, glandular antennae. The entrance mechanism is very peculiar. The velum is supplemented by membranes arising from the stalked glands of the step. The tripping mechanism of the door consists of three glandular hairs set in a triangle on the upper half of the door. One is mallet-shaped, placed at the inwardly directed apex of the triangle. The other two are at first large, globular, nearly sessile glands (*32* — 6). In maturity, the capital, containing a large mass of stiff mucilage, bursts in a regular fashion, releasing a long sausage-like mass of jelly which remains attached to the hair. Two of these hang down in front of the entrance, and with the mallet-shaped hair receive the impact of prey which trips the door (LLOYD 1932*a*). A Thibetan species (Brit. Mus.: L.S. and T. 802), similar to *U. multicaulis*, has a broad fan-shaped rostrum armed with radiating glands, which extend forward and in front of the entrance. *U. brachiata* is also like this (COMPTON) (*32* — 5, 7–9).

    U. longiciliata (*33* — 3, 4) is a unique terrestrial species of S. America, and has been described by MERL (1915). The traps are very small (0.3 mm.). The lower lip projects as a strong bifurcated rostrum, the arms extending laterally. The upper lip forms a short, slightly upturned beak. The middle piece of the door is exceptionally thick and bears a single tripping hair (MERL). This consists of a thin stalk and a disc shaped basal cell and a capital of spindle shape. It projects straight forward (LLOYD 1932*a*). The internal glands are few in number but large.

    A small group of species from India, East Indies and Australia includes *U. lateriflora, U. simplex* (Australian), *U. calliphysa* (Borneo) and two probably unnamed species from India and Ceylon, all terrestrial and small in size (*33* — 5–9). The minute (0.3 – 0.5 mm.) traps have a pronounced upper rostrum and a row of short glandular hairs on each side of the trap leading up to the lower angles of the entrance. Sometimes there is a frieze of low tubercles on each side above the mouth (STAPF). The tripping hairs (*33* — 8) stand in a prominent group, marked by sessile, transversely long capitals on the upper part of the door. The internal glands are few but large.

    We shall now speak of that variety of traps represented in the foregoing discussion by *U. monanthos* (p. 256) or alternatively by *U. dichotoma* (they are much alike). The structure of the entrance mechanism has been described. Beyond this is the form of the trap, with its appendages and glands.

The appendages, when a full complement is present, consist of a rostrum, upper (dorsal) wings and lower (ventral) wings (*34* — 1). The rostrum projects forward from the overhang; the upper wings arise one from each side of the trap above the door, and the lower wings extend each from a point near the insertion of the stalk up to the lower angles of the entrance. In the various species one pair or the other of the wings may be either suppressed or greatly enlarged or extended, with great differences in the character of their margins (*34; 35*). The rostrum is always present, but may be short or extended, to a maximum in *U. tubulata*, and sometimes once branched (*U. volubilis*) (*34* — 6). It will suffice to refer the reader to the figures, made with a minimum of detail, for some grasp of the great variety within this restricted group of purely Australian plants.

In *U. volubilis*, which grows anchored in rather deep water, there are three forms of traps (*34* — 6). Its runner stolons bear traps in groups of three, and these have wings crenately margined, and the rostrum is short. The shoots bear numerous ligulate leaves and among these, exposed directly to the water, are two kinds of trap, large, reaching a length of five mm. (this species has the largest trap) with rather short cylindrical stalks, so that they stand near the surface of the substrate; and smaller ones (2 mm. or less) on very long leafy stalks, and these stand 4–5 cm. above the substrate. The distinction between the water traps is not a sharp one for there are gradations of size and form, but they are on the whole quite recognizable. The traps in the substrate are similar to those of *U. monanthos* in that the wings, of which there are two pairs, are not laciniate; the rostrum is short and unbranched. The large water traps have a long, sometimes branched rostrum, and the edge of the shallow overhang bears additional fimbriae more or less branched, while the wings are deeply laciniate. The abundance of fimbriae seems to clutter up the front end of the trap. In the long stalked kinds, the ventral wings are much reduced in size and may or may not have a single thread-like lobe. The dorsal wings are single slender processes, as is also the rostrum, which may be once branched. This trap resembles much that of *U. tubulata*, which is a submersed floater. Similar behavior is seen in *U. Hookeri*, also an anchored submersed plant in which the traps are long stalked (*ca.* 1 cm.). It bears traps of various sizes, the largest 4 mm. long, to smaller ones 1.5 mm. long. In the large traps the wings are slender and fimbriate, but prominent, and the rostrum single, rather long and straight or curved downwards. In the small traps the ventral wings are represented by low ridges, the slender dorsal wings, and the single rostrum, all very long (*34* — 7).

In the little known floating species *U. tubulata*, (*35* — 8) the traps have a very long rostrum and filiform dorsal wings, without branches. The ventral wings are absent. In *U. Menziesii*, different in habit, being totally buried in wet quartz clay with only the leaf blades and flowers showing, there is complete uniformity of trap structure (*35* —

10, 11), but physiologically the traps behave differently, there being three sets, one growing downward, one growing laterally and one upward (*20 — 9*).

There are still other varieties of traps displaying various permutations of size and shape of the appendages. So far as known these are represented in *plate 35*.

Lastly the genus *Polypompholyx* (*36 — 1–9*), the trap of which was described with respect to the entrance mechanism on p. 257. It has a very special form in this genus (there is little variety), in which the stalk plays a special part of the approach to the door.

The form of the trap and a number of anatomical details were described by F. X. Lang in 1901 from material in the Goebel collection, which I examined later.

The traps are of various sizes, the largest measuring 4 mm. in length. For the most part they are smaller, about 1.5–2 mm. In one species (possibly *P. latifolia*, though Bentham did not admit this species) the traps are dimorphic both in size and structure (*36 — 8, 9*). In all the species (probably four) they present the following characters. Viewed from above, the body of the trap is seen to be roundly triangular with a forked rostrum in front and a broad wing on either side. The margins are entire but carry stiff hairs. The fork of the rostrum is seen to clasp the stalk, over which the whole forward part of the trap is inclined. The top of the trap body is almost flat — this is the upper side of the three sided body. Seen from below the trap body evidently has two lateral faces, from the upper angles of which the wings extend. The stalk, which now hides the rostrum, gradually swells on its approach to the trap, and is molded into two low ridges, one on each side, just before the insertion is reached. These ridges are strongly ciliated, forming guiding fences directing prey to the entrance of the trap, which is approached only laterally because of the contact of the rostrum on the stalk. The wings complete two funnel effects, one on each side. Viewed now from the side the stalk is seen to be increasingly massive as it approaches the trap, and this is due to a large intercellular space which inflates the lower moiety below the rostrum. The upper half is expanded into a ridge which becomes deeper under the rostrum, then to be reduced. The loss of height is, however, compensated for by a comb of stiff hairs with long, tapering capitals, and their ends curiously distorted (Lang) as if bent during development by impinging against the rostrum. This ridge being tightly pressed against the rostrum divides the approach to the door into two lateral vestibules, so that the prey must advance under the wings from behind, to be diverted by the combs of bristles on the sides of the stalk toward a space beneath the rostrum. This space has the wall of the trap for its floor and the rostrum and door for its roof, and is an antechamber leading to the entrance proper. Its floor is clothed with mucilaginous hairs with long whip-lash capitals, lying pointed toward the entrance. The roof, which is chiefly the door, bears similar hairs, longer toward the door insertion, shorter toward its free edge. The entrance is a small semi-circular hole in the trap wall, which stands at a steep angle with the floor of the antechamber. The semicircular edge of the entrance is clothed with pavement epithelium, the middle zone of which lies just within this edge. The outer zone, which carries the velum, faces outwardly (36 — 8, 9). The inner region bears glandular hairs of various forms, at first with conical capitals, then with bifids. Quadrifids of large size occupy the interior wall surface. The door lies almost at right angles to the plane of the threshold, result of the forward bending of the rostrum. The action of the door has been already described (p. 257). Histologically the door presents a unique feature in the very great depth of the inner course cells in the upper hinge region, the door gradually tapering in thickness toward the edge. Of this we may say that these thick cells can exert a strong tangential thrust so as to press the door selvage firmly against the pavement, the outer zone of which bears the velum, seen in living material at Perth, W. Australia. The door selvage is not thickened. Its cells are of equal thickness in both courses, and there is no obvious middle piece. This means that the door selvage must bend over the pavement, not impinge edgewise on it. The tripping mechanism consists of short, bent, glandular hairs, 30–40 in number, scattered on the surface of the door below the middle point (36 — 5).

The dimorphism in the traps of *P. latifolia* has been indicated. There are two sizes of traps. In the larger, the threshold behind the pavement bristles with a dense fringe of conical glands of graduated sizes, described by LANG. Inside this pale stand some bifid glands. In the small sized trap there are no conical glands. In their place there are glands with single-celled capitals of the form of the bifids and quadrifids. Inside the traps are bifids (36 — 8, 9).

The walls consist of four courses of cells, the two epiderms and two courses of parenchyma. The epiderms vary in thickness. The outer is thickest in the middle of the sides, and the inner thickest at the angles, here forming a hinge structure.

The total thickness of the three walls, which have four courses of cells throughout, is always greatest at the middle of their faces, producing a hinge effect at the angles. Further, the outer epidermis is always thin at the angles and progressively thicker toward the middle of the faces, while the inner is thick at the angles and thin elsewhere, the more readily allowing compression on the inside of the angles and on the outside of the faces. It is evident from mere inspection that these massive walls must exert a big pull when the trap is exhausted of water (36 — 7).

In closing this account one cannot but wonder at the astonishing variety of trap structure. It is not less astonishing that there is no evidence that one form of trap is superior to another in action. The fact of variety is one with the same phenomenon observed when we survey attentively some other unit of structure. It seems as though nature, or to deify her fruitfulness, Nature, is not nor ever has been content to make some one thing, however satisfactory, and to let it go at that. She must show that she is not bound to the details of a pattern that, in this case, she can make a whole shelf full of different kinds of traps, as if to puzzle you to pick the best.

Digestion. — GOEBEL remarked the great difficulty, because of their small size, of studying the traps of *Utricularia* to determine the presence or absence of digestive activity. It had of course been quite apparent to DARWIN, COHN, Mrs. TREAT and others that animals caught in the traps disintegrate, but the natural inference, that digestion was effected by the plant, was not sustained by evidence, for a few experiments done by DARWIN in which he introduced minute fragments of meat, albumen and cartilage into the traps, gave only negative results, and he concluded that *Utricularia* cannot digest its prey. BÜSGEN fared no better — he worked with an acid medium with which LUETZELBURG also got meagre results.

GOEBEL regarded *Utricularia* as capable of digestion because of its close relationship to *Pinguicula*, but confessed that no evidence had been forthcoming. LUETZELBURG (1910), one of his students, obtained evidence with sap expressed from large numbers of traps removed individually, ground up with clean sand and glycerin, and percolated. The extract thus obtained showed a slight activity, visible after 3 days, in an acid medium. It was, however, much more active in an alkaline medium, and the conclusion that a trypsin was present was arrived at.

During prolonged observation of the experiments it was noticed that there was never any odor of putrefaction, and culture tests showed that bacteria did not grow in the presence of the expressed juices, yet these could liquify gelatin in four days. The presence of an agent inhibiting the growth of bacteria was inferred and this inference was strengthened by experimental evidence that bacteria are only feebly produced in trap fluid put on a gelatin surface. This led to the discovery of benzoic acid in the trap fluid, this substance having been found also in the leaves and glands of *Pinguicula* by LOEW and ASO, and in the pitchers of *Cephalotus* by GOEBEL.

ADOWA (1924) attacked the same problem. He first made saline and acid (HCl) extracts of the whole plant, and tested their efficacy in digesting gelatin, fibrin, milk casein and egg-albumin. The tissues of the whole plant contain, he found, two proteoclastic ferments, alpha- and beta-protease, the latter active in an acid medium. The former is rendered a little more active with the addition of $CaCl_2$ to it in a neutral medium. He then made extracts of three lots of material (*a*) stems, (*b*) green (young) traps and (*c*) red and blue traps, and tested these separately. In neutral gelatin, the effects of these three extracts were in the ratios of 18.5 for green traps, 6.5 for colored traps, and 3.5 for stems; in alkaline gelatin the ratios were 22, 23.5 and 6. In acid gelatin the effects were rapid at first but stopped quickly, while in the alkaline and neutral media the action was continuous. The conclusions were drawn that (*1*) the extract of the traps contained more alpha-protease than that of the stems; (*2*) that of green traps affects alkaline gelatine over a long period (24 days) to the same extent as that of colored traps; (*3*) the extract of green traps acts more energetically on neutral gelatine than that of the colored traps; (*4*) the protease content of branches is very insignificant; (*5*) alkaline gelatin is the best medium for digestion by undiluted extracts, neutral gelatin for diluted extracts (50% and less); (*6*) beta-protease both from the branches and from the traps shows a weaker activity than alpha-protease, and (*7*) extracts diluted 8–16 times act in neutral but not in alkaline medium.

It seemed evident from all the foregoing that digestive ferments are present, but principally in the traps.

KIESEL (1924), however, took the opposite view. He found that fragments of fibrin were digested in the traps, but if acidified with 0.2% HCl were not. The trap fluid, obtained by means of a fine pipette directly from the traps and preserved under toluol showed no power to digest fibrin, gelatin or albumin. He concluded that the digestion in the traps of *Utricularia* is the work of microörganisms. What these might be was investigated by STUTZER (1926). Traps washed in sterile physiological solution were minced and the contents thus obtained were sown on agar plates. He found bacteria of the *Bacterium coli* group to be dominant and suggested that they play the important rôle of digestion. Other bacteria play a secondary rôle. Those of the kind found in the digestive tracts of insects etc., are also to be met with, but these he thought play the same role in the traps as there, namely, to conserve the nutrient mass during digestion and hinder the development of putrefactive bacteria. It is possible, in addition, that *Bacillus aquatilis communis*, one of the soil bacteria, takes some part in digestion, since it can digest albumin.

And there the matter stands at the moment. On the one hand, it is held that the presence of benzoic acid inhibits bacterial action, and that any digestive action is the work of the ferments secreted by the trap itself; on the other the digestion is referred to the activity of bacteria. HADA (1930) takes a middle ground, holding that "the animals captured . . . . . are decomposed not only by the enzyme secreted by the plant, but also by the bacteria which increase rapidly after the death of the animals." Since his paper is in Japanese, I do not know what evidence he puts forward.

Prey and their fate. — The presence of sugar as well as mucilage in the glandular hairs at the entrance of *U. vulgaris*, shown by LUETZEL-BURG, was thought by him to indicate that these hairs form a lure to attract animals. The presence of special groups of glands near the entrance in some species (*e.g. U. cornuta*) seems to support this view.

While it is true enough that animal prey captured by the traps of *Utricularia* sooner or later succumb and are digested, there are exceptions in organisms which are able to live and multiply in the restricted space of the interior of the trap, notably *Euglena, Heteronema, Phacus* (HEGNER) and probably others, including diatoms and desmids, often seen. There is at present no evidence of obligate relations; these forms seem to be caught probably accidentally, and can live inside the trap indefinitely, though HEGNER states that when plants are kept a long time in an aquarium, the *Euglena* runs out. Protozoa when captured generally succumb, but some remain alive for a long time, a fact noted long ago. The presence of decaying *Paramaecia* in the trap does not affect the *Euglenae*.

That *Paramaecium* is sometimes quickly killed and at others remains alive for a long time (75 min. to 17 days) (HEGNER) seems to indicate that the physiological conditions in the traps are not always uniform. LUETZELBURG thought he detected a paralysing effect of the extract which he used for digestion experiments on small crustaceans, but that it must be weak. HADA advanced the idea that animals are killed by being compressed by the walls in becoming convex. This can hardly be the case as animals have been seen to live, meanwhile freely moving, for days.

Appendix: —

Here in a position of obscurity I ask leave to present two models, in the form of mouse traps, designed *ad hoc*, to illustrate the way in which the trap of *Utricularia* has been and at present is thought to work.

Two models are offered. One, FIG. 10, represents the mechanism of the trap as conceived by COHN, DARWIN and others. In this the door is a passive check valve, easily pushed inwards, but not outwards. In the model a small hole in the bottom of the door allows the mouse to see the bait thus enhancing the effect of the lure by adding sight to smell. This model is an improvement on the *Utricularia* trap in having the bait on the inside. Its extreme simplicity is in contrast to that of the second model, FIG. 11, which affords an analog in which the

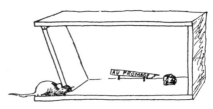

FIG. 10. — A mouse trap designed to embody the idea held by COHN and by DARWIN and others for fifteen years after them.

complexity of the *Utricularia* trap as now understood is suggested without exaggeration.

A description of this model is presently given. A box is provided with a door having two hinges (h_1, h_2). Below h_2 the part d_2 swings independently from that above, d_1. Pressure applied at the arrow pr cannot push in the door; but rotation of d_2 on h_2, so that its edge clears the stop (sp), allowing inward swing. Outward swing is prevented by a backstay st_4. A handle tr on d_2, actuated by a mouse, accomplishes inward opening by pulling on the string st_3, whereby the doodad (d) is pulled away from the top of the plunger pl, allowing play to the spring s_2. This spring then pulls on the string st_2 actuating the double pulley $p \times 2$, one element smaller than the other in the ratio $\frac{1}{3}$. The outer pulley pulls on st_1, swiftly opening the door. To this is attached a device called a booster, B, the purpose of which, like the sudden inward gush of water in nature, ensures the entrance of the mouse into the trap. This is now momentarily open, and of course would remain so unless power were available to close it again. This is supplied by an electric motor m which starts to rotate when an electrical circuit is closed by a contact point on the plunger coming into contact with e. The motor continues to rotate till the plunger, pushing the spring S_2 into its set posture, the door being pushed back into position by its spring S_1. When this is completed, the contact point on the plunger comes into contact with the contact point *e*, below, and the relay *r* then stops the motor. The power from the motor is applied to the plunger through the gear p_2 etc., ending in a cam *c*, the whole being adjusted so that the cam comes into a position which allows the lever *l* to swing downwards when the door is actuated again by, it is confidently hoped, a second mouse. In the meantime, the mouse first caught can employ his time admiring the interior effect, and possibly suggest improvements. A digestion chamber could of course be provided.

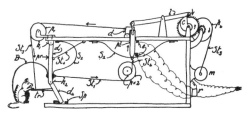

Fig. 11. — A mouse trap intended as a model embodying present ideas of the *Utricularia* trap as a mechanism (with apologies to HEATH ROBINSON).

A captious reader may find difficulty in accepting the analogy as complete. I can say only that he would be right; but at least a purpose is served, to indicate that the *Utricularia* is a pretty complex bit of mechanism.

Literature Cited:

ADOWA, A. N., Zur Frage nach den Fermenten von *Utricularia vulgaris* L., I. Bioch. Z. 150:101–107, 1924; II. 153:506–509, 1924.

BARNHART, J. H., Segregation of genera in *Lentibulariaceae*. Mem. N. Y. Bot. Gard. 6:39–64, 1916.

BATH, W., Über Kaulquappen in den Fangblasen von *U. vulgaris*. Sitzungsber. d. Ges. Naturforsch. Freunde Berlin 1905:153–155.

BENJAMIN, L., Über den Bau und die Physiologie der Utricularien. Botan. Zeitung 6:1–5; 17–23; 45–50; 57–61; 81–86, 1848.

BROCHER, FRANK, Le problème de l'Utriculaire. Ann. de Biol. lacustre 5:33–46, 1911.

BROCHER, F., A propos de la capture d'anophèles par les Utriculaires. Ann. Parasitol. 5: 46–47, 1927.

BRUMPT, E., Capture des larves de *Culicidées* par les plantes du genre *Utricularia*. Ann. de Parasit. humaine et compar. 3:403–411, 1925.

BUCHENAU, FRANZ, Morphologische Studien an deutschen Lentibularieen. Botan. Zeitung 23:61–66; 69–71; 77–80; 85–91; 93–99, 1865.

BÜSGEN, M., Über die Art und Bedeutung des Tierfangs bei *Utricularia vulgaris* L. Ber. d. deutsch. bot. Gesellsch. 6:55–63, 1888.

CANDOLLE, A. P. DE, Physiologie végétale II:528, 1832.

CHANDLER, BERTHA, *Utricularia emarginata* Benj. Ann. Bot. 24:549–555, 1910.

CLARKE, W. G. and R. GURNEY, Notes on the genus *Utricularia* and its distribution in Norfolk. Trans. Norfolk and Norwich Nat. Soc. 11:128–161, 1920–1921.

COHN, FERD., Über die Funktion der Blasen von *Aldrovanda* und *Utricularia*. Cohns Beiträge zur Biologie der Pflanzen 1(3):71–92, 1875.

COMPTON, R. H., The morphology and anatomy of *Utricularia brachiata* Oliver. New Phytologist 8:117–130, 1909.

CROUAN Frères, Observations sur un mode particulier de propagation des *Utricularia*. Bull. de la Soc. bot. de France 5:27–29, 1858.

CURRY, DALFERES P., Breeding of *Anopheles* mosquitoes among aquatic vegetation of Gatun Lake, accompanied by periodic long flights of *A. albimanus* Wied. Southern Med. Journ. 27:644–651, 1934.

CZAJA, A. TH., Ein allseitig geschlossenes, selektivpermeables System. Ber. d. deutsch. bot. Gesellsch. 40:381–385, 1923.

CZAJA, A. TH., Die Fangvorrichtung der *Utricularia*blase. Zeitschr. f. Bot. 14:705–729, 1922.
CZAJA, A. TH., Physikalisch-chemische Eigenschaften der Membran der *Utricularia*blase. Pflügers Arch. f. d. Ges. Physiol. 206:554–613, 1924.
DARWIN, CHARLES, Insectivorous Plants. New York 1875.
DEAN, B., Report on the supposed fish-eating plant. Commissioners of Fisheries of the State of New York, Report 18:183–197, 1890.
DRUDE, O., Die insektenfressenden Pflanzen. SCHENK'S Handbuch der Botanik I:113–146 (*Utricularia*, pp. 133–135), Breslau 1881.
EKAMBARAM, T., Irritability of the bladders in *Utricularia*. Agric. Journ. India 11:72–79, 1916.
EKAMBARAM, T., *Utricularia flexuosa* Vahl. Bot. Bull. of the Presidency College Madras, Sept., 1918:1–21.
EKAMBARAM, T., A note on the mechanism of the bladders of *Utricularia*. Journ. Indian Bot. Soc. 4:73–74, 1926.
FERMI, C. & BUSCAGLIONE, Die proteolytischen Enzyme im Pflanzenreiche. Centralbl. f. Bakt., Parasit. u. Pflanzenkr. II, 5:24–33; 63–66; 91–95; 125–134; 145–158, 1899.
FERNALD, M. L., Expedition to Nova Scotia. Rhodora 23:89–111, 1921.
FERNALD, M. L., Specific segregations and identities in some floras of eastern North America. Rhodora 33:25–63, 1931.
FRANÇA, C., Recherches sur les plantes carnivores, II. *Utricularia vulgaris*. Bol. Soc. Brot. 1, ser. 2:11–37, 1922.
GARDNER, G., Travels in the interior of Brazil 1836–1841. London 1846.
GATES, F. C., Heat and the flowering of *Utricularia resupinata*. Ecology 10(3):353–354, 1929.
GEDDES, PATRICK, Chapters in Modern Botany. New York 1893.
GIBBS, R. D., The trap of *Utricularia*. Torreya 29:85–94, 1929.
GISLEN, T., Beiträge zur Anatomie der Gattung *Utricularia*. Arkiv för Bot. 15:1–17, 1917.
GLÜCK, H., Biologische und morphologische Untersuchungen über Wasser- und Sumpfgewächse. Jena 1906.
GOEBEL, K., Vergleichende Entwicklungsgeschichte der Pflanzenorgane. SCHENK'S Handbuch der Botanik III:99–431, 1884. (*re Utricularia* etc., pp. 236–241.)
GOEBEL, K., Über die Jugendzustände der Pflanzen. Flora 72:1–45, 1889.
GOEBEL, K., Der Aufbau von *Utricularia*. Flora 72:291–297, 1889.
GOEBEL, K., Morphologische und biologische Studien, V. *Utricularia*. Ann. Jard. Bot. Buit. 9:41–119, 1891.
GOEBEL, K., Pflanzenbiologische Schilderungen, II. Marburg 1891.
GURNEY, ROBERT, *Utricularia* in Norfolk: the effects of drought and temperature. Trans. Norfolk and Norwich Nat. Soc. 11:260–266, 1921/22.
HADA, Y., The feeding habits of *Utricularia* (with English abstract). Trans. Sapporo Nat. Hist. Soc. 11:175–183, 1930.
HEGNER, R. W., The interrelations of protozoa and the utricles of *Utricularia*. Biol. Bull. 50:239–270, 1926.
HOEHNE, F. C., & KUHLMANN, J. G., Utricularias do Rio de Janeiro e seus arredores. Mem. Inst. Butantan 1:1–26, 1918.
HOVELACQUE, MAURICE, Recherches sur l'appareil végétative des Bignoniacées, Rhinanthacées, Orobanchées et Utriculariées. 765 pp., Lib. Acad. Méd. Paris, 1888 (*Utricularia*, pp. 635–745).
IM THURN, E. F., Among the Indians of Guyana. London 1883.
IM THURN, E. F. & D. OLIVER, The botany of the Roraima Expedition of 1884. Trans. Linn. Soc. Lond. ser. II, 2 (bot.), 1881–1888; Part 13:249–300, 1887.
IRMISCH, THILO, Botanische Mitteilung, I. Über *Utricularia minor*. Flora 41:33–37, 1858.
JANE, F. W. & WELLS, B. R., Observations on the seeds and seedlings of *Utricularia vulgaris* L. Trans. Norfolk and Norwich Naturalists Soc. 14:31–54, 1935.
KAMIENSKI, FR., Vergleichende Untersuchungen über die Entwicklungsgeschichte der Utricularien. Botan. Zeitung 35:761–729, 1877.
KAMIENSKI, FR., *Lentibulariaceae*. Natürliche Pflanzenfamilien 4, Abt. 3b:108–123, 1895.
KIESEL, A., Études sur la nutrition de l'*Utricularia vulgaris*. Ann. Inst. Pasteur 38:879–891, 1924.
KRUCK, M., Physiologische und zytologische Studien über die *Utricularia*blase. Bot. Arch. 33:257–309, 1931.
LANG, F. X., Untersuchungen über Morphologie, Anatomie und Samenentwicklung von *Polypompholyx* and *Byblis*. Flora 88:149–206, 1901.
LLOYD, F. E., The mechanism of the watertight door of the *Utricularia* trap. Plant Physiol. 4:87–102, 1929.
LLOYD, F. E., The range of structural and functional variation in the traps of *Utricularia*. Flora 125:260–276, 1931.
LLOYD, F. E., The range of structural and functional variety in the traps of *Utricularia* and *Polypompholyx*. Flora 126:303–328, 1932a.

LLOYD, F. E., Is the door of *Utricularia* an irritable mechanism? Canadian Journ. Res. 7:386–425, 1932*b*.
LLOYD, F. E., The structure and behaviour of *Utricularia purpurea*. Canadian Journ. Res. 8:234–252, 1933*a*.
LLOYD, F. E., Carnivorous plants — a review with contributions. Presidential Address, Trans. Roy. Soc. of Canada, Ser. III, 27:35–101, 1933*b*.
LLOYD, F. E., The types of entrance mechanisms of the traps of *Utricularia* (including *Polypompholyx*). Presidential Address, Section K–Botany, B. A. A. S., Leicester, Sept. 1933*c*, pp. 183–218.
LLOYD, F. E., Additional observations on some *Utriculariaceae*. Canadian Journ. Res. 10:557–562, 1934.
LLOYD, F. E., *Utricularia*. Biol. Reviews 10:72–110, 1935*a*.
LLOYD, F. E., Struktur und Funktion des Eintrittsmechanismus bei *Utricularia*. Beih. z. Bot. Centralbl. A, 54:292–320, 1935*b*.
LLOYD, F. E., The traps of *Utricularia*. Proc. Sixth Intern. Botan. Congress, Sept. 1935, 1:54–73, 1936*a*.
LLOYD, F. E., The trap of *Utricularia capensis*, how it works. Journ. S. Afr. Bot., 2:75–94, 1936*b*.
LLOYD, F. E., Notes on *Utricularia*, with special reference to Australia, with descriptions of four new species. Victorian Naturalist 53:91–112, 1936*c*.
LLOYD, F. E., Further notes on Australian *Utricularia* with a correction. Victorian Naturalist 53: 163–166, 1937*a*.
LLOYD, F. E., *Utricularia*: its development from the seed. Journ. S. Afr. Bot. 3:155–164, 1937*b*.
LUETZELBURG, P. v., Beiträge zur Kenntnis der *Utricularia*. Flora 100:145–212, 1910.
MATHESON, ROBERT, The utilization of aquatic plants as aids in mosquito control. Amer. Nat. 64:56–86, 1930.
MAYR, F. X., Hydropoten an Wasser- und Sumpfpflanzen. Diss. Erlangen, 1914. Beih. Bot. Centralbl. I, 32:278–371, 1915.
MEIERHOFER, HANS, Beiträge zur Kenntnis der Anatomie und Entwickelungsgeschichte der *Utricularia*-Blasen. Flora 90:84–113, 1902.
MERL, E. M., Beiträge zur Kenntnis der Utricularien und Genliseen. Flora 108:127–200, 1915.
MERL, E. M., Biologische Studien über die *Utricularia*blase. Flora 115:59–74, 1922.
MERL, E. M., Beiträge zur Kenntnis der brasilianischen Utricularien. Flora 118–119: 386–392, 1925.
MERL, E. M., A new Brazilian species of the genus *Utricularia*. Bull. Torr. Bot. Club 61:367–371, 1934.
MERZ, M., Untersuchungen über die Samenentwickelung der Utricularien. Flora 84:69–87, 1897.
MEYEN, F. J. F., Neues System der Pflanzenphysiologie. Berlin 1837.
MEYER, F. J., Zur Frage der Funktion der Hydropoten. Ber. d. D. Bot. Gesellsch. 53:542–546, 1935.
MORREN, ÉD., La théorie des plantes carnivores et irritables. Bull. de l'Acad. Roy. Belg. II, 60:1–60 (repaged?), 1875.
MOSELY, H. N., Bull. U. S. Fish Commission 4:259, 1884/5.
NOLD, R. H., Die Funktion der Blase von *Utricularia vulgaris* (Ein Beitrag zur Elektrophysiologie der Drüsenfunktion). Beihefte Bot. Centralb. 52:415–448, 1934.
OLIVER, DANIEL, The Indian species of *Utricularia*. Journ. Linnean Soc., Bot., 3:169–176, 1859.
OPPENHEIMER, C., Die Fermente und ihre Wirkungen. 5. Aufl., 2:1106–1108, 1925.
PORSILD, M. P., Stray contributions to the flora of Greenland, VI–XII. Medd. om Grønland, Komm. f. Videnskab. Undersøg. i Grønland 93:1–94, 1935 (*Utricularia*, pp. 25–34).
PRÁT, S., Plasmolyse und Permeabilität. Ber. d. D. Bot. Gesellsch. 41:225–227, 1923.
PRINGSHEIM, N., Über die Bildungsvorgänge am Vegetationskegel von *Utricularia vulgaris*. Monatsbericht k. Akad. d. Wiss. 1869:92–116.
RIDLEY, H. N., On the foliar organs of a new species of *Utricularia* from St. Thomas, West Africa. Ann. Bot. 2:305–3c8, 1888.
ROSSBACH, G. B., Aquatic Utricularias. Rhodora 41:113–128, 1939.
ST. HILAIRE, A. DE, Voyages dans les provinces du Rio de Janeiro et du Minas Geraes. Paris 1830.
SCHENCK, H., Beiträge zur Kenntnis der Utricularien. Pringsheim's Jahrb. f. wissensch. Bot. 18:218–235, 1887.
SCHIMPER, A. F. W., Notizen über insectenfressenden Pflanzen. Botan. Zeitung 40:225–234; 241–248, 1882.
SCHWARTZ, O., Plantae novae vel minus cognitae Australiae tropicae, Rep. spec. nov. reg. veg. 24:80–109, 1927.
SIMMS, G. E. Bull. U. S. Fish Commission 4:257, 1884/5.
SIMMS, G. E. & H. N. MOSELY, Naturforscher 17:276, 1884. Ref. in Centralbl. f. Agriculturchemie 14:69, 1885.

SKUTCH, A. F., The capture of prey by the bladderwort, A review of the physiology of the bladders. New Phytologist 27:261–297, 1928.

STAPF, O., *Lentibulariaceae, in* Flora of Tropical Africa. London, 1906.

STAPF, O., *Lentibulariaceae* (of Borneo). Journ. Linn. Soc., Bot., 42:115, 1914.

STEPHENS, EDITH L., Carnivorous plants of the Cape Peninsula. Journ. Bot. Soc. South Africa, Part IX:20–24, 1923.

STUTZER, M. J., Zur Biologie der *Utricularia vulgaris.* Arch. Hydrobiol. 17:730–735, 1926.

THOMPSON, G. M., On the fertilization of flowering plants (*Lentibulariaceae*). Trans. and Proc. N. Zealand Inst. 13:278–281, 1881.

TIEGHEM, PH. VAN, Anatomie de l'utriculaire commune. Ann. Sci. Nat. Bot. V, 10:54–58, 1869; C. R. Acad. Sci. Paris 67:1063–1066, 1868.

TOPP, C. A., Notes on the genus *Utricularia.* Victorian Naturalist 1:71–74, 1884.

TOPP, C. A., Note on *Utricularia dichotoma.* Victorian Naturalist 3:74–75, 1886.

TREAT, MARY, Plants that eat animals. N. Y. Daily Tribune, 1 Feb. 1875. Reprinted without illustrations in Gardeners' Chronicle, March 6, 1875: 303–304.

TREAT, MARY, Is the valve of *Utricularia* sensitive? Harper's New Monthly Mag. 52:382–387, 1876.

TREVIRANUS, C. L., Noch etwas über die Schläuche der Utricularien. Bot. Zeit. 6:444–448, 1848.

ULE, E., Über Standortsanpassungen einiger Utricularien in Brazilien. Ber. deutsch. bot. Ges. 16:308–314, 1898.

UPHOF, J. C. TH., Einiges zur Biologie der terrestrischen Utricularien. Oest. bot. Zeit. 82: 207–212, 1933.

WARMING, E., Bidrag til Kundskaben om *Lentibulariaceae.* Vidensk. Medd. nat. For. Copenhagen, Nos. 3–7:33–58, 1874.

WEHRLE, EMIL, Studien über Wasserstoffionenkonzentrationsverhältnisse und Besiedelung an Algenstandorten in der Umgebung von Freiburg im Breisgau. Zeitschr. f. Bot. 19: 209–287, 1927.

WITHYCOMBE, C. L., Observations on the bladderwort. Knowledge 39:238–241, 1916.

WITHYCOMBE, C. L., On the function of the bladders in *Utricularia vulgaris.* Journ. Linnean Soc., Bot., 46:401–413, 1922–1924. Paper published in 1923.

WYLIE, R. B. & YOCOM, A. E., The endosperm of *Utricularia.* Univ. of Iowa Studies Nat. Hist. 10:3–181, My., 1923.

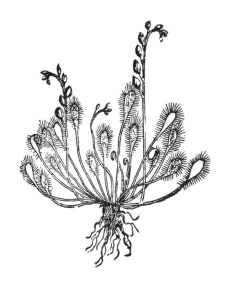

PLATES

— *Plate 1.* —

FIG. 1. — *Heliamphora nutans* (grown at the Edinburgh Botanical Garden).

FIG. 2. — *H. Macdonaldae* (Photograph by Dr. G. H. H. TATE taken on Mt. Duida, Venezuela).

FIG. 3. — *Sarracenia purpurea* (Photograph by CHARLES MACNAMARA, Ontario).

FIG. 4. — *S. purpurea:* a leaf cut lengthwise.

FIG. 5. — *S. purpurea:* view facing the opening.

FIG. 6. — *S. Drummondii.*

FIG. 7. — *S. flava.*

FIG. 8. — *S. psittacina.*

FIG. 9. — *S. minor* (Photograph by Professor J. C. TH. UPHOF).

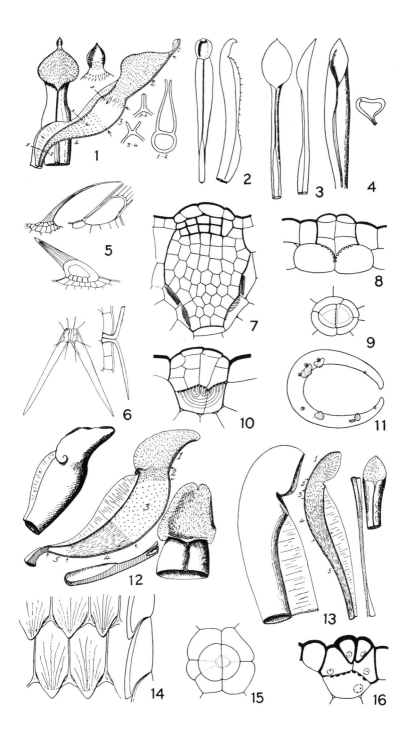

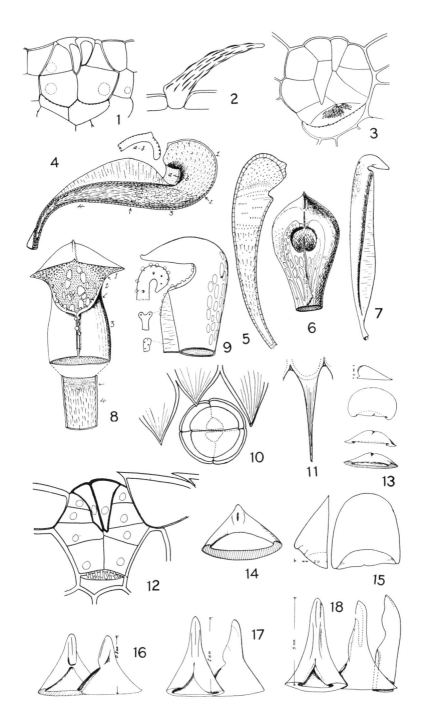

— *Plate 4.* —

FIG. 1. — *Darlingtonia californica*, as seen growing 25 miles east of Crescent City, Calif.

FIG. 2. — The same, in flower in early spring (Photograph by Dr. FRANK MORTON JONES, taken in Plumas Co., Calif., 1920).

FIG. 3. — The same, flowers (near Florence, Oregon).

FIG. 4. — The same. View looking up into the dome of the leaf.

FIG. 5. — The same. A leaf split lengthwise.

FIG. 6. — *Nepenthes Mastersiana*. A pitcher split lengthwise, showing the waxy zone above and the glandular zone below.

FIG. 7. — *N. ventricosa*.

FIG. 8. — *N. Balfouriana* (*N. mixta* × *Mastersiana*).

FIG. 9. — *N. ampullaria*.

FIG. 10. — *N. bicalcarata*.

FIG. 11. — *N. ampullaria*, looking into a pitcher.

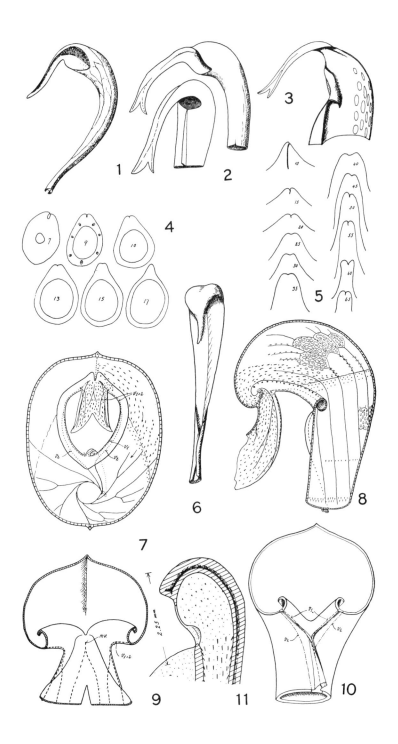

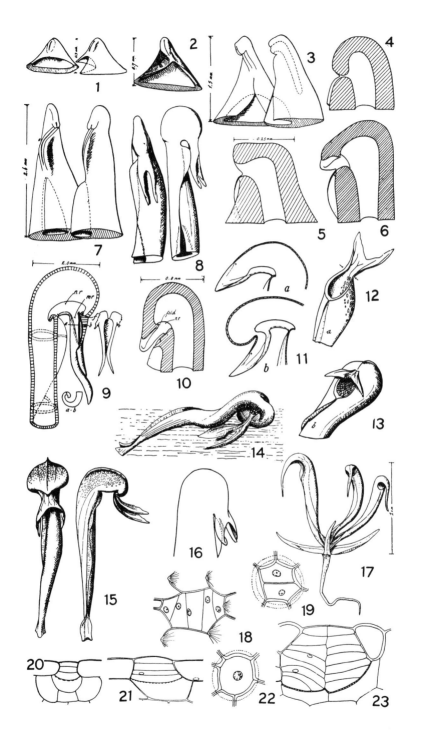

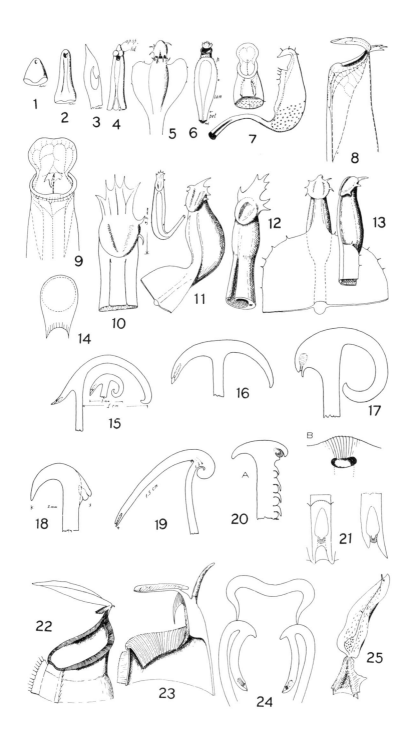

— *Plate 8.* —

FIGS. 1–20. — *Nepenthes.*

FIGS. 1–3. — Stellate hairs, sometimes emergent, sometimes in pits.

FIG. 4. — Tufted hair, producing the rusty pubescence of *Nepenthes.* There are several varieties of form.

FIGS. 5 and 6. — Front and lateral views of the peculiar stomata on the waxy zone of the interior of the pitcher.

FIG. 7. — Front and lateral views of the epidermis clothing the peristome; *a–b* and *c–d* correspond in position. *N. ampullaria* (*cf.* FIGS. 17 and 18).

FIG. 8. — Nectar gland from inner surface of the lid.

FIGS. 9 and 10. — Digestive glands from two species, in section; *cut.* suberized course of cells.

FIG. 11. — Front view of a digestive gland, standing in its pocket.

FIG. 12. — Epidermal cells of the peristome of *N. Lowii.*

FIG. 13. — Nectar gland of the peristome edge, *N. ampullaria.* The outermost course of cells is suberized.

FIG. 14. — Digestive gland in young, thin-walled condition of *N. ampullaria.*

FIG. 15. — External alluring (nectar) gland from the midrib of the blade. *S*, suberized layer.

FIG. 16. — Nectar gland from the ridge beneath the lid, of *N. Tiveyi. S,* suberized course of cells.

FIG. 17. — Transverse section of epidermis of the peristome of *N. ampullaria.* The cells appear ridged.

FIG. 18. — The ridges are seen to be due to the overlying of next cells (*see also* FIG. 7).

FIG. 19. — Quite young stage of development of a pitcher and lid in section, showing folding of the lid and origin of the inner peristome ridge as an outgrowth of the wall.

FIG. 20. — Transverse section of the petiole showing it to be bifacial.

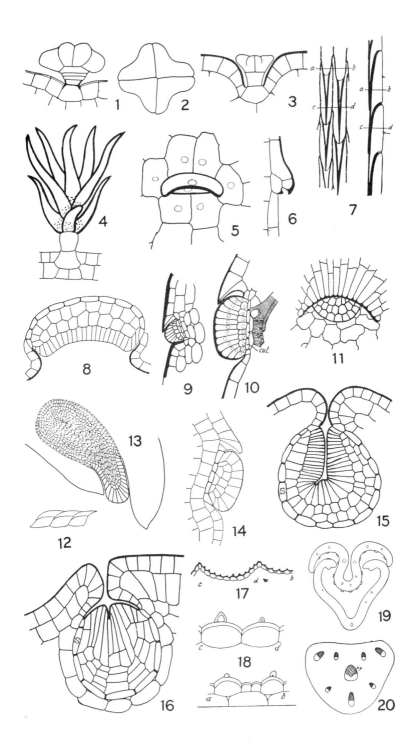

— Plate 9. —

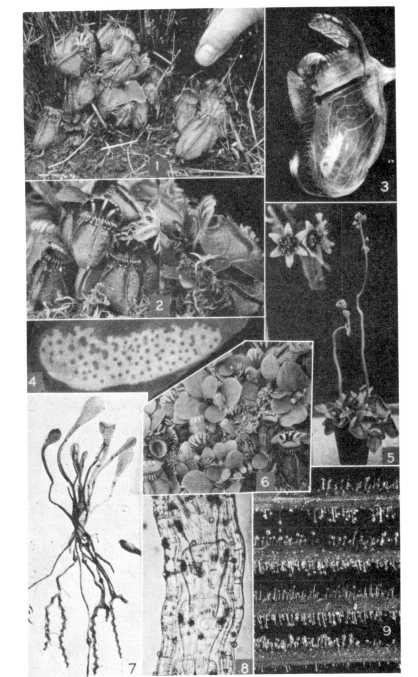

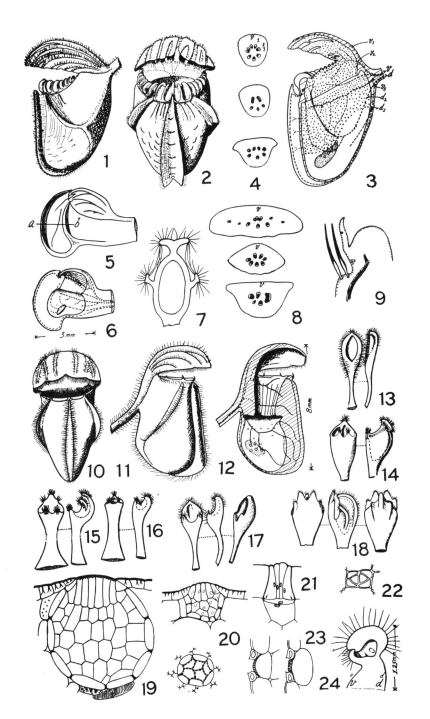

— *Plate 11.* —

FIGS. 1–11. — *Genlisea.*

FIGS. 1–4, 7, 8 and 10. — Series showing the development of the trap.

FIG. 5. — A single plant (from Brazil) × 2; *inf.*, inflorescence stalk; *t.*, trap.

FIG. 6. — Portion of an arm laid open of *G. ornata*. In this species the number of rows of detentive hairs is small. The position of the glands and the shape of the inner epidermal cells (on a larger scale) are indicated.

FIG. 7. — A trap in which the arms are beginning to develop; *vent.*, ventral view; *lat.*, lateral view.

FIG. 8. — Distal end of a young trap showing the arms in a stage of growth later than that seen in FIG. 4. Dotted lines indicate veins, as in FIG. 7.

FIG. 9. — Mature trap, one arm having been laid open and shown in its posture thereafter. A portion of the laid-open arm at *a* is shown above and to the right; below this, the sections along *a–b* and *c–d* are shown.

FIG. 10. — A mature trap. The numbered lines indicate the positions of the sections shown in PLATE 12.

FIG. 11. — A portion of the oral termination of the tube, with the adjacent portion of an arm, diagrammed in perspective. Note prey caught, seen through the window cut in the wall, on the right.

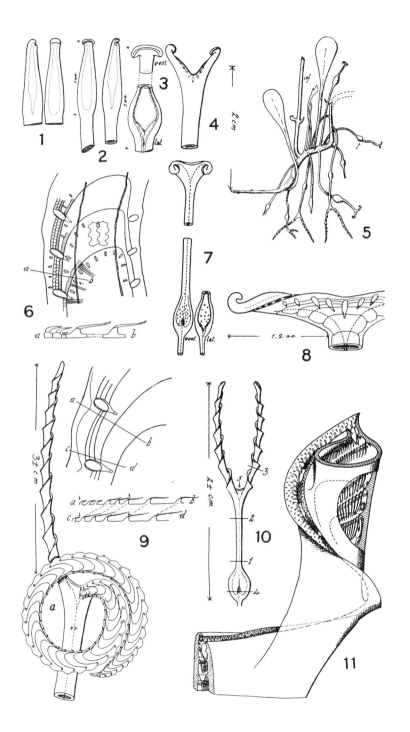

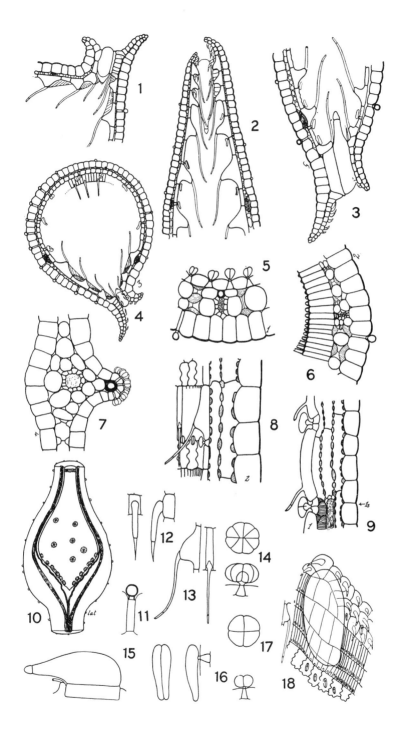

— *Plate 13.* —

Fig. 1. — *Byblis gigantea* (W. Australia). Inset: commensal (true) bug, as yet undescribed.

Fig. 2. — *Drosophyllum lusitanicum*, in culture (Munich). Right, a piece of a leaf with captured prey.

Fig. 3. — The same (Photograph by Dr. A. QUINTANILHA).

Fig. 4. — *Pinguicula vulgaris* (Alberta, Canada). × ½.

Fig. 5. — At left of numeral, a piece of a leaf of *Byblis;* at right of numeral a part of a leaf of *Drosera capensis.*

Fig. 6. — *Pinguicula vulgaris.* Two views of the same plant taken 24 hours apart to show leaf movements. Collected 20 mi. east of Crescent City, Calif.

Fig. 7. — *Drosera capensis.* × ½.

Fig. 8. — Time-lapse motion pictures of *D. capensis*, showing leaf movements. Total period about one and one half hours.

Fig. 9. — *D. rotundifolia*, a leaf with captured prey.

Fig. 10. — *Pinguicula vulgaris*, a small area of leaf surface with the mucilage glands in the focal plane of the camera lens.

Fig. 11. — The same, with the focal plane of the lens at the level of the digestive glands. A captured insect is seen.

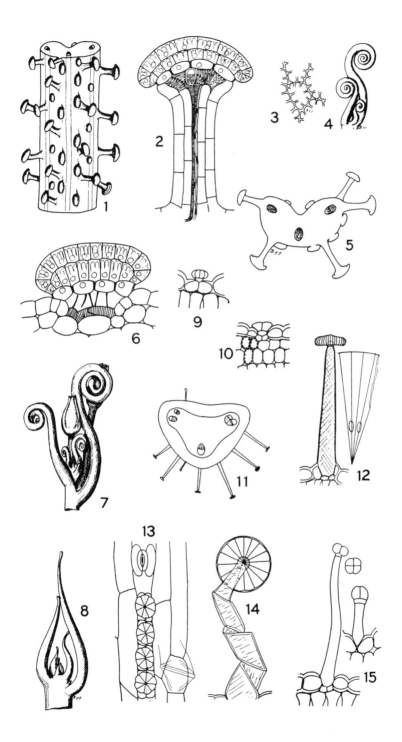

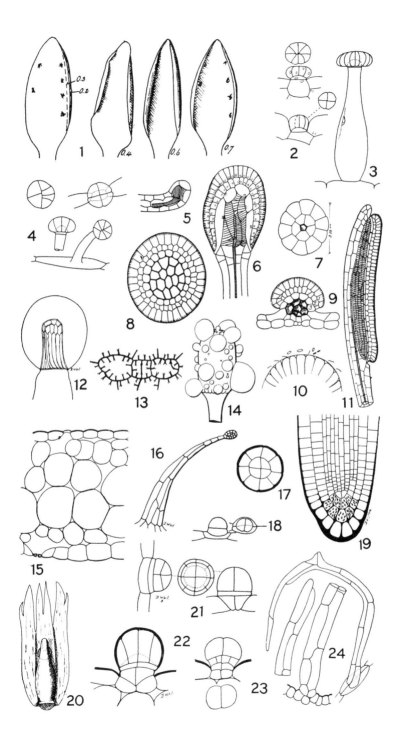

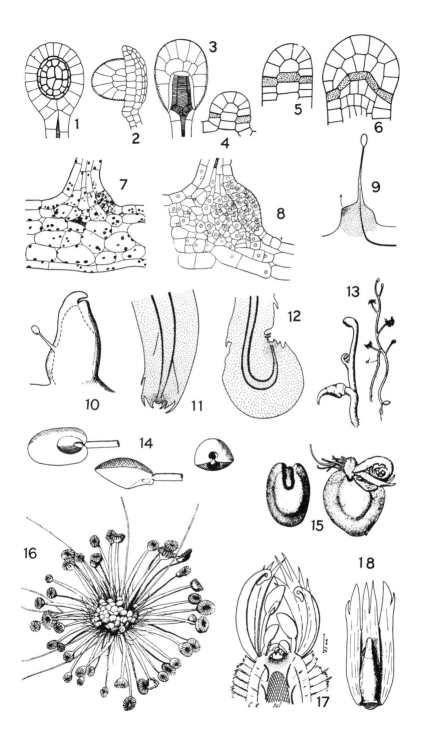

— *Plate 17.* —

Fig. 1. — Aggregation in the stalk cells of *Drosera rotundifolia*. These photographs were provided by Dr. Å. ÅKERMAN. A and B, successive photographs of the same field taken 2 minutes apart; B and C, taken 15 minutes apart.

Fig. 2. — *Dionaea muscipula* (Photograph by Dr. CORNELIA M. SMITH).

Fig. 3. — *Dionaea* leaf which has captured a Harvest-man or Harvest-spider (*Phalangium* sp.).

Fig. 4. — *Drosera gigantea*. This species grows to a height of four feet (Western Australia).

Fig. 5. — *Aldrovanda vesiculosa* (Silesia). On the right of the numeral 5, half a whorl of eight leaves, axial view.

Fig. 6. — *Dionaea*. Moving pictures taken at one-sixteenth of a second intervals. The last one was taken half an hour later.

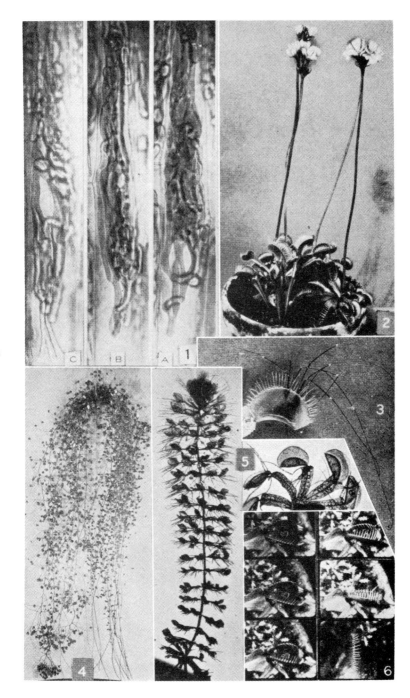

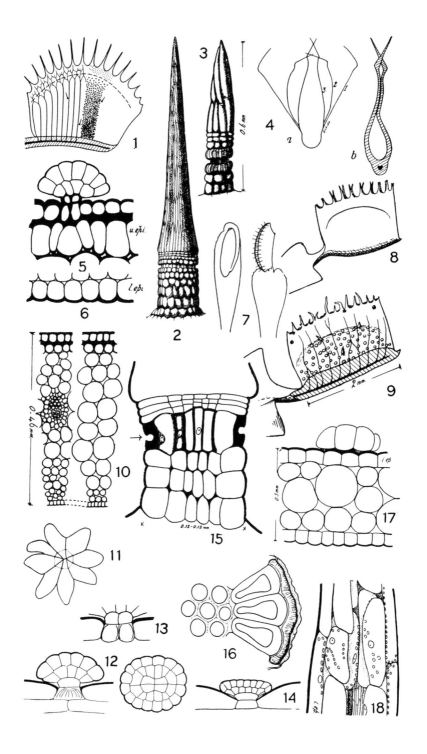

— Plate 19. —

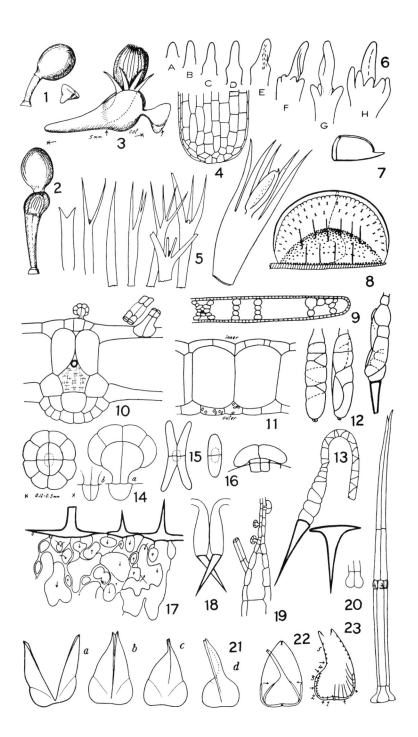

— Plate 20. —

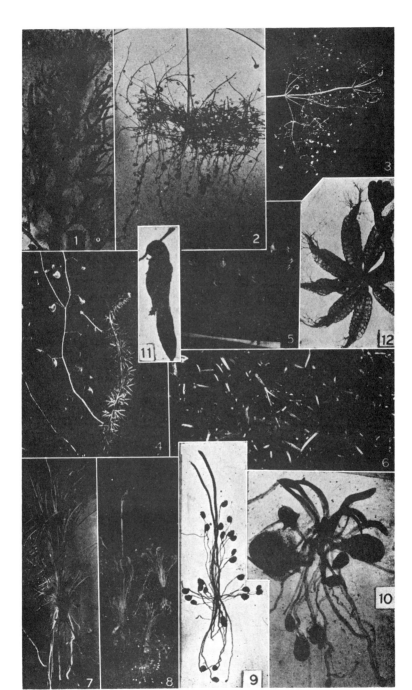

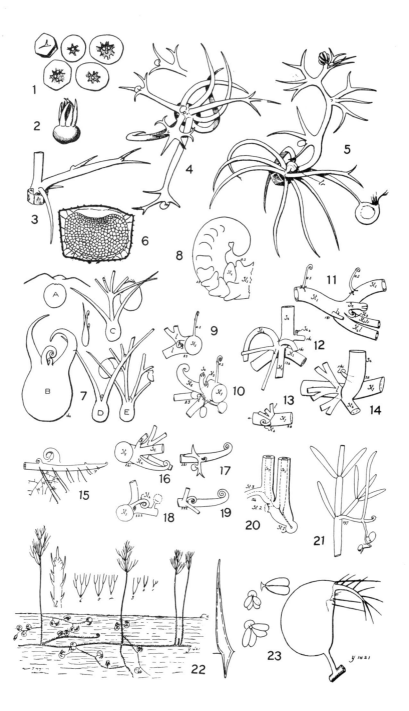

— *Plate 22.* —

1, l_2, primary and secondary leaves; *st*, with sub-numerals, stolons; *tr*, trap; *pod*, podium; *e*, embryo.

Figs. 1–11 and 28. — *U. monanthos.*

Figs. 1–3. — Early germination, during which the primary leaf develops precociously.

Fig. 4. — A primary trap develops in the place of a primary stolon.

Figs. 5 and 6. — Normal germination.

Fig. 7. — The upper moiety of the embryo has developed into a very long podium.

Figs. 8 and 9. — Two aspects of the same embryo. Partial concrescence of the primary trap with its axillary bud, and of the whole with the primary leaf.

Fig. 10. — Seedling with a well-developed podium.

Fig. 11. — The bud which produces the scape is far advanced.

Fig. 12. — *U. orbiculata.*

Figs. 13 and 14. — *U. capensis.* Fig. 13, primary leaf bearing adventive traps each with an axillary bud in adaxial position.

Figs. 15 and 16. — *U. rosea.*

Figs. 17–22. — *U. bifida.* Fig. 18, precocious development of primary leaf; later emergence of primary stolon from podium (3d, 4th, 5th and 6th drawings of the series to left of numeral 18); fig. 19, lateral origin, near base of embryo, of primary leaf; fig. 20, concrescence of primary leaf and stolon; fig. 21, the primary vegetation point has produced only a leaf, while an adventitious growing point has emerged laterally, bearing otherwise normal leaf and stolon; fig. 22, primary stolon apparently from primary leaf.

Figs. 23–26. — *Polypompholyx tenella.*

Fig. 27. — *U. Barnesii* (Ms. name).

Fig. 28. — *U. monanthos.* A stage of development following that shown in fig. 3.

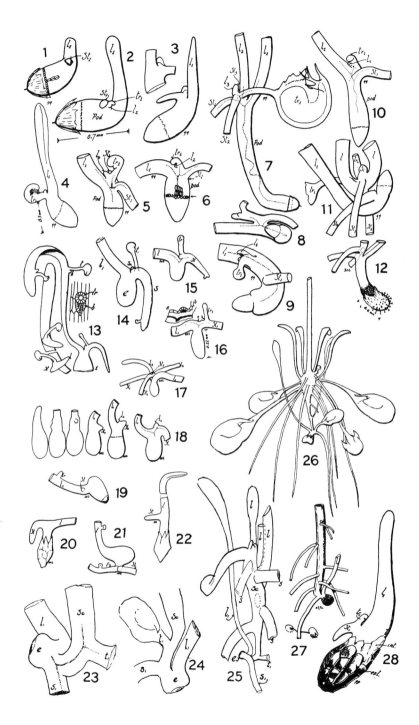

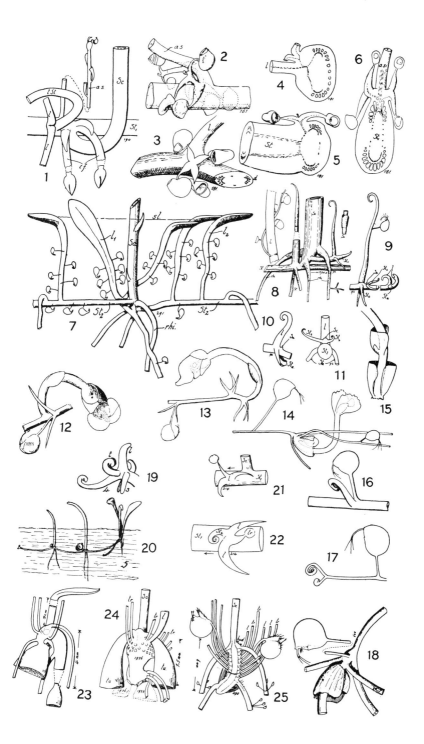

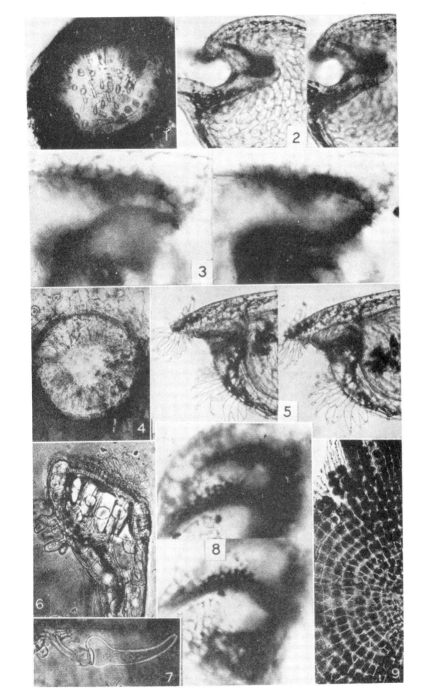

— Plate 25. —

Fig. 1. — *Utricularia Deightonii* (Ms. name) aff. *peltata*. Sagittal section of trap.

Fig. 2. — Sagittal section of entrance to trap of *U. peltata.*

Fig. 3. — The same, of trap of *U. gibba* showing very approximately the normal (but not set) posture of the door and velum.

Fig. 4. — Profile of the door and velum in the set posture, in an entirely whole trap of *U. emarginata.* The lens has, of necessity, to penetrate a considerable thickness of tissues, and hence a sharp picture is unobtainable. The velum is seen as a bulbous mass just above the threshold and in front of the lower door edge.

Fig. 5. — Sagittal section of door and velum, *U. gibba* — the same as in Fig. 3, but at higher magnification to show details of structure.

Fig. 6. — View as from the inside of the trap of the middle reach of the velum in *U. vulgaris.*

Fig. 7. — *U. gibba*. Transverse section of the threshold with the velum, from which its origin can be discerned.

Fig. 8. — The same. View of the velum as one looks into the entrance.

Fig. 9. — *U. intermedia* (or *U. vulgaris*). View looking down on the pavement, showing, however, only a narrow middle fore and aft strip. The velum is at the lower edge of the picture. The outer, middle and inner zones are discernible.

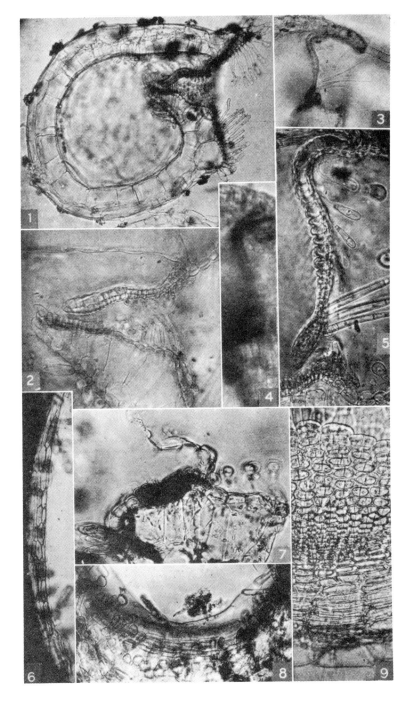

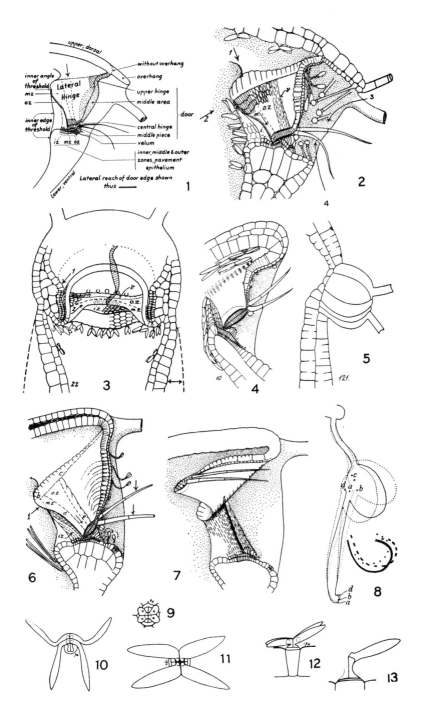

— Plate 27. —

FIG. 1. — Trap of *Utricularia biloba*. Only a few of the bifid and quadri-fid hairs are shown.

FIG. 2. — Entrance of *U. purpurea*, sagittal section. The door is regarded as transparent.

FIG. 3. — The same, the door in open and closed postures.

FIG. 4. — Trap of *U. elephas* Luetz.

FIG. 5. — Trap of *Utricularia (Biovularia) olivacea*.

FIG. 6. — Front view of door of same to show the six tripping bristles.

FIG. 7. — Traps of *U. resupinata* displaying dimorphism.

FIG. 8. — Trap of *U. exoleta* (Queenlad).

FIG. 9. — Trap of *U. neottioides*.

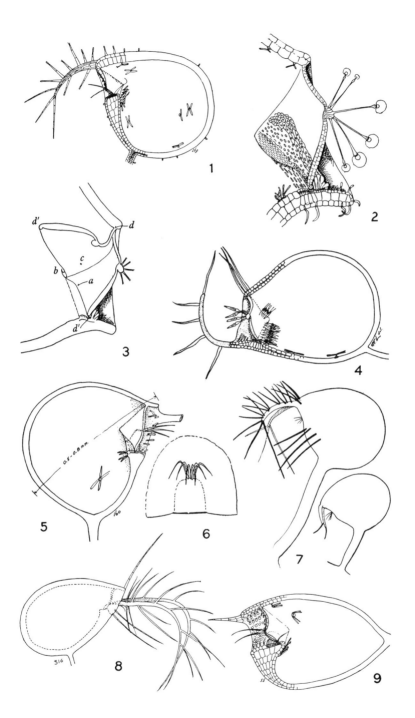

1

2

3

_d'_   _d_

_c_

_b_

_a_

_d'_

4

5   0.5-0.8mm   6

7

8   316   9

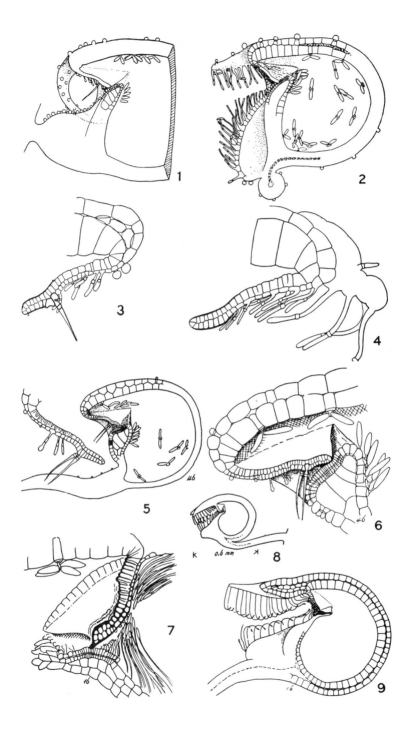

— *Plate 29.* —

FIGS. 1–13. — *Utricularia*.

FIG. 1. — Diagrammatic representation of the histology of the door. Above, view *en face* of the door seen from the inside of the trap; below, section through *a–b*.

FIG. 2. — Sagittal section of the door: *7*, upper hinge; *2*, middle area; *5*, central hinge; *4*, middle piece; *cut*, cuticle; *cel*, cellulose.

FIG. 3. — Cells of the inner course of a portion of the door, the central hinge approximately in the middle; the bases of the tripping bristles shown in dotted lines. Numerous props.

FIG. 4. — Transverse section of the threshold at the middle point, showing the velum. The posture of the door edge in broken lines.

FIG. 5. — Section through the lateral reach, near its outer end, of the threshold in *U. purpurea*. The posture of the door thrusting against the pavement indicated by the oblique arrows. The direction of water pressure against the door and velum shown by the arrows below.

FIG. 6. — Surface hairs of *U. purpurea; a*, sickle-shaped, glandular (mucilage) hairs; *b, c*, young stage of oil-bearing hairs; *d–g*, mature stage of same, showing oil deposit held by the raised cuticle.

FIG. 7. — Glandular hairs of the central boss of the door of *U. purpurea*, shown in developmental stages, numbered serially.

FIG. 8. — Diagram of wall structure, showing the inner quadrifid (*left*) and the outer spherical glands. Vascular tissue between the two cell courses.

FIG. 9. — Peltate leaves of *U.* sp. aff. *peltata* (from Angola). They bear a deep coating of mucilage on their upper surfaces.

FIG. 10. — Mucilage glands of the same with their heavy loads of stiff mucilage (*b*); *c*, scheme of branching: *a*, leaf, with three branches (stolons of second order) emerging from the primary stolon seen axially.

FIG. 11. — *U. gibba*, schematized to show relation of door and threshold in the wide-angle type of entrance (*cf. 30 — 3*). The angular relation of the door posture (*p–d*) to the general level of the threshold (*p–t*) is ca. 90 ; *r*, relaxed posture of door; *s*, set posture; *pr*, various possible directions of impact of prey on the tripping bristles; *uh*, upper hinge; *ch*, central hinge; *lh*, lateral hinge; *a*, middle piece.

FIG. 12. — Narrow angle door: its shape and areas (*cf. 30 — 4*) and, below, the areas of the threshold, of *U. capensis*; *uh*, upper, and *lh*, lateral hinge; *ma*, middle area; *mp*, middle piece; *oz*, outer zone of pavement; *mz*, middle zone; and *iz*, inner zone, of same.

FIG. 13. — Wide angle door (*U. gibba* or *vulgaris* etc.); *ch*, central hinge.

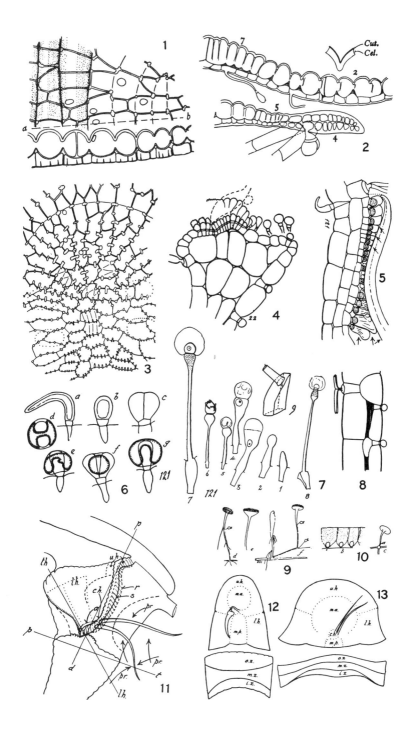

— *Plate 30.* —

FIGS. 1–8. — *Utricularia cornuta.*

FIG. 1. — The trap in lateral and frontal views.

FIG. 2. — Entrance, with alluring glands below, from in front.

FIG. 3. — Sagittal section of entrance. The door (d_1) is shown in the set posture; d_2 its open posture; d_3 normal relaxed posture and d_4, totally relaxed posture, as when the trap is punctured; *dt*, direction of thrust of lateral hinge; *ot*, longitudinal thrust of door; *c*, component of the two thrusts; *dh*, inner angle of threshold, as also in FIG. 5.

FIG. 4. — The door seen from in front. Inner course cells in double outline. Lettering as above.

FIG. 5. — View of pavement from above as from point *d*, FIG. 3; *oz*, *mz*, *iz*, outer, middle and inner zones of pavement; *de*, position of door edge.

FIG. 6. — Section through door and threshold taken as between *c* and *d*, FIG. 3; 1, set, and 2 relaxed posture of door, approximately.

FIG. 7. — Section of same through *d*, FIG. 3. Broken lines indicate opening flexures.

FIG. 8. — Section of same through *c*, FIG. 3; *mp*, middle piece; *t*, rear part of middle zone of pavement indicated in outline; *d*, dotted line indicating the thrust of the door edge into the soft pavement cells (arrows indicate the thrust of the lateral hinges).

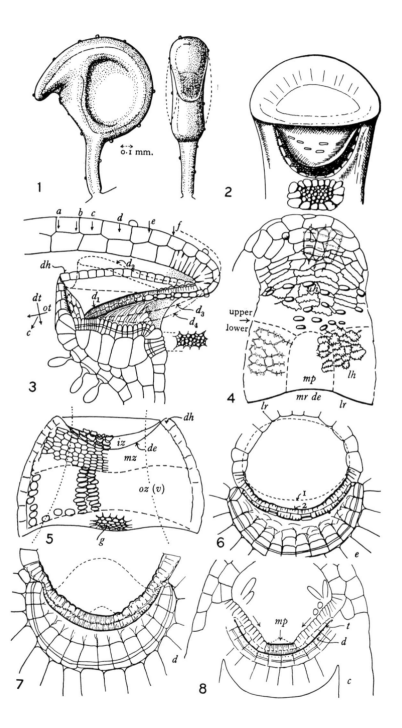

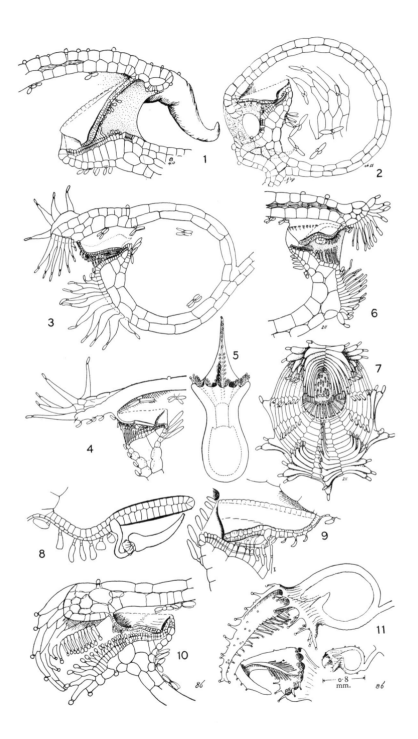

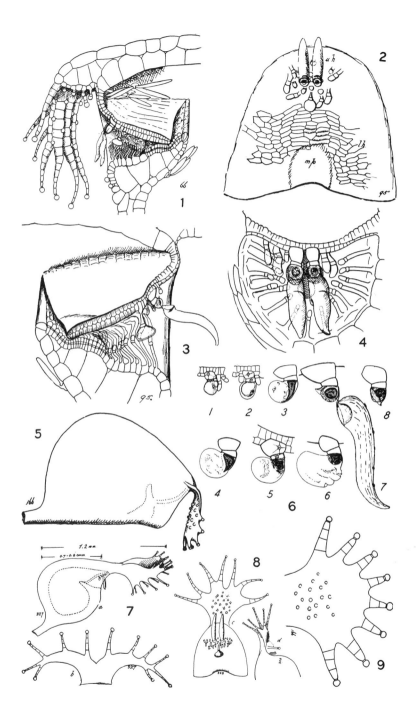

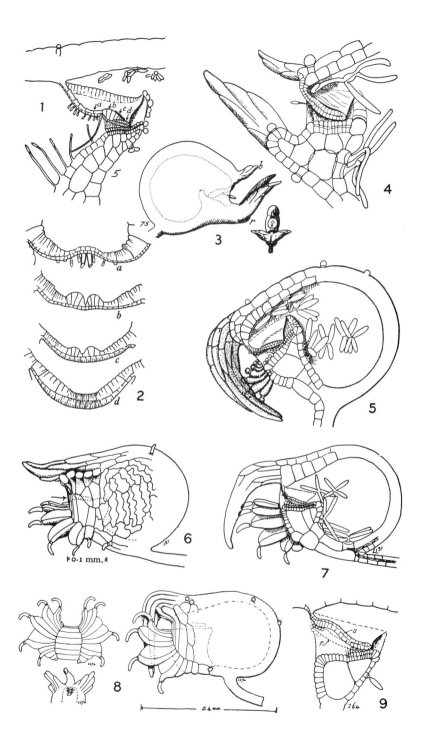

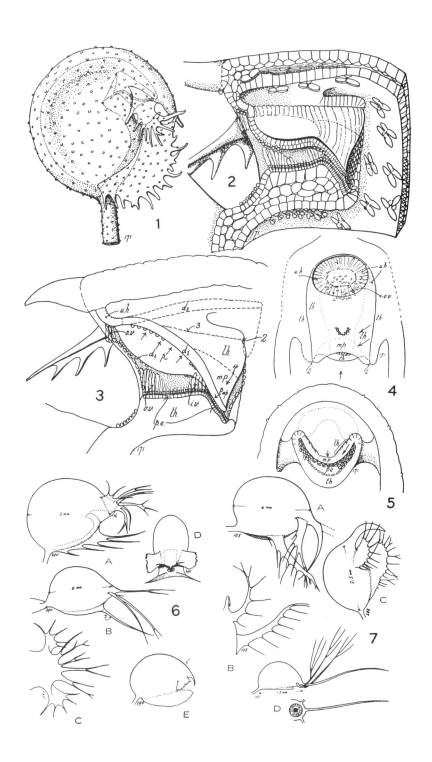

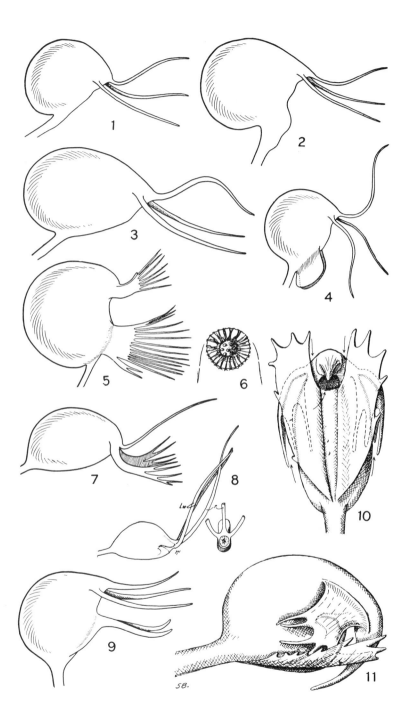

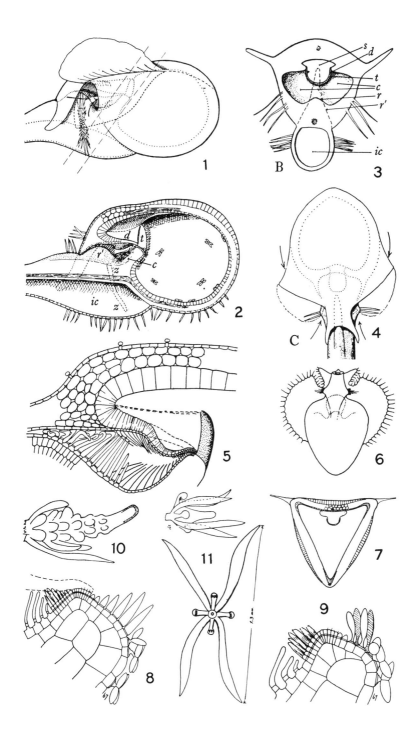

— *Plate 37.* —

Moving pictures showing the action of the trap of *Utricularia*, and of the sensitive hairs of *Dionaea* (all frames are 1/16 sec. apart, except in FIG. 2, in which they are. 1/160 sec. apart, and in FIG. 1A, which is time lapse) : —

FIG. 1A. — *Utricularia purpurea.* Trap showing the exhaustion of the contained water and the consequent collapse of the walls, indicated by the distortion of a contained bubble of air. Moving picture: time lapse spread over about 2 hours.

FIG. 1B. — The same, viewed edgewise, before and after action.

FIG. 2. — *U. vulgaris.* View looking into the entrance showing the opening of the door (in 1/160 sec.) and the subsequent closing in 4/160 sec. The open door is seen in the third frame from top. The round object in front of the door is the knob of a glass probe.

FIG. 3. — *U. vulgaris.* The capture of a copepod. The trap was set in a shallow glass tank with walls to guide the copepod to the mouth of the trap.

FIG. 4. — The same. The lateral profile of a trap before and after (*below*) actuation.

FIG. 5. — *Dionaea muscipula.* Bending and straightening of a sensitive hair.

FIG. 6. — The "Darwin experiment," referred to in the text: the sudden disappearance of colored particles (here particles of carbon) resting on the door, on its actuation by a needle point slowly moved across the entrance.

FIG. 7. — *U. gibba*, capturing a larva.

FIG. 8. — *U. purpurea.* A trap swallowing a bubble.

FIG. 9. — *U. vulgaris.* Trap swallowing a glass bead and, in doing so, jumping at the probe. The trap had been removed from the plant.

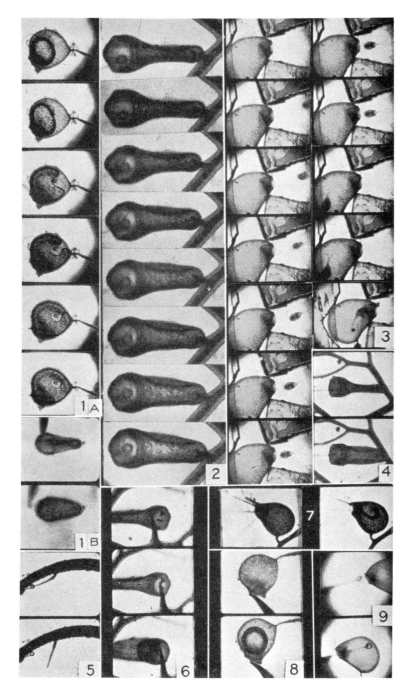

— Plate 38. —

Animation of the trap of *U. gibba*, by Mr. HAROLD PEBERDY, illustrating its action in the capture of prey (Courtesy of the Associated Screen News, Montreal).

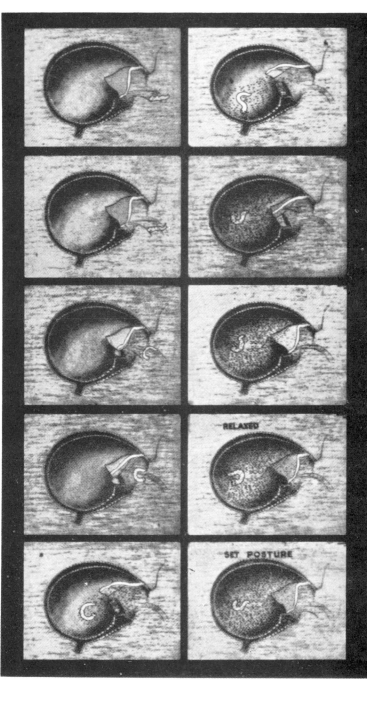

INDEX of PLANT and ANIMAL NAMES

AUTHOR INDEX

A CATALOGUE OF SELECTED DOVER BOOKS
IN ALL FIELDS OF INTEREST

A CATALOGUE OF SELECTED DOVER BOOKS
IN ALL FIELDS OF INTEREST

AMERICA'S OLD MASTERS, James T. Flexner. Four men emerged unexpectedly from provincial 18th century America to leadership in European art: Benjamin West, J. S. Copley, C. R. Peale, Gilbert Stuart. Brilliant coverage of lives and contributions. Revised, 1967 edition. 69 plates. 365pp. of text.

21806-6 Paperbound $3.00

FIRST FLOWERS OF OUR WILDERNESS: AMERICAN PAINTING, THE COLONIAL PERIOD, James T. Flexner. Painters, and regional painting traditions from earliest Colonial times up to the emergence of Copley, West and Peale Sr., Foster, Gustavus Hesselius, Feke, John Smibert and many anonymous painters in the primitive manner. Engaging presentation, with 162 illustrations. xxii + 368pp.

22180-6 Paperbound $3.50

THE LIGHT OF DISTANT SKIES: AMERICAN PAINTING, 1760-1835, James T. Flexner. The great generation of early American painters goes to Europe to learn and to teach: West, Copley, Gilbert Stuart and others. Allston, Trumbull, Morse; also contemporary American painters—primitives, derivatives, academics—who remained in America. 102 illustrations. xiii + 306pp. 22179-2 Paperbound $3.50

A HISTORY OF THE RISE AND PROGRESS OF THE ARTS OF DESIGN IN THE UNITED STATES, William Dunlap. Much the richest mine of information on early American painters, sculptors, architects, engravers, miniaturists, etc. The only source of information for scores of artists, the major primary source for many others. Unabridged reprint of rare original 1834 edition, with new introduction by James T. Flexner, and 394 new illustrations. Edited by Rita Weiss. $6\frac{5}{8}$ x $9\frac{5}{8}$.

21695-0, 21696-9, 21697-7 Three volumes, Paperbound $15.00

EPOCHS OF CHINESE AND JAPANESE ART, Ernest F. Fenollosa. From primitive Chinese art to the 20th century, thorough history, explanation of every important art period and form, including Japanese woodcuts; main stress on China and Japan, but Tibet, Korea also included. Still unexcelled for its detailed, rich coverage of cultural background, aesthetic elements, diffusion studies, particularly of the historical period. 2nd, 1913 edition. 242 illustrations. lii + 439pp. of text.

20364-6, 20365-4 Two volumes, Paperbound $6.00

THE GENTLE ART OF MAKING ENEMIES, James A. M. Whistler. Greatest wit of his day deflates Oscar Wilde, Ruskin, Swinburne; strikes back at inane critics, exhibitions, art journalism; aesthetics of impressionist revolution in most striking form. Highly readable classic by great painter. Reproduction of edition designed by Whistler. Introduction by Alfred Werner. xxxvi + 334pp.

21875-9 Paperbound $3.00

ALPHABETS AND ORNAMENTS, Ernst Lehner. Well-known pictorial source for decorative alphabets, script examples, cartouches, frames, decorative title pages, calligraphic initials, borders, similar material. 14th to 19th century, mostly European. Useful in almost any graphic arts designing, varied styles. 750 illustrations. 256pp. 7 x 10. 21905-4 Paperbound $4.00

PAINTING: A CREATIVE APPROACH, Norman Colquhoun. For the beginner simple guide provides an instructive approach to painting: major stumbling blocks for beginner; overcoming them, technical points; paints and pigments; oil painting; watercolor and other media and color. New section on "plastic" paints. Glossary. Formerly *Paint Your Own Pictures*. 221pp. 22000-1 Paperbound $1.75

THE ENJOYMENT AND USE OF COLOR, Walter Sargent. Explanation of the relations between colors themselves and between colors in nature and art, including hundreds of little-known facts about color values, intensities, effects of high and low illumination, complementary colors. Many practical hints for painters, references to great masters. 7 color plates, 29 illustrations. x + 274pp. 20944-X Paperbound $3.00

THE NOTEBOOKS OF LEONARDO DA VINCI, compiled and edited by Jean Paul Richter. 1566 extracts from original manuscripts reveal the full range of Leonardo's versatile genius: all his writings on painting, sculpture, architecture, anatomy, astronomy, geography, topography, physiology, mining, music, etc., in both Italian and English, with 186 plates of manuscript pages and more than 500 additional drawings. Includes studies for the Last Supper, the lost Sforza monument, and other works. Total of xlvii + 866pp. 7⅞ x 10¾. 22572-0, 22573-9 Two volumes, Paperbound $12.00

MONTGOMERY WARD CATALOGUE OF 1895. Tea gowns, yards of flannel and pillow-case lace, stereoscopes, books of gospel hymns, the New Improved Singer Sewing Machine, side saddles, milk skimmers, straight-edged razors, high-button shoes, spittoons, and on and on . . . listing some 25,000 items, practically all illustrated. Essential to the shoppers of the 1890's, it is our truest record of the spirit of the period. Unaltered reprint of Issue No. 57, Spring and Summer 1895. Introduction by Boris Emmet. Innumerable illustrations. xiii + 624pp. 8½ x 11⅝. 22377-9 Paperbound $8.50

THE CRYSTAL PALACE EXHIBITION ILLUSTRATED CATALOGUE (LONDON, 1851). One of the wonders of the modern world—the Crystal Palace Exhibition in which all the nations of the civilized world exhibited their achievements in the arts and sciences—presented in an equally important illustrated catalogue. More than 1700 items pictured with accompanying text—ceramics, textiles, cast-iron work, carpets, pianos, sleds, razors, wall-papers, billiard tables, beehives, silverware and hundreds of other artifacts—represent the focal point of Victorian culture in the Western World. Probably the largest collection of Victorian decorative art ever assembled—indispensable for antiquarians and designers. Unabridged republication of the Art-Journal Catalogue of the Great Exhibition of 1851, with all terminal essays. New introduction by John Gloag, F.S.A. xxxiv + 426pp. 9 x 12. 22503-8 Paperbound $5.00

A HISTORY OF COSTUME, Carl Köhler. Definitive history, based on surviving pieces of clothing primarily, and paintings, statues, etc. secondarily. Highly readable text, supplemented by 594 illustrations of costumes of the ancient Mediterranean peoples, Greece and Rome, the Teutonic prehistoric period; costumes of the Middle Ages, Renaissance, Baroque, 18th and 19th centuries. Clear, measured patterns are provided for many clothing articles. Approach is practical throughout. Enlarged by Emma von Sichart. 464pp. 21030-8 Paperbound $3.50

ORIENTAL RUGS, ANTIQUE AND MODERN, Walter A. Hawley. A complete and authoritative treatise on the Oriental rug—where they are made, by whom and how, designs and symbols, characteristics in detail of the six major groups, how to distinguish them and how to buy them. Detailed technical data is provided on periods, weaves, warps, wefts, textures, sides, ends and knots, although no technical background is required for an understanding. 11 color plates, 80 halftones, 4 maps. vi + 320pp. 6⅛ x 9⅛. 22366-3 Paperbound $5.00

TEN BOOKS ON ARCHITECTURE, Vitruvius. By any standards the most important book on architecture ever written. Early Roman discussion of aesthetics of building, construction methods, orders, sites, and every other aspect of architecture has inspired, instructed architecture for about 2,000 years. Stands behind Palladio, Michelangelo, Bramante, Wren, countless others. Definitive Morris H. Morgan translation. 68 illustrations. xii + 331pp. 20645-9 Paperbound $3.00

THE FOUR BOOKS OF ARCHITECTURE, Andrea Palladio. Translated into every major Western European language in the two centuries following its publication in 1570, this has been one of the most influential books in the history of architecture. Complete reprint of the 1738 Isaac Ware edition. New introduction by Adolf Placzek, Columbia Univ. 216 plates. xxii + 110pp. of text. 9½ x 12¾. 21308-0 Clothbound $12.50

STICKS AND STONES: A STUDY OF AMERICAN ARCHITECTURE AND CIVILIZATION, Lewis Mumford.One of the great classics of American cultural history. American architecture from the medieval-inspired earliest forms to the early 20th century; evolution of structure and style, and reciprocal influences on environment. 21 photographic illustrations. 238pp. 20202-X Paperbound $2.00

THE AMERICAN BUILDER'S COMPANION, Asher Benjamin. The most widely used early 19th century architectural style and source book, for colonial up into Greek Revival periods. Extensive development of geometry of carpentering, construction of sashes, frames, doors, stairs; plans and elevations of domestic and other buildings. Hundreds of thousands of houses were built according to this book, now invaluable to historians, architects, restorers, etc. 1827 edition. 59 plates. 114pp. 7⅞ x 10¾ 22236-5 Paperbound $4.00

DUTCH HOUSES IN THE HUDSON VALLEY BEFORE 1776, Helen Wilkinson Reynolds. The standard survey of the Dutch colonial house and outbuildings, with constructional features, decoration, and local history associated with individual homesteads. Introduction by Franklin D. Roosevelt. Map. 150 illustrations. 469pp. 6⅝ x 9¼. 21469-9 Paperbound $5.00

AGAINST THE GRAIN (A REBOURS), Joris K. Huysmans. Filled with weird images, evidences of a bizarre imagination, exotic experiments with hallucinatory drugs, rich tastes and smells and the diversions of its sybarite hero Duc Jean des Esseintes, this classic novel pushed 19th-century literary decadence to its limits. Full unabridged edition. Do not confuse this with abridged editions generally sold. Introduction by Havelock Ellis. xlix + 206pp. 22190-3 Paperbound $2.50

VARIORUM SHAKESPEARE: HAMLET. Edited by Horace H. Furness; a landmark of American scholarship. Exhaustive footnotes and appendices treat all doubtful words and phrases, as well as suggested critical emendations throughout the play's history. First volume contains editor's own text, collated with all Quartos and Folios. Second volume contains full first Quarto, translations of Shakespeare's sources (Belleforest, and Saxo Grammaticus), Der Bestrafte Brudermord, and many essays on critical and historical points of interest by major authorities of past and present. Includes details of staging and costuming over the years. By far the best edition available for serious students of Shakespeare. Total of xx + 905pp. 21004-9, 21005-7, 2 volumes, Paperbound $7.00

A LIFE OF WILLIAM SHAKESPEARE, Sir Sidney Lee. This is the standard life of Shakespeare, summarizing everything known about Shakespeare and his plays. Incredibly rich in material, broad in coverage, clear and judicious, it has served thousands as the best introduction to Shakespeare. 1931 edition. 9 plates. xxix + 792pp. 21967-4 Paperbound $4.50

MASTERS OF THE DRAMA, John Gassner. Most comprehensive history of the drama in print, covering every tradition from Greeks to modern Europe and America, including India, Far East, etc. Covers more than 800 dramatists, 2000 plays, with biographical material, plot summaries, theatre history, criticism, etc. "Best of its kind in English," *New Republic*. 77 illustrations. xxii + 890pp. 20100-7 Clothbound **$10.00**

THE EVOLUTION OF THE ENGLISH LANGUAGE, George McKnight. The growth of English, from the 14th century to the present. Unusual, non-technical account presents basic information in very interesting form: sound shifts, change in grammar and syntax, vocabulary growth, similar topics. Abundantly illustrated with quotations. Formerly *Modern English in the Making*. xii + 590pp. 21932-1 Paperbound $3.50

AN ETYMOLOGICAL DICTIONARY OF MODERN ENGLISH, Ernest Weekley. Fullest, richest work of its sort, by foremost British lexicographer. Detailed word histories, including many colloquial and archaic words; extensive quotations. Do not confuse this with the Concise Etymological Dictionary, which is much abridged. Total of xxvii + 830pp. 6½ x 9¼. 21873-2, 21874-0 Two volumes, Paperbound $7.90

FLATLAND: A ROMANCE OF MANY DIMENSIONS, E. A. Abbott. Classic of science-fiction explores ramifications of life in a two-dimensional world, and what happens when a three-dimensional being intrudes. Amusing reading, but also useful as introduction to thought about hyperspace. Introduction by Banesh Hoffmann. 16 illustrations. xx + 103pp. 20001-9 Paperbound $1.00

POEMS OF ANNE BRADSTREET, edited with an introduction by Robert Hutchinson. A new selection of poems by America's first poet and perhaps the first significant woman poet in the English language. 48 poems display her development in works of considerable variety—love poems, domestic poems, religious meditations, formal elegies, "quaternions," etc. Notes, bibliography. viii + 222pp.
22160-1 Paperbound $2.50

THREE GOTHIC NOVELS: THE CASTLE OF OTRANTO BY HORACE WALPOLE; VATHEK BY WILLIAM BECKFORD; THE VAMPYRE BY JOHN POLIDORI, WITH FRAGMENT OF A NOVEL BY LORD BYRON, edited by E. F. Bleiler. The first Gothic novel, by Walpole; the finest Oriental tale in English, by Beckford; powerful Romantic supernatural story in versions by Polidori and Byron. All extremely important in history of literature; all still exciting, packed with supernatural thrills, ghosts, haunted castles, magic, etc. xl + 291pp.
21232-7 Paperbound $3.00

THE BEST TALES OF HOFFMANN, E. T. A. Hoffmann. 10 of Hoffmann's most important stories, in modern re-editings of standard translations: Nutcracker and the King of Mice, Signor Formica, Automata, The Sandman, Rath Krespel, The Golden Flowerpot, Master Martin the Cooper, The Mines of Falun, The King's Betrothed, A New Year's Eve Adventure. 7 illustrations by Hoffmann. Edited by E. F. Bleiler. xxxix + 419pp.   21793-0 Paperbound $3.00

GHOST AND HORROR STORIES OF AMBROSE BIERCE, Ambrose Bierce. 23 strikingly modern stories of the horrors latent in the human mind: The Eyes of the Panther, The Damned Thing, An Occurrence at Owl Creek Bridge, An Inhabitant of Carcosa, etc., plus the dream-essay, Visions of the Night. Edited by E. F. Bleiler. xxii + 199pp.   20767-6 Paperbound $2.00

BEST GHOST STORIES OF J. S. LEFANU, J. Sheridan LeFanu. Finest stories by Victorian master often considered greatest supernatural writer of all. Carmilla, Green Tea, The Haunted Baronet, The Familiar, and 12 others. Most never before available in the U. S. A. Edited by E. F. Bleiler. 8 illustrations from Victorian publications. xvii + 467pp.   20415-4 Paperbound $3.00

MATHEMATICAL FOUNDATIONS OF INFORMATION THEORY, A. I. Khinchin. Comprehensive introduction to work of Shannon, McMillan, Feinstein and Khinchin, placing these investigations on a rigorous mathematical basis. Covers entropy concept in probability theory, uniqueness theorem, Shannon's inequality, ergodic sources, the E property, martingale concept, noise, Feinstein's fundamental lemma, Shanon's first and second theorems. Translated by R. A. Silverman and M. D. Friedman. iii + 120pp.   60434-9 Paperbound $2.00

SEVEN SCIENCE FICTION NOVELS, H. G. Wells. The standard collection of the great novels. Complete, unabridged. *First Men in the Moon, Island of Dr. Moreau, War of the Worlds, Food of the Gods, Invisible Man, Time Machine, In the Days of the Comet.* Not only science fiction fans, but every educated person owes it to himself to read these novels. 1015pp.   (USO) 20264-X Clothbound $6.00

LAST AND FIRST MEN AND STAR MAKER, TWO SCIENCE FICTION NOVELS, Olaf Stapledon. Greatest future histories in science fiction. In the first, human intelligence is the "hero," through strange paths of evolution, interplanetary invasions, incredible technologies, near extinctions and reemergences. Star Maker describes the quest of a band of star rovers for intelligence itself, through time and space: weird inhuman civilizations, crustacean minds, symbiotic worlds, etc. Complete, unabridged. v + 438pp. (USO) 21962-3 Paperbound $3.00

THREE PROPHETIC NOVELS, H. G. WELLS. Stages of a consistently planned future for mankind. *When the Sleeper Wakes*, and *A Story of the Days to Come*, anticipate *Brave New World* and *1984*, in the 21st Century; *The Time Machine*, only complete version in print, shows farther future and the end of mankind. All show Wells's greatest gifts as storyteller and novelist. Edited by E. F. Bleiler. x + 335pp. (USO) 20605-X Paperbound $3.00

THE DEVIL'S DICTIONARY, Ambrose Bierce. America's own Oscar Wilde— Ambrose Bierce—offers his barbed iconoclastic wisdom in over 1,000 definitions hailed by H. L. Mencken as "some of the most gorgeous witticisms in the English language." 145pp. 20487-1 Paperbound $1.50

MAX AND MORITZ, Wilhelm Busch. Great children's classic, father of comic strip, of two bad boys, Max and Moritz. Also Ker and Plunk (Plisch und Plumm), Cat and Mouse, Deceitful Henry, Ice-Peter, The Boy and the Pipe, and five other pieces. Original German, with English translation. Edited by H. Arthur Klein; translations by various hands and H. Arthur Klein. vi + 216pp. 20181-3 Paperbound $2.00

PIGS IS PIGS AND OTHER FAVORITES, Ellis Parker Butler. The title story is one of the best humor short stories, as Mike Flannery obfuscates biology and English. Also included, That Pup of Murchison's, The Great American Pie Company, and Perkins of Portland. 14 illustrations. v + 109pp. 21532-6 Paperbound $1.50

THE PETERKIN PAPERS, Lucretia P. Hale. It takes genius to be as stupidly mad as the Peterkins, as they decide to become wise, celebrate the "Fourth," keep a cow, and otherwise strain the resources of the Lady from Philadelphia. Basic book of American humor. 153 illustrations. 219pp. 20794-3 Paperbound $2.00

PERRAULT'S FAIRY TALES, translated by A. E. Johnson and S. R. Littlewood, with 34 full-page illustrations by Gustave Doré. All the original Perrault stories— Cinderella, Sleeping Beauty, Bluebeard, Little Red Riding Hood, Puss in Boots, Tom Thumb, etc.—with their witty verse morals and the magnificent illustrations of Doré. One of the five or six great books of European fairy tales. viii + 117pp. 8⅛ x 11. 22311-6 Paperbound $2.00

OLD HUNGARIAN FAIRY TALES, Baroness Orczy. Favorites translated and adapted by author of the *Scarlet Pimpernel*. Eight fairy tales include "The Suitors of Princess Fire-Fly," "The Twin Hunchbacks," "Mr. Cuttlefish's Love Story," and "The Enchanted Cat." This little volume of magic and adventure will captivate children as it has for generations. 90 drawings by Montagu Barstow. 96pp. (USO) 22293-4 Paperbound $1.95

THE RED FAIRY BOOK, Andrew Lang. Lang's color fairy books have long been children's favorites. This volume includes Rapunzel, Jack and the Bean-stalk and 35 other stories, familiar and unfamiliar. 4 plates, 93 illustrations x + 367pp.
21673-X Paperbound $2.50

THE BLUE FAIRY BOOK, Andrew Lang. Lang's tales come from all countries and all times. Here are 37 tales from Grimm, the Arabian Nights, Greek Mythology, and other fascinating sources. 8 plates, 130 illustrations. xi + 390pp.
21437-0 Paperbound $2.75

HOUSEHOLD STORIES BY THE BROTHERS GRIMM. Classic English-language edition of the well-known tales — Rumpelstiltskin, Snow White, Hansel and Gretel, The Twelve Brothers, Faithful John, Rapunzel, Tom Thumb (52 stories in all). Translated into simple, straightforward English by Lucy Crane. Ornamented with headpieces, vignettes, elaborate decorative initials and a dozen full-page illustrations by Walter Crane. x + 269pp.
21080-4 Paperbound **$2.00**

THE MERRY ADVENTURES OF ROBIN HOOD, Howard Pyle. The finest modern versions of the traditional ballads and tales about the great English outlaw. Howard Pyle's complete prose version, with every word, every illustration of the first edition. Do not confuse this facsimile of the original (1883) with modern editions that change text or illustrations. 23 plates plus many page decorations. xxii + 296pp.
22043-5 Paperbound $2.75

THE STORY OF KING ARTHUR AND HIS KNIGHTS, Howard Pyle. The finest children's version of the life of King Arthur; brilliantly retold by Pyle, with 48 of his most imaginative illustrations. xviii + 313pp. 6⅛ x 9¼.
21445-1 Paperbound $2.50

THE WONDERFUL WIZARD OF OZ, L. Frank Baum. America's finest children's book in facsimile of first edition with all Denslow illustrations in full color. The edition a child should have. Introduction by Martin Gardner. 23 color plates, scores of drawings. iv + 267pp.
20691-2 Paperbound $3.50

THE MARVELOUS LAND OF OZ, L. Frank Baum. The second Oz book, every bit as imaginative as the Wizard. The hero is a boy named Tip, but the Scarecrow and the Tin Woodman are back, as is the Oz magic. 16 color plates, 120 drawings by John R. Neill. 287pp.
20692-0 Paperbound $2.50

THE MAGICAL MONARCH OF MO, L. Frank Baum. Remarkable adventures in a land even stranger than Oz. The best of Baum's books not in the Oz series. 15 color plates and dozens of drawings by Frank Verbeck. xviii + 237pp.
21892-9 Paperbound $2.25

THE BAD CHILD'S BOOK OF BEASTS, MORE BEASTS FOR WORSE CHILDREN, A MORAL ALPHABET, Hilaire Belloc. Three complete humor classics in one volume. Be kind to the frog, and do not call him names . . . and 28 other whimsical animals. Familiar favorites and some not so well known. Illustrated by Basil Blackwell. 156pp.
(USO) 20749-8 Paperbound $1.50

CATALOGUE OF DOVER BOOKS

EAST O' THE SUN AND WEST O' THE MOON, George W. Dasent. Considered the best of all translations of these Norwegian folk tales, this collection has been enjoyed by generations of children (and folklorists too). Includes True and Untrue, Why the Sea is Salt, East O' the Sun and West O' the Moon, Why the Bear is Stumpy-Tailed, Boots and the Troll, The Cock and the Hen, Rich Peter the Pedlar, and 52 more. The only edition with all 59 tales. 77 illustrations by Erik Werenskiold and Theodor Kittelsen. xv + 418pp. 22521-6 Paperbound $3.50

GOOPS AND HOW TO BE THEM, Gelett Burgess. Classic of tongue-in-cheek humor, masquerading as etiquette book. 87 verses, twice as many cartoons, show mischievous Goops as they demonstrate to children virtues of table manners, neatness, courtesy, etc. Favorite for generations. viii + 88pp. 6½ x 9¼. 22233-0 Paperbound $1.50

ALICE'S ADVENTURES UNDER GROUND, Lewis Carroll. The first version, quite different from the final Alice in Wonderland, printed out by Carroll himself with his own illustrations. Complete facsimile of the "million dollar" manuscript Carroll gave to Alice Liddell in 1864. Introduction by Martin Gardner. viii + 96pp. Title and dedication pages in color. 21482-6 Paperbound $1.25

THE BROWNIES, THEIR BOOK, Palmer Cox. Small as mice, cunning as foxes, exuberant and full of mischief, the Brownies go to the zoo, toy shop, seashore, circus, etc., in 24 verse adventures and 266 illustrations. Long a favorite, since their first appearance in St. Nicholas Magazine. xi + 144pp. 6⅝ x 9¼. 21265-3 Paperbound $1.75

SONGS OF CHILDHOOD, Walter De La Mare. Published (under the pseudonym Walter Ramal) when De La Mare was only 29, this charming collection has long been a favorite children's book. A facsimile of the first edition in paper, the 47 poems capture the simplicity of the nursery rhyme and the ballad, including such lyrics as I Met Eve, Tartary, The Silver Penny. vii + 106pp. (USO) 21972-0 Paperbound $1.25

THE COMPLETE NONSENSE OF EDWARD LEAR, Edward Lear. The finest 19th-century humorist-cartoonist in full: all nonsense limericks, zany alphabets, Owl and Pussycat, songs, nonsense botany, and more than 500 illustrations by Lear himself. Edited by Holbrook Jackson. xxix + 287pp. (USO) 20167-8 Paperbound $2.00

BILLY WHISKERS: THE AUTOBIOGRAPHY OF A GOAT, Frances Trego Montgomery. A favorite of children since the early 20th century, here are the escapades of that rambunctious, irresistible and mischievous goat—Billy Whiskers. Much in the spirit of Peck's Bad Boy, this is a book that children never tire of reading or hearing. All the original familiar illustrations by W. H. Fry are included: 6 color plates, 18 black and white drawings. 159pp. 22345-0 Paperbound $2.00

MOTHER GOOSE MELODIES. Faithful republication of the fabulously rare Munroe and Francis "copyright 1833" Boston edition—the most important Mother Goose collection, usually referred to as the "original." Familiar rhymes plus many rare ones, with wonderful old woodcut illustrations. Edited by E. F. Bleiler. 128pp. 4½ x 6⅜. 22577-1 Paperbound $1.00

"ESSENTIAL GRAMMAR" SERIES

All you really need to know about modern, colloquial grammar. Many educational shortcuts help you learn faster, understand better. Detailed cognate lists teach you to recognize similarities between English and foreign words and roots—make learning vocabulary easy and interesting. Excellent for independent study or as a supplement to record courses.

ESSENTIAL FRENCH GRAMMAR, Seymour Resnick. 2500-item cognate list. 159pp.
(EBE) 20419-7 Paperbound $1.50

ESSENTIAL GERMAN GRAMMAR, Guy Stern and Everett F. Bleiler. Unusual short-cuts on noun declension, word order, compound verbs. 124pp.
(EBE) 20422-7 Paperbound $1.25

ESSENTIAL ITALIAN GRAMMAR, Olga Ragusa. 111pp.
(EBE) 20779-X Paperbound $1.25

ESSENTIAL JAPANESE GRAMMAR, Everett F. Bleiler. In Romaji transcription; no characters needed. Japanese grammar is regular and simple. 156pp.
21027-8 Paperbound $1.50

ESSENTIAL PORTUGUESE GRAMMAR, Alexander da R. Prista. vi + 114pp.
21650-0 Paperbound $1.35

ESSENTIAL SPANISH GRAMMAR, Seymour Resnick. 2500 word cognate list. 115pp.
(EBE) 20780-3 Paperbound $1.25

ESSENTIAL ENGLISH GRAMMAR, Philip Gucker. Combines best features of modern, functional and traditional approaches. For refresher, class use, home study. x + 177pp.
21649-7 Paperbound $1.75

A PHRASE AND SENTENCE DICTIONARY OF SPOKEN SPANISH. Prepared for U. S. War Department by U. S. linguists. As above, unit is idiom, phrase or sentence rather than word. English-Spanish and Spanish-English sections contain modern equivalents of over 18,000 sentences. Introduction and appendix as above. iv + 513pp.
20495-2 Paperbound $3.50

A PHRASE AND SENTENCE DICTIONARY OF SPOKEN RUSSIAN. Dictionary prepared for U. S. War Department by U. S. linguists. Basic unit is not the word, but the idiom, phrase or sentence. English-Russian and Russian-English sections contain modern equivalents for over 30,000 phrases. Grammatical introduction covers phonetics, writing, syntax. Appendix of word lists for food, numbers, geographical names, etc. vi + 573 pp. 6⅛ x 9¼.
20496-0 Paperbound $5.50

CONVERSATIONAL CHINESE FOR BEGINNERS, Morris Swadesh. Phonetic system, beginner's course in Pai Hua Mandarin Chinese covering most important, most useful speech patterns. Emphasis on modern colloquial usage. Formerly *Chinese in Your Pocket.* xvi + 158pp.
21123-1 Paperbound $1.75

PLANETS, STARS AND GALAXIES: DESCRIPTIVE ASTRONOMY FOR BEGINNERS, A. E. Fanning. Comprehensive introductory survey of astronomy: the sun, solar system, stars, galaxies, universe, cosmology; up-to-date, including quasars, radio stars, etc. Preface by Prof. Donald Menzel. 24pp. of photographs. 189pp. 5¼ x 8¼.
21680-2 Paperbound $2.50

TEACH YOURSELF CALCULUS, P. Abbott. With a good background in algebra and trig, you can teach yourself calculus with this book. Simple, straightforward introduction to functions of all kinds, integration, differentiation, series, etc. "Students who are beginning to study calculus method will derive great help from this book." Faraday House Journal. 308pp. 20683-1 Clothbound $2.50

TEACH YOURSELF TRIGONOMETRY, P. Abbott. Geometrical foundations, indices and logarithms, ratios, angles, circular measure, etc. are presented in this sound, easy-to-use text. Excellent for the beginner or as a brush up, this text carries the student through the solution of triangles. 204pp. 20682-3 Clothbound $2.00

BASIC MACHINES AND HOW THEY WORK, U. S. Bureau of Naval Personnel. Originally used in U.S. Naval training schools, this book clearly explains the operation of a progression of machines, from the simplest—lever, wheel and axle, inclined plane, wedge, screw—to the most complex—typewriter, internal combustion engine, computer mechanism. Utilizing an approach that requires only an elementary understanding of mathematics, these explanations build logically upon each other and are assisted by over 200 drawings and diagrams. Perfect as a technical school manual or as a self-teaching aid to the layman. 204 figures. Preface. Index. vii + 161pp. 6½ x 9¼. 21709-4 Paperbound $2.50

THE FRIENDLY STARS, Martha Evans Martin. Classic has taught naked-eye observation of stars, planets to hundreds of thousands, still not surpassed for charm, lucidity, adequacy. Completely updated by Professor Donald H. Menzel, Harvard Observatory. 25 illustrations. 16 x 30 chart. x + 147pp. 21099-5 Paperbound $2.00

MUSIC OF THE SPHERES: THE MATERIAL UNIVERSE FROM ATOM TO QUASAR, SIMPLY EXPLAINED, Guy Murchie. Extremely broad, brilliantly written popular account begins with the solar system and reaches to dividing line between matter and nonmatter; latest understandings presented with exceptional clarity. Volume One: Planets, stars, galaxies, cosmology, geology, celestial mechanics, latest astronomical discoveries; Volume Two: Matter, atoms, waves, radiation, relativity, chemical action, heat, nuclear energy, quantum theory, music, light, color, probability, antimatter, antigravity, and similar topics. 319 figures. 1967 (second) edition. Total of xx + 644pp. 21809-0, 21810-4 Two volumes, Paperbound $5.75

OLD-TIME SCHOOLS AND SCHOOL BOOKS, Clifton Johnson. Illustrations and rhymes from early primers, abundant quotations from early textbooks, many anecdotes of school life enliven this study of elementary schools from Puritans to middle 19th century. Introduction by Carl Withers. 234 illustrations. xxxiii + 381pp.
21031-6 Paperbound $4.00

THE PHILOSOPHY OF THE UPANISHADS, Paul Deussen. Clear, detailed statement of upanishadic system of thought, generally considered among best available. History of these works, full exposition of system emergent from them, parallel concepts in the West. Translated by A. S. Geden. xiv + 429pp.

21616-0 Paperbound $3.50

LANGUAGE, TRUTH AND LOGIC, Alfred J. Ayer. Famous, remarkably clear introduction to the Vienna and Cambridge schools of Logical Positivism; function of philosophy, elimination of metaphysical thought, nature of analysis, similar topics. "Wish I had written it myself," Bertrand Russell. 2nd, 1946 edition. 160pp.

20010-8 Paperbound $1.50

THE GUIDE FOR THE PERPLEXED, Moses Maimonides. Great classic of medieval Judaism, major attempt to reconcile revealed religion (Pentateuch, commentaries) and Aristotelian philosophy. Enormously important in all Western thought. Unabridged Friedländer translation. 50-page introduction. lix + 414pp.

(USO) 20351-4 Paperbound $4.50

OCCULT AND SUPERNATURAL PHENOMENA, D. H. Rawcliffe. Full, serious study of the most persistent delusions of mankind: crystal gazing, mediumistic trance, stigmata, lycanthropy, fire walking, dowsing, telepathy, ghosts, ESP, etc., and their relation to common forms of abnormal psychology. Formerly *Illusions and Delusions of the Supernatural and the Occult.* iii + 551pp.   20503-7 Paperbound $4.00

THE EGYPTIAN BOOK OF THE DEAD: THE PAPYRUS OF ANI, E. A. Wallis Budge. Full hieroglyphic text, interlinear transliteration of sounds, word for word translation, then smooth, connected translation; Theban recension. Basic work in Ancient Egyptian civilization; now even more significant than ever for historical importance, dilation of consciousness, etc. clvi + 377pp. 6½ x 9¼.

21866-X Paperbound $4.95

PSYCHOLOGY OF MUSIC, Carl E. Seashore. Basic, thorough survey of everything known about psychology of music up to 1940's; essential reading for psychologists, musicologists. Physical acoustics; auditory apparatus; relationship of physical sound to perceived sound; role of the mind in sorting, altering, suppressing, creating sound sensations; musical learning, testing for ability, absolute pitch, other topics. Records of Caruso, Menuhin analyzed. 88 figures. xix + 408pp.

21851-1 Paperbound $3.50

THE I CHING (THE BOOK OF CHANGES), translated by James Legge. Complete translated text plus appendices by Confucius, of perhaps the most penetrating divination book ever compiled. Indispensable to all study of early Oriental civilizations. 3 plates. xxiii + 448pp.   21062-6 Paperbound $3.50

THE UPANISHADS, translated by Max Müller. Twelve classical upanishads: Chandogya, Kena, Aitareya, Kaushitaki, Isa, Katha, Mundaka, Taittiriyaka, Brhadaranyaka, Svetasvatara, Prasna, Maitriyana. 160-page introduction, analysis by Prof. Müller. Total of 670pp. 20992-X, 20993-8 Two volumes, Paperbound $7.50

MATHEMATICAL PUZZLES FOR BEGINNERS AND ENTHUSIASTS, Geoffrey Mott-Smith. 189 puzzles from easy to difficult—involving arithmetic, logic, algebra, properties of digits, probability, etc.—for enjoyment and mental stimulus. Explanation of mathematical principles behind the puzzles. 135 illustrations. viii + 248pp.

20198-8 Paperbound $2.00

PAPER FOLDING FOR BEGINNERS, William D. Murray and Francis J. Rigney. Easiest book on the market, clearest instructions on making interesting, beautiful origami. Sail boats, cups, roosters, frogs that move legs, bonbon boxes, standing birds, etc. 40 projects; more than 275 diagrams and photographs. 94pp.

20713-7 Paperbound $1.00

TRICKS AND GAMES ON THE POOL TABLE, Fred Herrmann. 79 tricks and games—some solitaires, some for two or more players, some competitive games—to entertain you between formal games. Mystifying shots and throws, unusual caroms, tricks involving such props as cork, coins, a hat, etc. Formerly *Fun on the Pool Table*. 77 figures. 95pp.

21814-7 Paperbound $1.25

HAND SHADOWS TO BE THROWN UPON THE WALL: A SERIES OF NOVEL AND AMUSING FIGURES FORMED BY THE HAND, Henry Bursill. Delightful picturebook from great-grandfather's day shows how to make 18 different hand shadows: a bird that flies, duck that quacks, dog that wags his tail, camel, goose, deer, boy, turtle, etc. Only book of its sort. vi + 33pp. $6\frac{1}{2}$ x $9\frac{1}{4}$.   21779-5 Paperbound $1.00

WHITTLING AND WOODCARVING, E. J. Tangerman. 18th printing of best book on market. "If you can cut a potato you can carve" toys and puzzles, chains, chessmen, caricatures, masks, frames, woodcut blocks, surface patterns, much more. Information on tools, woods, techniques. Also goes into serious wood sculpture from Middle Ages to present, East and West. 464 photos, figures. x + 293pp.

20965-2 Paperbound $2.50

HISTORY OF PHILOSOPHY, Julián Marías. Possibly the clearest, most easily followed, best planned, most useful one-volume history of philosophy on the market; neither skimpy nor overfull. Full details on system of every major philosopher and dozens of less important thinkers from pre-Socratics up to Existentialism and later. Strong on many European figures usually omitted. Has gone through dozens of editions in Europe. 1966 edition, translated by Stanley Appelbaum and Clarence Strowbridge. xviii + 505pp.   21739-6 Paperbound $3.50

YOGA: A SCIENTIFIC EVALUATION, Kovoor T. Behanan. Scientific but non-technical study of physiological results of yoga exercises; done under auspices of Yale U. Relations to Indian thought, to psychoanalysis, etc. 16 photos. xxiii + 270pp.

20505-3 Paperbound $2.50